HEINEMANN COORDINATED SCI

BIOLOGY

Richard Fosbery • Jean McLean

Contents

SECTION D: VARIATION, INHERITANCE AND EVOLUTION

CHAPTER 6: VARIATION AND INHERITANCE

CHAPTER 7: EVOLUTION, SELECTION AND IMPROVEMENT

SECTION E: THE ENVIRONMENT

CHAPTER 8: ORGANISMS AND THEIR ENVIRONMENT

CHAPTER 9: HUMAN IMPACT ON THE ENVIRONMENT

Heinemann Educational Publishers
Halley Court, Jordan Hill, Oxford, OX2 8EJ
a division of Reed Educational & Professional Publishing Ltd

OXFORD FLORENCE PRAGUE MADRID ATHENS
MELBOURNE AUCKLAND KUALA LUMPUR
SINGAPORE TOKYO IBADAN NAIROBI KAMPALA
JOHANNESBURG GABORONE PORTSMOUTH NH
CHICAGO MEXICO CITY SAO PAULO

First published 1996

ISBN 0 435 58000 0

2000 99 98 97 96
10 9 8 7 6 5 4 3 2 1

Designed and typeset by Ken Vail Graphic Design

Illustrated by: Simon Girling and Associates (Mike Lacey), Nick Hawken, Squires Graphics, Ken Vail Graphic Design.

Cover design by Ken Vail Graphic Design

Cover photo by Bruce Coleman/K. Taylor (Inset: Bruce Coleman)

Printed and bound in Spain by Mateu Cromo

Acknowledgements

The authors and publishers would like to thank the following for permission to use photographs:

p 4 *T*: NHPA. **p 4** *ML, MR* & *BL*: Bruce Coleman. **p 4** Snake: Oxford Scientific Films. **p 4** *BR*: Bruce Coleman. **p 5** *L, M* & *R*: Bruce Coleman. **p 6** *T*: SPL. **p 6** *B*: Biophoto. **p 7** *R*: Bridgeman Art Library. **p 7** *L*: SPL. **p 8** *BL*: SPL. **p 8** *BR*: Biophoto. **p 9**: SPL. **p 10** *T* & *M*: SPL. **p 11** *T*: SPL. **p 11** *M*: SPL. **p 11** *ML, BL* & *BR*: Microscopix. **p 18** *T*: Network/Martin Mayer. **p 19** *TL, TR, BL* & *BR*: Roger Scruton. **p 20** *T*: SPL. **p 20** *BL*: National Medical Slide Bank. **p 22** *B*: Biophoto. **p 23**: SPL. **p 26** *L*: Allsport/Richard Martin. **p 26** *R*: N.H.P.A. **p 27** *R*: Allsport/Mike Powell. **p 27** *L*: Biophoto. **p 29** *B*: SPL. **p 32**: SPL. **p 33**: Peter Gould. **p 34** *L, R* & *B*: SPL. **p 35** *T*: SPL. **p 35** *L*: SPL. **p 36** *L*: SPL. **p 36** *B*: Peter Gould. **p 38**: SPL. **p 40**: SPL. **p 41** *T*: SPL. **p 41** *BR*: Roger Scruton. **p 42**: Allsport/Steve Morton. **p 44**: J Allan Cash. **p 49** *T*: Roger Scruton. **p 49** *M*: SPL. **p 49** *BL*: SPL. **p 52**: Network/John Sturrock. **p 54**: Collections/Liz Stores. **p 57**: Collections/A Sieveking. **p 58** *T, M*&*B*: SPL. **p 60** *T* & *L*: SPL. **p 61**: Ace Photos. **p 62** *ML*: SPL. **p 62** *T*: SPL. **p 62** *MR*: SPL. **p 62** *B*: Still Pictures/M. Ostergaad. **p 64**: Hulton Deutsch. **p 65** *L* &*R*: Network/Gideon Mendel. **p 66**: Ace Photo. **p 67** *TL* & *TR*: SPL. **p 67** *B*: Tony Stone Images. **p 68** *T*: Kobal Collection. **p 69**: Advertising Archives/HEA. **p 75** *M, BL* & *BR*: Peter Gould. **p 76**: Peter Gould. **p 77**: Bruce Coleman. **p 78**: Skyscan. **p 79** *T*: NHPA. **p 79** *B*: Plant Environmental Laboratory/Dept of Agriculture/University of Reading. **p 82** *T*: Bruce Coleman/M P *L* Fogden. **p 82** *R*: O.S.F./Harold Taylor. **p 82** *BL*: SPL. **p 83**: SPL. **p 84** *T*: Bruce Coleman. **p 85** seedlings A, B, C & D: Horticulture Research International. **p 85** *M*: Environmental Picture Library. **p 86** *T*: Harry Smith. **p 86** *B*: Bruce Coleman. **p 87** *T*: Harry Smith. **p 87** *B*: CSF/Harold Taylor. **p 88** *TR*: SPL. **p 88** *B*: The Garden Picture Library. **p 89** *TR*: The Garden Picture Library. **p 89** *ML* & *R*: Holt Studios Int. **p 89** *B*: Peter Gould. **p 91**: The Garden Picture Library. **p 94** *MR, BL* & *BR*: NHPA. **p 95** *TR, ML, BR*: NHPA. **p 95** *BL*: Bruce Coleman. **p 96**: Sally Greenhill. **p 97** *T, M*: Hulton Deutsch. **p 98**: Network/Oliver Martef. **p 99**: Holt Studios Int. **p 100** *T* & *M*: SPL. **p 100** *BL* & *BR*: Biophoto Assocs. **p 102** *T, BL, M* & *R*: SPL. **p 104**: Richard & Sally Greenhill. **p 105**: Biophotos. **p 106** *R*: NHPA. **p 106** *L*: SPL. **p 108** *TL*: Bruce Coleman. p 108 *TR, ML* & *MR*: NHPA. **p 109** *T*: Holt Studios Int. **p 112**: SPL. **p 114**: SPL. **p 116**: Sygma/P. Robert. **p 117** *T*: SPL. **p 117** *M*: Holt Studios Int. **p 117** *B*: Down's Syndrome Assoc. **p 118**: SPL. **p 119**: Mansell Collection. **p 120** *T* & inset: Bruce Coleman. **p 120** *BL* & *BR*: Natural History Museum. **p 121** *T*: Forschungs Institut und Naturmuseum Senckenburg. **p 121** *B*: Ardea. **p 121** *M*: Geoscience Features. **p 122** *TL* & *TR*: Bruce Coleman. **p 122** *B*: Natural History Museum. **p 123** *T*: Neville Hollingworth. **p 123** *BR*: Natural History Museum. **p 124** *R*: Ardea. **p 124** *L* & finches: Mary Evans Picture Library. **p 125** *T*: Ardea. **p 125** *B*: NHPA. **p 126** *T* & *M*: NHPA. **p 126** *B*: Ironbridge Gorge Museum Trust/Science Museum. **p 125** *ML* & *MR*: SPL. **p 128** *T*: J. Allan Cash. **p 128** *MR*: South American Pictures. **p 128** *ML* & *B*: NHPA. **p 132** *T*: Holt Studios. **p 132** *B*: SPL. **p 138** *T* & *BL*: Bruce Coleman. **p 138** *BR*: NHPA. **p 140** *T*: Bruce Coleman. **p 140** *B*: Holt Studios Int. **p 141** *L* & *R*: Bruce Coleman. **p 142** *TL, ML, BL, B, BR* & woodland: Bruce Coleman. **p 142** *MR*: Roger Scruton. **p 142** *TR*: Holt Studios Int. **p 144**: Environmental Picture Library/Graham Burns. **p 146**: Bruce Coleman. **p 149**: O.S.F. p 150: Ardea. **p 152** *T*: NHPA. **p 152** *M* & *B*: Bruce Coleman. **p 153** *L* & *R*: Bruce Coleman. **p 154** *T* & *B*: Bruce Coleman. **p 155** Bruce Coleman. **p 156** *T*: Bruce Coleman. **p 156** *MR*: NHPA. **p 156** *BL* & *BR*: Holt Studios Int. **p 159** *T*: SPL. **p 159** *ML*: Holt Studios Int. **p 159** *MR*: O.S.F. **p 160** *R*: Holt Studios Int. **p 160** *L*: Environmental Picture Library. **p 162** *T* & *M*: Bruce Coleman. **p 163**: Holt Studios Int. **p 164**: Roger Scruton. **p 165**: NHPA. **p 167** *T, ML* & *MR, B*: Holt Studios Int. **p 169**: Bruce Coleman. **p 172**: SPL. **p 174** *T*: Bruce Coleman. **p 174** *B*: Holt Studios Int. **p 175** *T*: NHPA. **p 175** *B*: Holt Studios Int.

p 20: poster was originally published in the *ABC of Nutrition* ©1992 by the BMJ Publishing Group, and is reproduced with their permission; **p 52**: diagram from Nuffield Foundation; *p 54*: diagram of 'Exploded Nerve' taken from *Biology: A Modern Introduction* by B.S.Beckett, ©Oxford University Press, reproduced by permission; **p 73**: graph from Welcome Centre; **p 112**: illustration 'Packing DNA into chromosonne' taken from *Advanced Biology,* Mackean & Clegg publ. and reproduced by permission of John Murry (Publishers) Ltd; **p 125**: Newton Abbot for the map, taken from *Evolution Expanded* by Peter Hutchinson ©1982; **p 130**: diagram from BBSRC; **p 134**: drawing taken from *Biology for Today* by E.RNeal and K.Neal, published by Blanford Press; **p 161**: table of pollutants of air, water and land, reprinted from *Pollution and Health* by kind permission of Daniels Publishing; **p 164**: illustration 'Organic Pollution: Inverterbrates' taken from *Lower Plants,* by C.J.Clegg, publ and reproduced by permission of John Murry (Publishers) Ltd; **p 165**: graph from The Royal Society of Chemistry; **p 166**: the pyramid: showing DDT concentrates (Sheet 34), **p 171**: graph of CO2 Concentrations, and **p 175**: map, all from WWF UK, Data Support for Education Service. special thanks to Carol Inskipp for supplying this information to the author; **p 172** and **p 173**: graphs from Hodder & Stoughton, taken from *Global Environment Issues* by Smith and Warr ©1991; **p 177**: table from British Agrochemicals Association; **p 177**: graph from Blackwell Publishers from *Applied Ecology* by Newman; **p 177**: table taken from *BTO News 199 (7-8/1995),* British Trust for Ornithology;

The publishers have made every effort to trace the copyright holders, but if they have inadvertently overlooked any, they will be pleased to make the necessary arrangements at the first opportunity.

How to use this book

Heinemann Coordinated Science:Biology has been written for your GCSE course and contains all the information you will need over the next two years for your exam syllabus.

This book has five sections. Each section matches one of the major themes in the National Curriculum.

What is in a section?

The sections are organised into double-page spreads. Each spread has:

Colour-coded sections so you can quickly find the one you want.

Clear text and pictures to explain the science.

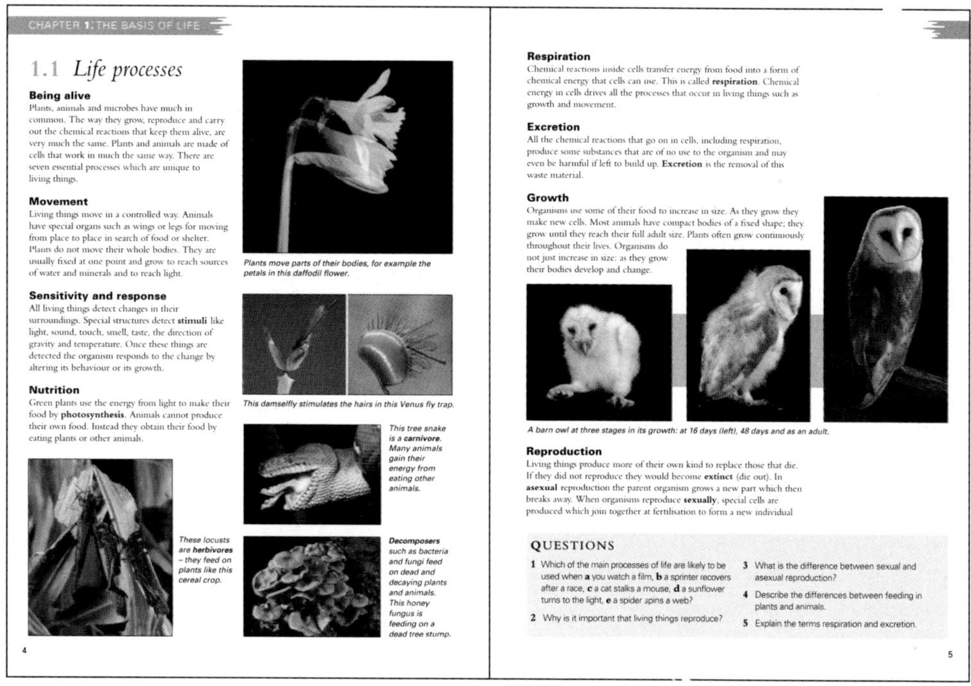

CHAPTER 1: THE BASIS OF LIFE

1.1 *Life processes*

Being alive
Plants, animals and microbes have much in common. The way they grow, reproduce and carry out the chemical reactions that keep them alive, are very much the same. Plants and animals are made of cells that work in much the same way. There are seven essential processes which are unique to living things.

Movement
Living things move in a controlled way. Animals have special organs such as wings or legs for moving from place to place in search of food or shelter. Plants do not move their whole bodies. They are usually fixed at one point and grow to reach sources of water and minerals and to reach light.

Sensitivity and response
All living things detect changes in their surroundings. Special structures detect **stimuli** like light, sound, touch, smell, taste, the direction of gravity and temperature. Once these things are detected the organism responds to the change by altering its behaviour or its growth.

Nutrition
Green plants use the energy from light to make their food by **photosynthesis**. Animals cannot produce their own food. Instead they obtain their food by eating plants or other animals.

These locusts are ***herbivores*** *– they feed on plants like this cereal crop.*

Plants move parts of their bodies, for example the petals in this daffodil flower.

This damselfly stimulates the hairs in this Venus fly trap.

This tree snake is a ***carnivore****. Many animals gain their energy from eating other animals.*

Decomposers *such as bacteria and fungi feed on dead and decaying plants and animals. This honey fungus is feeding on a dead tree stump.*

4

Respiration
Chemical reactions inside cells transfer energy from food into a form of chemical energy that cells can use. This is called **respiration**. Chemical energy in cells drives all the processes that occur in living things such as growth and movement.

Excretion
All the chemical reactions that go on in cells, including respiration, produce some substances that are of no use to the organism and may even be harmful if left to build up. **Excretion** is the removal of this waste material.

Growth
Organisms use some of their food to increase in size. As they grow they make new cells. Most animals have compact bodies of a fixed shape; they grow until they reach their full adult size. Plants often grow continuously throughout their lives. Organisms do not just increase in size: as they grow their bodies develop and change.

A barn owl at three stages in its growth: at 16 days (left), 48 days and as an adult.

Reproduction
Living things produce more of their own kind to replace those that die. If they did not reproduce they would become **extinct** (die out). In **asexual** reproduction the parent organism grows a new part which then breaks away. When organisms reproduce **sexually**, special cells are produced which join together at fertilisation to form a new individual

QUESTIONS

1 Which of the main processes of life are likely to be used when **a** you watch a film, **b** a sprinter recovers after a race, **c** a cat stalks a mouse, **d** a sunflower turns to the light, **e** a spider spins a web?

2 Why is it important that living things reproduce?

3 What is the difference between sexual and asexual reproduction?

4 Describe the differences between feeding in plants and animals.

5 Explain the terms respiration and excretion.

5

Questions to help check your understanding of the important ideas on the spread.

At the end of each section, there are double-page spreads of longer questions. These are to help you find out if you understand the key ideas in that section. They can also help you revise.

Assessment and resource pack

All the answers for questions in this student book are in the *Heinemann Coordinated Science: Higher Biology Assessment and resource pack.*

Biologists study living things. Exciting discoveries are being made all the time in the different areas of biology. Our knowledge of biology is constantly changing. You can find out about these discoveries by watching TV programmes like *Tomorrow's World*, *Horizon* or *Equinox* or by listening to the radio or reading newspapers and magazines. Your school may subscribe to a magazine called *Catalyst*, which is written for students taking GCSE Science.

Asking questions

Biologists make discoveries by **observing** humans, animals and plants. Here are some examples of these observations.

- Some people eat a lot of food but never put on weight.
- Swallows, swifts and house martins are found in Britain only in the summer.
- Some plants, such as the stemless thistle, grow on chalky (alkaline) soils, but never on acid soils.
- House plants grow much better if they are given a fertiliser.
- There are diseases that are common in some families but not in others.

Science is about being curious. Where do swifts go in the winter? What stops plants growing in different soils? Do all types of fertiliser have the same effect on plants? What causes disease? We ask questions about what we observe.

Making predictions

Scientists make suggestions about their observations and then try to collect evidence to support their ideas. They try to explain what they have seen and make **predictions** about what will happen in **experiments**. In an experiment a scientist investigates the effects of different factors.

Planning investigations

You will have to **plan** the experiments you carry out to test your predictions. Before you start ask to see an example of a piece of practical work done by another pupil. This may help you to set out your own work.

First be sure you know just what you are investigating. Identify the factor you intend to change in your experiment. It might be temperature, light intensity, quantity of fertiliser or type of soil. Think about the effect that your chosen factor may have. Base your predictions on your knowledge and always write down the facts on which you based your predictions. Use this book to help you find the information you need, but be prepared to look elsewhere as well.

Select the apparatus you need and decide how to use it. Think ahead about the results you will collect.

- What should you count or measure?
- What will you use to obtain **accurate** results?

Plan carefully so that you are sure you have a **valid** experiment. Have you designed an experiment that really tests your prediction? Think about all the factors that may affect your experiment. You should investigate the effect of one factor and keep all the others constant. This ensures that your results are due to the factor you are investigating, and not to anything else that you may not have thought about.

If appropriate you should include a **control**, in which only the factor you are investigating is absent. Try, if there is time, to **repeat** your experiment to be sure that your results are **reliable** and can be repeated.

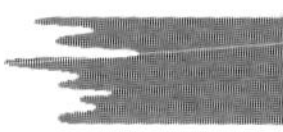

Obtaining and analysing evidence

When you have collected your data, present it clearly.

- Can you use a graph to help you to analyse your results?
- What type of graph will you draw?

Use tables of data and draw graphs whenever you can. Make sure calculations are written out clearly for other people to follow. Look for a pattern in your results. You may find some results which do not fit the pattern. Any results which do not fit the pattern are said to be **anomalous** results and they should not be included if you calculate any averages. See if your results **support** the prediction you made. Often the data collected in experiments do not agree with the prediction and therefore the prediction has to be **rejected** or changed in some way. Don't worry if this happens.

When you write conclusions always refer to your results quoting the data you collected. You might also quote data from other sources. This is important: use data like evidence in a courtroom trial. Use your knowledge to **explain** the results you collected.

Evaluating evidence

All scientists **evaluate** their work. This means they look at it critically. You must do the same. Look at the way you collected results: did you take really accurate measurements? It is often difficult in biology experiments to collect enough data in the time allowed. How would you improve your experiment if you had more time? If your results are not very conclusive what would you do next? The results of one experiment often pose as many questions as they answer. Never stop asking questions and making predictions.

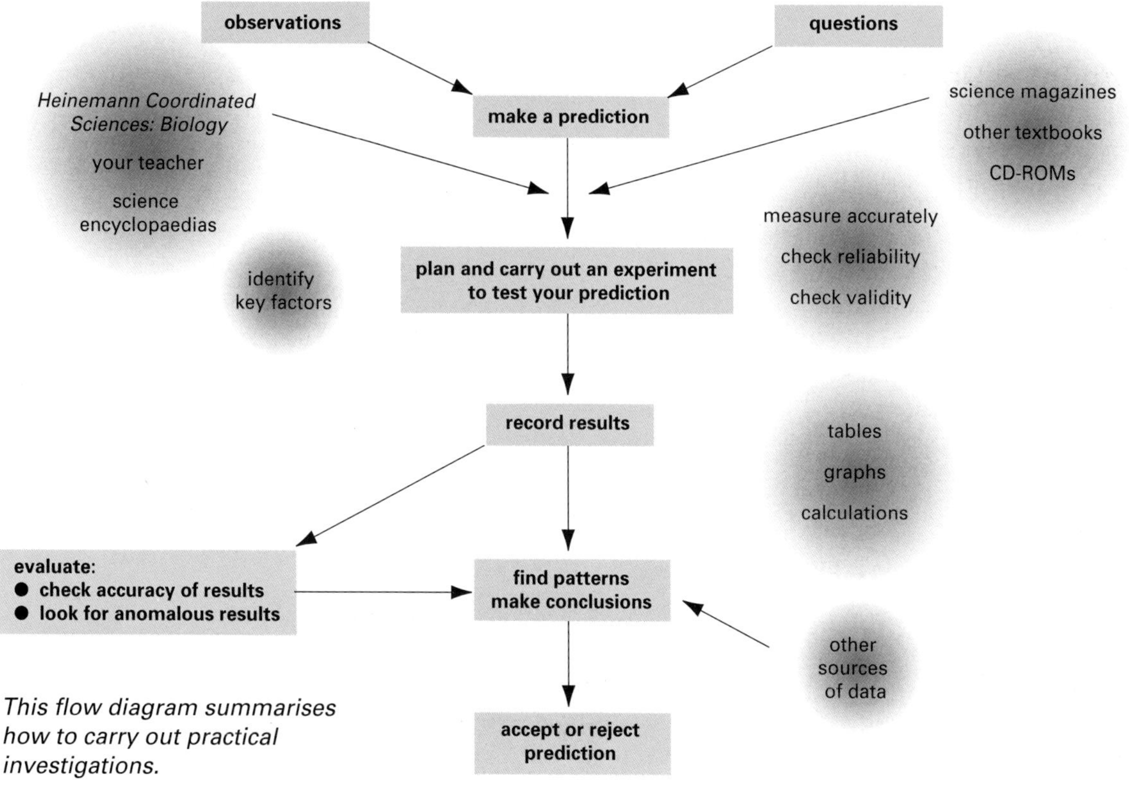

This flow diagram summarises how to carry out practical investigations.

1.1 *Life processes*

Being alive

Plants, animals and microbes have much in common. The way they grow, reproduce and carry out the chemical reactions that keep them alive, are very much the same. Plants and animals are made of cells that work in much the same way. There are seven essential processes which are unique to living things.

Plants move parts of their bodies, for example the petals in this daffodil flower.

Movement

Living things move in a controlled way. Animals have special organs such as wings or legs for moving from place to place in search of food or shelter. Plants do not move their whole bodies. They are usually fixed at one point and grow to reach sources of water and minerals and to reach light.

Sensitivity and response

All living things detect changes in their surroundings. Special structures detect **stimuli** like light, sound, touch, smell, taste, the direction of gravity and temperature. Once these things are detected the organism responds to the change by altering its behaviour or its growth.

This damselfly stimulates the hairs in this Venus fly trap.

Nutrition

Green plants use the energy from light to make their food by **photosynthesis**. Animals cannot produce their own food. Instead they obtain their food by eating plants or other animals.

*These locusts are **herbivores** – they feed on plants like this cereal crop.*

*This tree snake is a **carnivore**. Many animals gain their energy from eating other animals.*

***Decomposers** such as bacteria and fungi feed on dead and decaying plants and animals. This honey fungus is feeding on a dead tree stump.*

Respiration

Chemical reactions inside cells transfer energy from food into a form of chemical energy that cells can use. This is called **respiration**. Chemical energy in cells drives all the processes that occur in living things such as growth and movement.

Excretion

All the chemical reactions that go on in cells, including respiration, produce some substances that are of no use to the organism and may even be harmful if left to build up. **Excretion** is the removal of this waste material.

Growth

Organisms use some of their food to increase in size. As they grow they make new cells. Most animals have compact bodies of a fixed shape; they grow until they reach their full adult size. Plants often grow continuously throughout their lives. Organisms do not just increase in size: as they grow their bodies develop and change.

A barn owl at three stages in its growth: at 16 days (left), 48 days and as an adult.

Reproduction

Living things produce more of their own kind to replace those that die. If they did not reproduce they would become **extinct** (die out). In **asexual** reproduction the parent organism grows a new part which then breaks away. When organisms reproduce **sexually**, special cells are produced which join together at fertilisation to form a new individual

QUESTIONS

1 Which of the main processes of life are likely to be used when **a** you watch a film, **b** a sprinter recovers after a race, **c** a cat stalks a mouse, **d** a sunflower turns to the light, **e** a spider spins a web?

2 Why is it important that living things reproduce?

3 What is the difference between sexual and asexual reproduction?

4 Describe the differences between feeding in plants and animals.

5 Explain the terms respiration and excretion.

1.2 Organs and tissues

Body systems

Living things need to feed, grow and reproduce and carry out all the other functions of life. Humans have seven majc **body systems** to carry out these functions. These body systems are composed of **organs** such as the heart, stomac brain and lungs. Each organ carries out one major functioi as part of an **organ system**.

Organ system	Organs
feeding and digestive	mouth, gullet, stomach, intestines, pancreas, liver
transport	heart, arteries, veins
urinary	liver, kidneys, bladder
reproductive	ovaries, testes, uterus
sensory	eye, ear, tongue, skin, nose
coordination	brain, spinal cord, nerves
breathing	windpipe, lungs, diaphragm

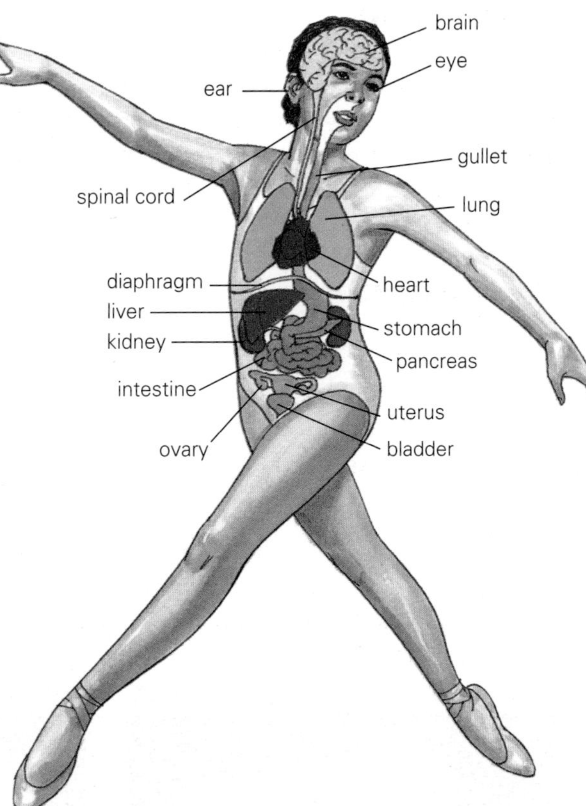

This shows the position in the human body of some of the major organs.

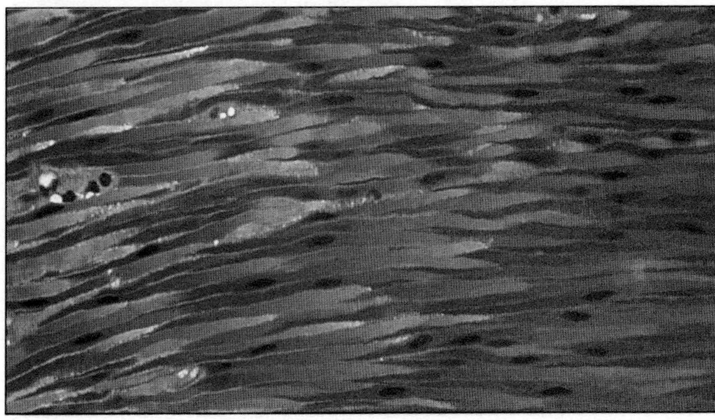

This is a photograph of smooth muscle tissue from the stomach. Its action mixes food with the digestive juices made by glandular tissue.

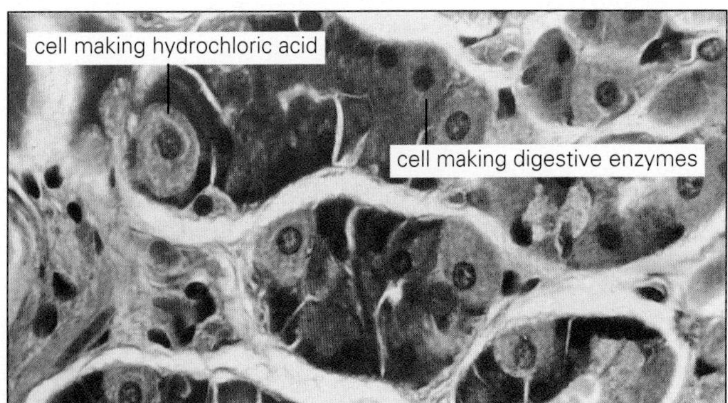

These cells are part of the glandular tissue in the lining of the stomach. Some cells make hydrochloric acid which kills bacteria in our food. Others make digestive enzymes.

Tissues and organs

An organ does one or several major functions for the body. The stomach digests food and helps protect us against infection, the kidney removes waste from the blood, and sense organs such as the eye and ear make us aware of our surroundings.

Organs are made of several different **tissues**. A tissue consists of many cells, which work together to perform one function. For example,

- **muscle tissue** is made from cells that cause movement
- **nervous tissue** contains cells which transmit information helping to coordinate the body
- **fat tissue** contains cells that store fat as a supply of energy.

Many organs contain different types of tissue. The heart is part of a transport system and consists of muscle tissue, nerve tissue and fat tissue. These tissues work together to pump blood around the body. The wall of the stomach consists of muscle tissue and glandular tissue.

Plant organs

Flowering plants have a body structure made of four main organs: leaf, stem, root and flower. These organs are made from a small number of tissues. While plants may not have complex bodies like animals they are capable of a very wide range of chemical reactions. Photosynthesis is just one example.

Plant tissues

The tissues in plants are used for

- protection
- storage of food and water
- photosynthesis
- transport and support.

Throughout the body of a plant there is a transport tissue that takes water from the roots to all the parts of the plant. This tissue is the **xylem**. It is like the pipework in a house. Xylem is also a support tissue for plants.

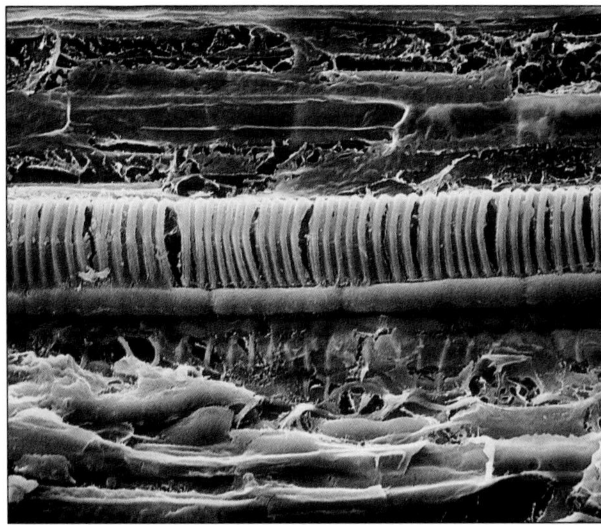

This is xylem tissue that transports water to all parts of a plant. The individual 'pipes' are chains of hollow cells often strengthened with rings of hard material to stop them breaking or collapsing.

Plant organs

QUESTIONS

1 Make a table showing the main systems and the organs of which they are made **a** for a human and **b** for a plant.

2 Explain the following terms: organ system, organ and tissue.

3 Explain why the stomach contains **a** muscle tissue and **b** glandular tissue.

4 What is the function of xylem in a plant?

5 Why do you think animals have more organs than plants?

1.3 *Cells*

Working together

Your tissues are made of millions of cells, each with its own function. A cell is the smallest unit of life able to control its own activities. It relies on the rest of the body to provide it with the raw materials it needs to survive and to remove its waste. Cells depend on each other. Survival of the whole organism depends on them working together efficiently.

Plant and animal cells

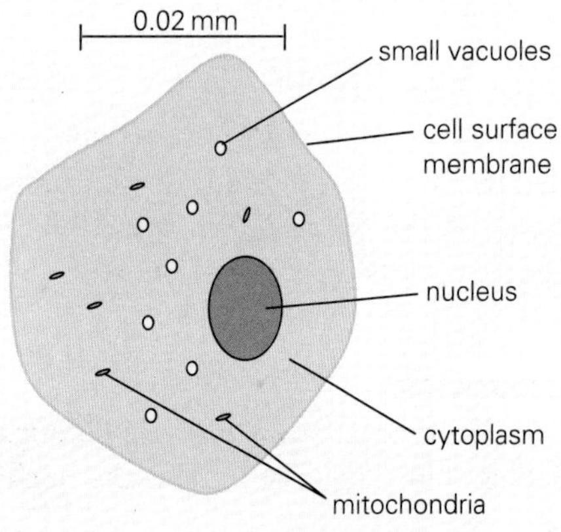

*This diagram shows an **animal cell**.*

0.04 mm
cytoplasm
cell wall
cell surface membrane
large central vacuole
nucleus
chloroplast
mitochondria
membrane surrounding vacuole
starch grain

*This diagram shows a **plant cell**. It is a cell from a leaf.*

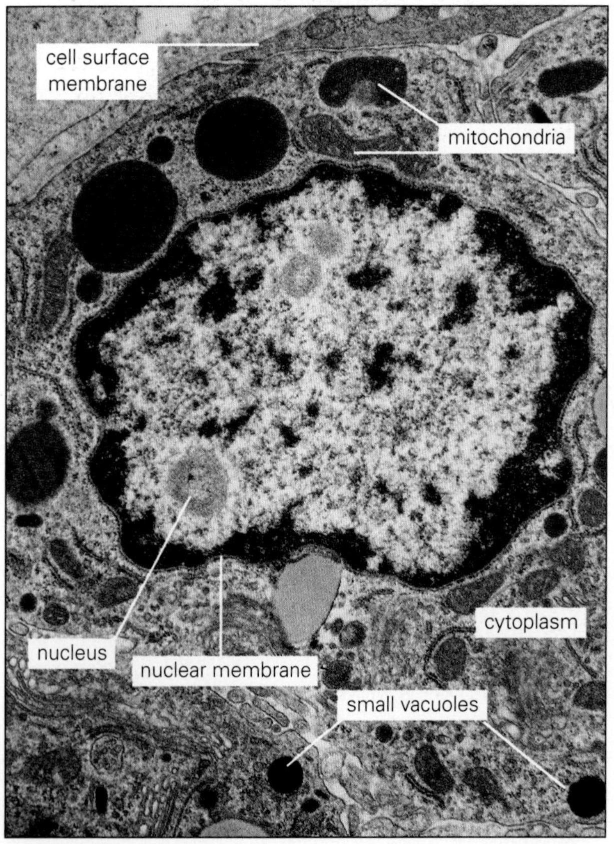

This electron micrograph shows a human cheek cell.

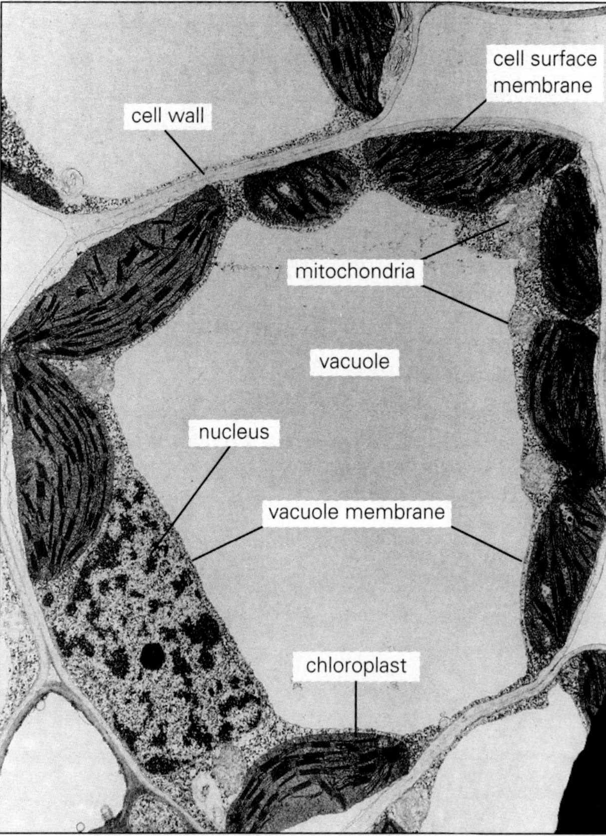

This electron micrograph shows a single leaf cell.

Similarities

You can see from the diagrams and photographs that both plant and animal cells have similarities.

- **Cytoplasm** Most of the chemical reactions that occur in cells take place in the cytoplasm. Most of the cytoplasm is water, but it contains many large molecules in solution so has the consistency of a partly set jelly.
- **Cell surface membrane** The cell surface membrane controls the movement of substances in and out of the cell.
- **Nucleus** This contains **chromosomes**, which are made of DNA (see 6.11). Nuclei control the activities of cells by sending instructions to the cytoplasm.

Differences

In some ways plant cells are different from animal cells. Plant cells:

- are usually larger than animal cells.
- are surrounded by a **cell wall**. A plant cell wall contains **cellulose** which supports and strengthens it.
- often have **chloroplasts**. Chloroplasts contain the green pigment chlorophyll, which absorbs light for photosynthesis. Chlorophyll is only found in chloroplasts.
- have large **vacuoles**. These are filled with **cell sap** which is a solution in water of substances needed by the cell. The solution also presses outwards on the cell wall, which is rigid. This helps to support stems, leaves, roots and flowers.

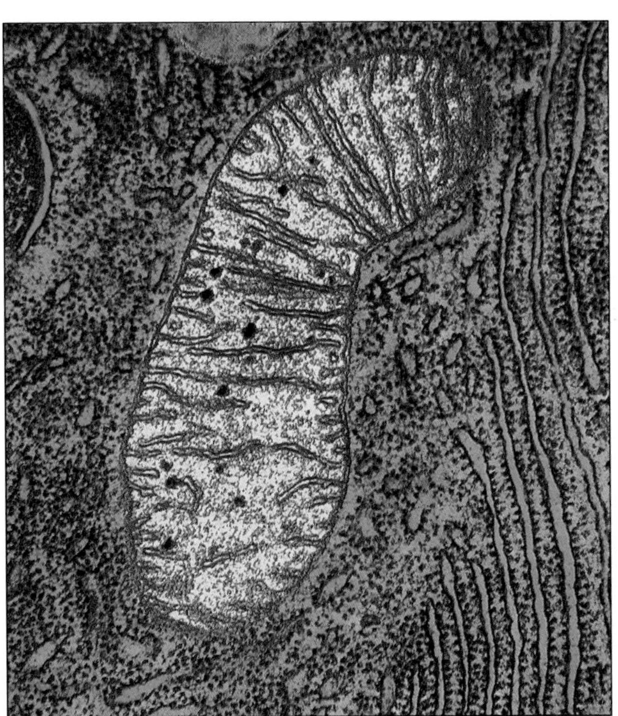

Mitochondria

Membranes inside cells surround small compartments or organelles. The largest of these is the nucleus.

Most of the energy used by cells is produced in organelles called **mitochondria** (singular, **mitochondrion**). Cells keep and concentrate most of the chemicals needed for the chemical reactions of respiration in the mitochondria. This is a more efficient arrangement than having these chemicals distributed randomly throughout the cytoplasm. Cells which use a great deal of energy have many mitochondria.

The mitochondrion (× 20 000). This organelle is found in both plant and animal cells.

QUESTIONS

1 Explain the following terms: cell, nucleus, cytoplasm and cell surface membrane.

2 List the structures that are found in both plant and animal cells.

3 Make a table to show the differences between plant and animal cells.

4 What are the functions of the following in plant cells: chloroplast, cell wall, vacuole?

5 Explain why some cells have many mitochondria.

1.4 *Scanners and microscopes*

Looking inside

You can look inside the human body using X–rays to view the hard parts of the body, such as the skeleton. Radio waves transmitted through the body give scans of the soft tissues and organs as well as the bones. These are used to give cross sections or slices of the body. Computers can build 3D images of organs from a series of cross sections. These imaging techniques can show what is happening in the soft organs of the body such as the brain, heart, lungs, stomach, liver and kidneys.

Cells are very small

Cells are too small to see without the aid of a microscope. Biologists use two types of microscope

- the light microscope, and
- the electron microscope.

Light microscopes

Using a light microscope, a magnified image is made using light waves. Light microscopes are used to look at small organisms and at living tissues and cells. You can watch many processes such as cell division (see 6.4) through a light microscope.

A light microscope can magnify up to 400 times. It uses two lenses: an eyepiece lense, which you look through; and an objective lens, which is slightly above the object you are looking at. Look out for photographs in this book taken through light microscopes.

The table shows how to calculate the total magnification of an image in a light microscope using one eyepiece lens (× 10) and three different objective lenses (× 5, × 10 and × 40).

	Total magnification with objective lenses		
eyepiece lens × 10	**objective lens**		
	× 5	× 10	× 40
Total magnification	× 50	× 100	× 400

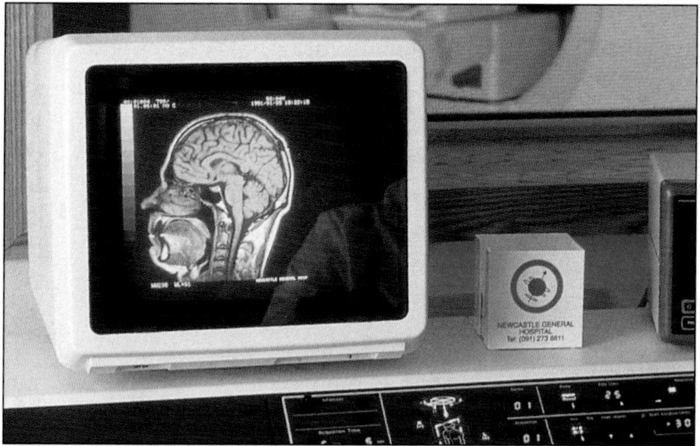

This image of the brain and spinal cord was produced by radio waves in a whole body scanner. Bones and soft tissues are visible.

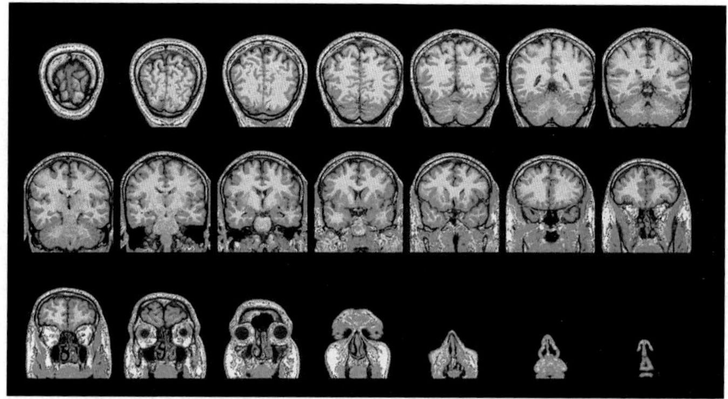

This photograph shows a series of scans through the head from the back (top left) to the tip of the nose (lower right). These images are useful in diagnosing brain tumours.

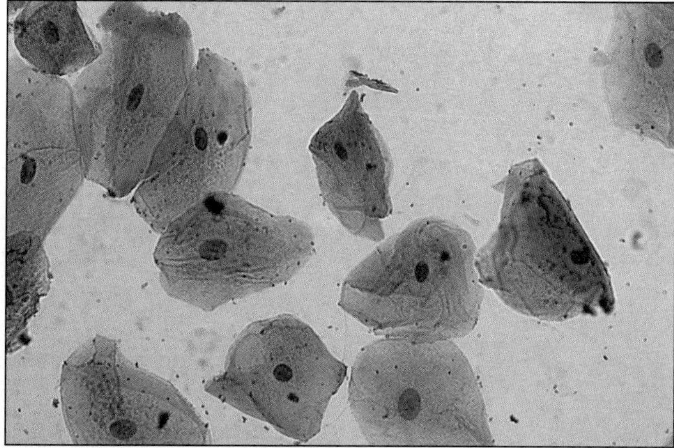

These cells have been scraped from inside the mouth and stained to show cytoplasm and nuclei.

Tissues from animals and plants are often not easy to see with the light microscope because they are transparent. To show them clearly a stain like iodine or methylene blue may be used.

The best light microscopes do not give good images at magnifications greater than × 1500. At magnifications greater than this the images we see become blurred and indistinct.

Electron microscopes

An electron microscope reveals more detail. It uses a beam of electrons, not light, to form an image. When tissues are prepared for the electron microscope they must be cut into very thin sections so that electrons will penetrate the tissue. The sections are stained to give contrast so you see dark and light areas in electron microscope photographs. Some of the photographs in this book are taken with an electron microscope but have been coloured to make them more attractive.

Cells must be completely free of water before you can look at them with an electron microscope. As a result of the drying process they are killed so you cannot see living cells as you can with the light microscope.

Magnifications up to × 250 000 are possible with an electron microscope without losing clarity. Look at the photographs in this book which have been taken with an electron microscope (for example in 1.2).

The person using this scanning electron microscope is looking at two images of an insect's leg. The scan on the right shows enlarged detail of the image on the left.

The surfaces of animals, plants and microbes can be viewed in a scanning electron microscope to give 3D images. The material is first coated in a metal and then scanned with an electron beam to give very detailed images.

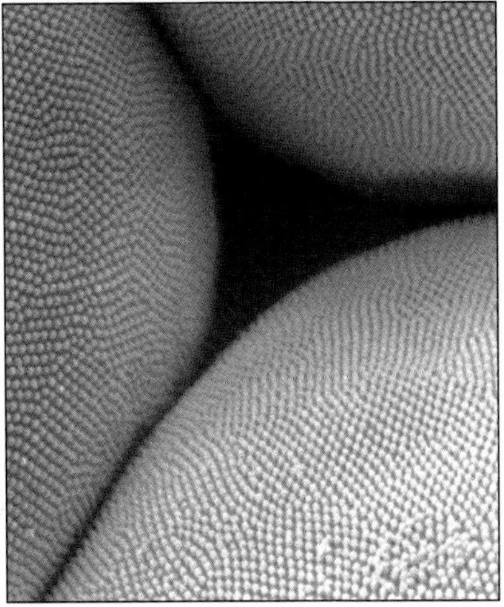

Scanning electron microscopes give 3D images like these of a mosquito's head. The image at the top is enlarged × 50, on the left × 500, and on the right × 5000.

QUESTIONS

1 Describe how it is possible to produce images of the whole human body.

2 Explain how to calculate the total magnification using a light microscope.

3 Summarise the advantages and disadvantages of using light and electron microscopes.

1.5 *Diffusion and active transport*

Diffusion

Molecules in gases move about in a random fashion. They move about freely, colliding with one another and, in the end, filling up any available space. This spreading out is called **diffusion**.

Diffusion happens when there is a high concentration of molecules in one place and a lower concentration in another. This difference in concentrations is known as a **concentration gradient**. Molecules move from areas where there is a high concentration to where there is a low concentration, that is *down* the concentration gradient.

The motion of molecules causes them to spread out evenly, mixing until the concentration throughout the available space is the same. Once this has happened there is no concentration gradient. Diffusion occurs in the same way in liquids, but more slowly.

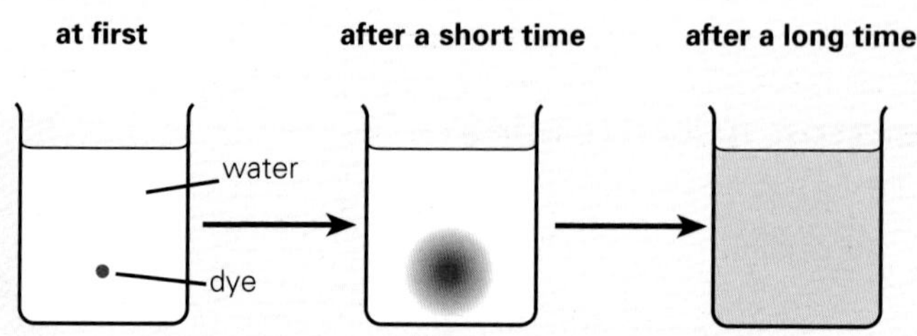

When a drop of dye is put into a beaker of water it gradually spreads through the water in the beaker by diffusion.

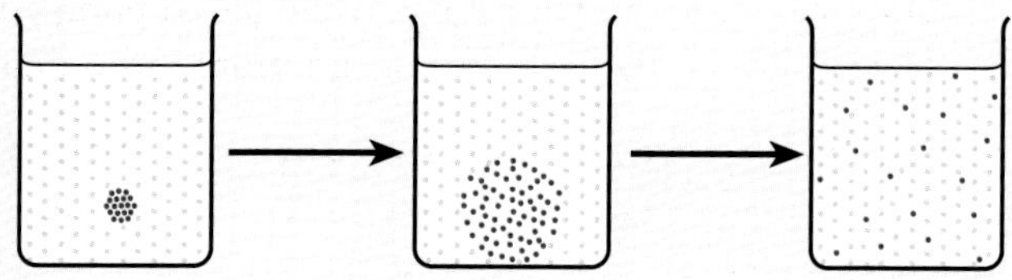

This shows that the molecules of the dye are spreading out through the water.

Diffusion in cells

Diffusion is one of the ways in which molecules move into and out of cells. Molecules move down their concentration gradient across the cell surface membrane. This does not require cells to use energy so the movement of molecules through the cell membrane by diffusion is **passive**. Diffusion is made more efficient by:

- having a short distance for molecules to diffuse
- maintaining a steep concentration gradient
- increasing the surface area over which diffusion occurs.

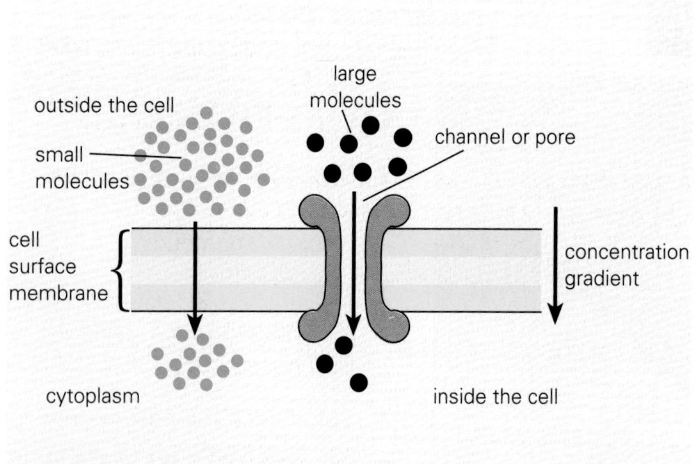

This diagram shows a cross-section of a membrane. Larger molecules diffuse through special channels made of protein.

Cell membranes

All cells are surrounded by a cell surface membrane. A membrane is very thin and forms a boundary between cells and their surroundings. Cell surface membranes control the movement of molecules in and out of cells. They are **partially permeable** allowing only small molecules like oxygen, carbon dioxide and water to pass through very easily but not larger molecules. Cell surface membranes have channels or pores to take up large molecules.

Plant cells have cell walls in addition to cell surface membranes. Cell walls are fully permeable to water and all dissolved substances. They are not a barrier to large molecules.

Adapted for diffusion

Animals and plants rely on diffusion for the exchange of carbon dioxide and oxygen with their surroundings. In animals, oxygen diffuses from the air across the lining of the lungs into the blood; carbon dioxide diffuses in the opposite direction (see 2.6).

Some cells are adapted for diffusion. Human lungs provide a good example. The surface of the lungs where oxygen and carbon dioxide are exchanged is lined by a very thin layer of cells. There is a short **diffusion distance** between the air and the blood so it only takes an oxygen molecule about 0.0004 seconds to travel across. You maintain steep concentration gradients for oxygen and carbon dioxide by continually breathing in more air. This keeps a high concentration of oxygen in your lungs while blood pumped into the lungs by your heart has less oxygen and more carbon dioxide.

The lungs provide a very large **surface area** available for this diffusion. If the total surface area of the lungs was all stretched out it would cover about 70 m^2 (about half the area of a tennis court).

Other cells are adapted in a similar way, for example the villi in the small intestine (see 2.3), leaf cells (see 5.1) and root hair cells (see 5.5). These all provide large surface areas for efficient diffusion.

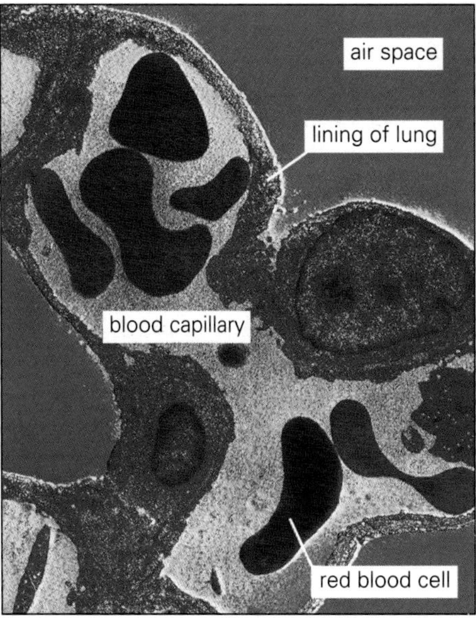

These cells form the lining of the lungs (see 2.6). They are very thin so that oxygen and carbon dioxide do not have far to diffuse. The distance between the air and the blood is only 0.001 mm.

Active transport

Cells do not obtain all the substances they need by diffusion. Often the required substances are in very low concentrations in the surroundings. Cells can move these molecules *against* their concentration gradient across the cell surface membrane and keep them at high concentration inside the cytoplasm.

This is **active transport**. The cells use energy from respiration to move molecules across membranes. You will find examples of this in plant roots (see 5.6) and in the kidney (see 2.11).

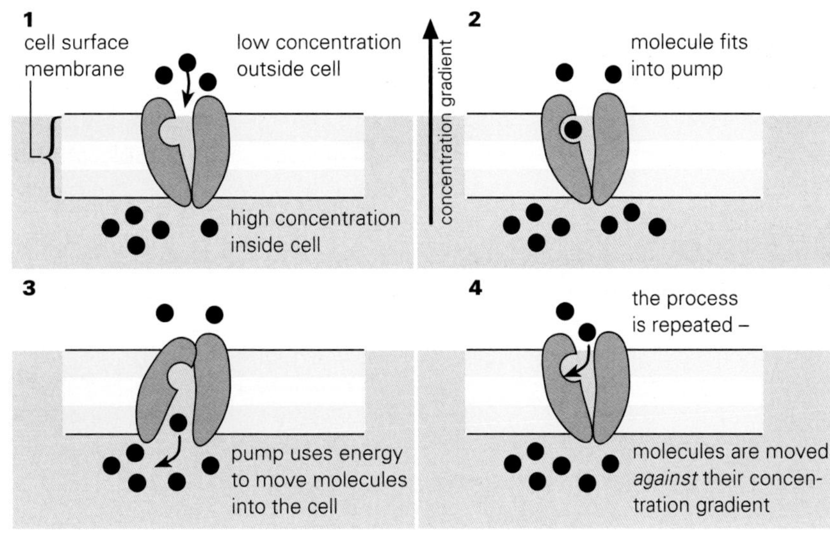

Active transport enables cells to absorb substances such as sugars and minerals as ions from very dilute solutions.

QUESTIONS

1 Explain the following terms: cell surface membrane, partially permeable, diffusion, concentration gradient.

2 Describe the process of diffusion and explain why it happens.

3 Why is diffusion described as a passive process?

4 Explain why diffusion is important to plants and animals.

5 Describe two ways in which human cells are adapted to increase the efficiency of diffusion.

1.6 *Osmosis*

A special type of diffusion

Cells contain large molecules which do not diffuse through cell surface membranes. The partially permeable cell membranes allow small molecules like water to pass through but large molecules cannot. When a cell is surrounded by a solution which is more dilute than the one inside it, water diffuses into the cell through the surface membrane. This diffusion of water across a partially permeable membrane from a dilute solution to a more concentrated one is called **osmosis**.

The diagram shows a bag made of an artificial membrane called Visking tubing. The tubing represents the partially permeable membrane of a cell and the concentrated sugar solution represents its cytoplasm. The tubing is immersed in water as shown.

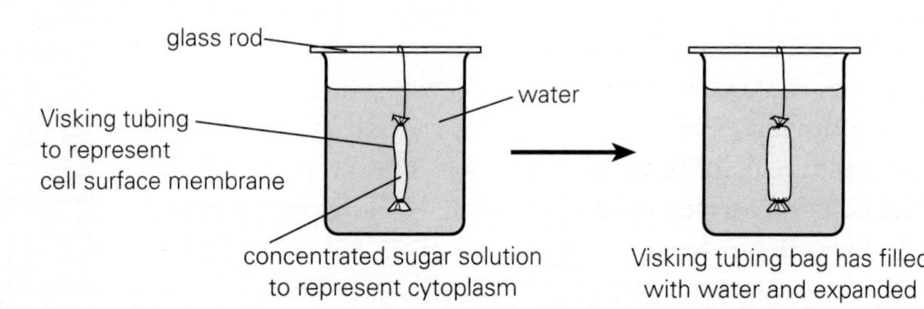

The Visking tubing bag is a model of a cell. After a little while it fills up with water.

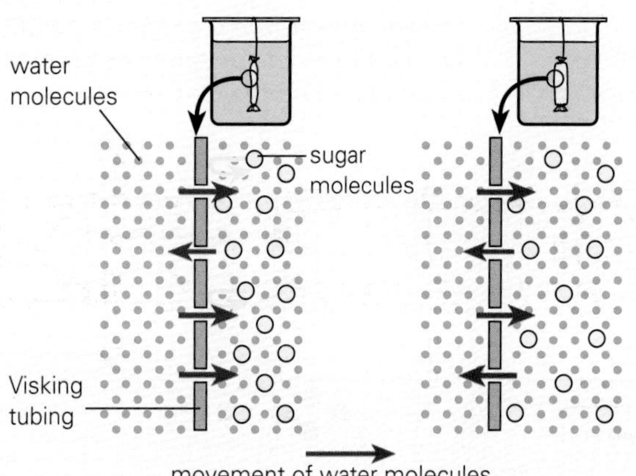

In this model small water molecules can pass through holes in the membrane. The sugar molecules are larger and so stay inside the cell.

More water molecules diffuse across the Visking tubing membrane into the sugar solution than move in the opposite direction. The sugar molecules in the tubing cannot easily diffuse out of the bag because they cannot pass through the tubing.

If the water in the beaker was replaced with a dilute sugar solution, there would still be a concentration gradient and water would diffuse in the same direction into the more concentrated solution.

Osmosis is a special type of diffusion in which two solutions are separated by a partially permeable membrane which allows the movement of water molecules, but not the large molecules like sugar. Water diffuses from a dilute solution to a concentrated one.

Animal cells and osmosis

Red blood cells contain a solution of salts and other substances. When placed in distilled water they expand. This happens because water diffuses through the cell surface membrane into the cells by osmosis. The membrane of each cell is slightly elastic, but it cannot stretch very much so the cells burst. The diagram shows this.

When placed in a strong salt solution red blood cells shrink. This time water diffuses out of the cells by osmosis and the cells decrease in volume. To prevent cells swelling or shrinking, the plasma in which red blood cells are suspended must not become too dilute or too concentrated.

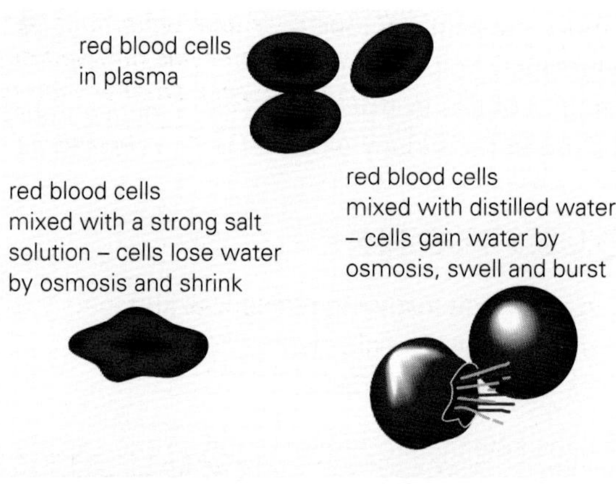

This shows what happens to red blood cells in plasma, in salt solution and in distilled water.

Plant cells and osmosis

This investigation shows the importance of osmosis to plants. Small pieces of potato of equal size and shape are placed in solutions of distilled water, dilute sugar and concentrated sugar. Changes to their shape and size are noted.

In water plant cells increase in size. Water enters the cells by osmosis causing them to swell a little because the cell wall will stretch slightly (the cells are turgid). The cells do not burst because cell walls are tough and strong. This increase in size is reversible – if the cells are placed into a strong sugar solution they decrease in size. This is because water diffuses out of the cells by osmosis. If the sugar solution is strong enough then the vacuole in the cell shrinks pulling the cell membrane and cytoplasm away from the cell wall, known as **plasmolysis** (the cells are not turgid). If many of the cells are like this then the plant will wilt.

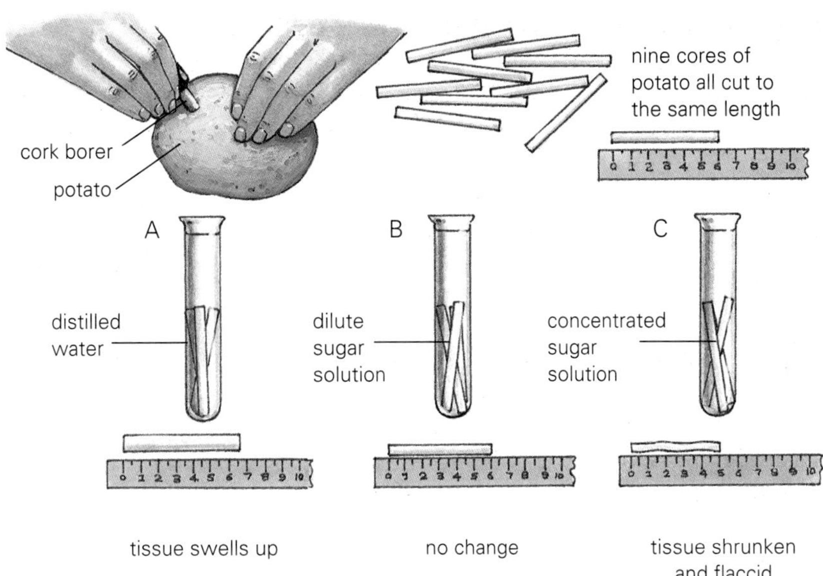

Investigating osmosis in plant tissues.

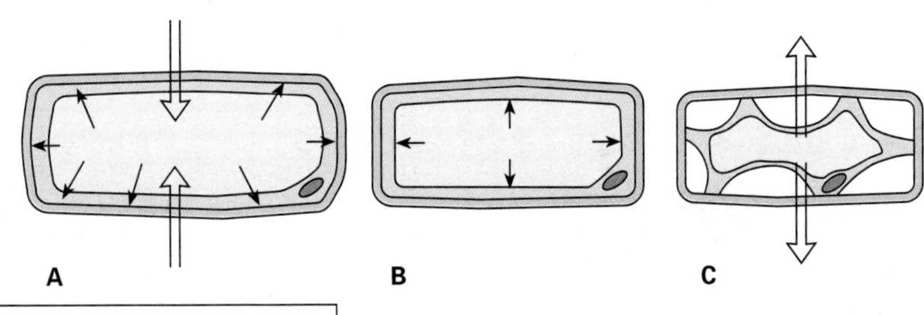

***A** Absorption of water by osmosis makes cells firm and turgid. They have all increased in mass and lengthened a little.*

***B** The vacuole contains a solution of salts and other substances. These cells have not gained or lost water. They have not changed in mass or length.*

***C** The cells lose water and become flabby (flaccid). Water has diffused out by osmosis leaving the cells smaller than before.*

key
diffusion of water
pressure exerted by vacuole on cell wall

This diagram shows what happens to the cells in the potato cores A, B and C above.

QUESTIONS

1 Explain why osmosis is a special kind of diffusion.

2 Explain why red blood cells burst when placed in water.

3 Why do plant cells not burst when placed in water?

4 Explain why plant cells kept in a strong sugar solution will show plasmolysis.

5 Plan an investigation to find out what happens to the mass of small onions when placed in different concentrations of salt solutions.

SECTION A: QUESTIONS

1 Explain how animals and plants feed.

2 Write a list of the stimuli to which animals and plants respond.

3 Describe how the movement of animals differs from the movement of plants.

4 State whether the following are cells, tissues or organs:
xylem, leaf, muscle, liver, stomach, stem, root.

5 Outline briefly how organ systems in humans provide the body with:

a food

b oxygen.

6 Make labelled drawings of an animal cell and a plant cell.

7 Where in a plant cell are the following found: cellulose, starch, protein, DNA?

8 Put the following parts of a plant cell in order of increasing size:
protein molecule, mitochondrion, nucleus, chloroplast, chromosome.

9 The epidermis is the tissue that covers the surfaces of leaves. The drawing shows an epidermis as seen through a light microscope.

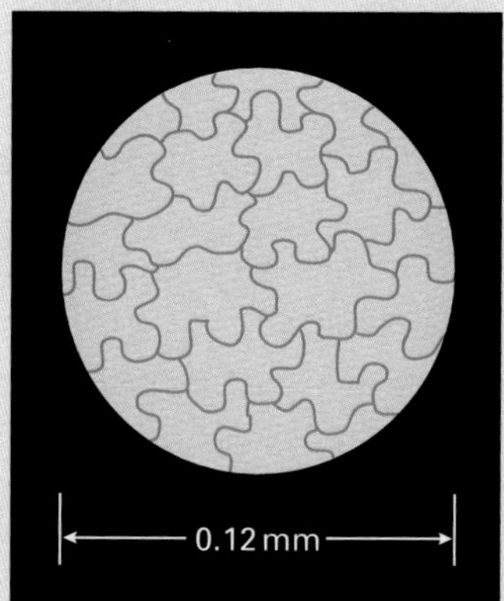

a Calculate the area of the field of view in mm^2 (area of circle = πr^2).

b Count the number of complete cells you can see in the picture and calculate how many there are in 1 mm^2.

c Suggest a function for these cells.

10a Explain how diffusion occurs.

b Describe how you would find out if Visking tubing is permeable to a coloured reagent such as iodine.

c Explain why cell surface membranes are described as partially permeable.

d Explain why cells use active transport to absorb substances from their surroundings.

11 Describe how the following cells help to maximise diffusion:

a cells lining the small intestine

b cells lining the lungs.

12 The drawing shows two different views of muscle cells from the lining of the stomach.

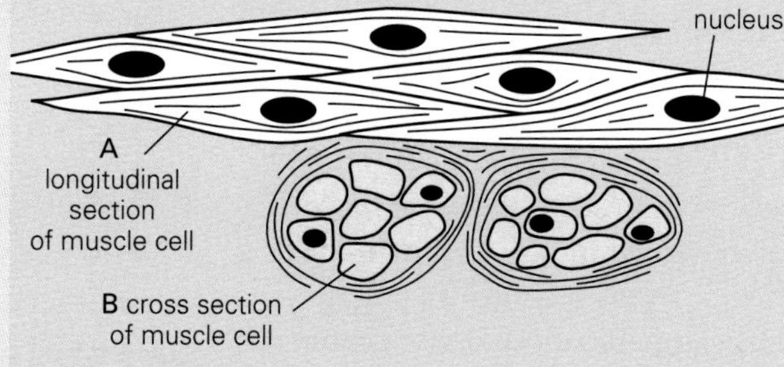

a Explain why nuclei are only seen in a few of the cells in **B**.

b Describe the function of muscle tissue in the stomach.

13 Five pieces of Visking tubing 14 cm long were tied at one end and each filled with a different sugar solution until they weighed 10 g. After filling, the air was expelled from the tubing and it was tied at the other end. The bags were then suspended in beakers of distilled water. After six hours they were taken out, surface dried and reweighed. The results are shown in the table.

Concentration of sugar solution (g per litre)	Mass after 6 hours (g)
60	12.3
120	15.8
180	18.4
240	20.0
300	21.4

a Draw a graph of the results shown in the table.
b Explain these results.
c Describe how you would improve the reliability of these results.
d Predict what you think will happen if the bags are left in the beakers of water for a further 24 hours.

14 Sultanas are dried grapes. They contain a large quantity of sugar. Thirty of them were divided into two groups of fifteen and used in an experiment on osmosis. First their volume was measured by placing them into a measuring cylinder containing water. Then fifteen of them were placed into a beaker of strong sugar solution and the other fifteen were placed in distilled water. After 24 hours they were taken out and the volumes measured again. The results are shown in the table.

Time (hours)	Volume of sultanas (cm^3)	
	in sugar solution	in distilled water
0	5.0	4.0
24	8.0	12.0

a Write out the steps you would take to measure the volume of the sultanas accurately.
b Explain the changes in volume of the sultanas which were kept for 24 hours in:
  i water
  ii sugar solution.
c What would you expect to happen to the sultanas if they were transferred from distilled water to a strong sugar solution?

15 A drop of blood was put on a microscope slide and mixed with some strong salt solution. A coverslip was added and the cells observed under high power.
a **i** Describe what you would see happening to the red blood cells as you observed them under the microscope.
  ii Give an explanation for your answer.
b Another drop of blood was mixed with some distilled water on a microscope slide. When observed at high power, no cells were visible at all. Explain this result.
c Describe the appearance of plant cells under the microscope after they have been kept in a strong salt solution.
d Describe what would happen to plant cells that were then transferred from a strong salt solution to distilled water.

16 Six cores were cut from a potato, weighed and then placed into six different sugar solutions. After 24 hours they were removed, surface dried and reweighed. The results are shown below.

Concentration of sugar solution (g per litre)	Mass of cores (g)	
	at the beginning	after 24 hours
0	3.60	4.00
40	3.20	3.32
80	3.04	2.97
120	3.64	3.32
160	2.75	2.30
200	2.95	2.28

a Make a table to show the change in mass of each core.
b Calculate the percentage change in mass of each core.
c Plot a graph of percentage change against concentration of sugar solution.
d Why is it better to think about percentage change rather than actual change in mass?
e Explain fully why some cores increased in mass while others showed a decrease.
f **i** Describe how you would find the sugar concentration in which the cores would not change in mass.
  ii Explain why, at one sugar concentration, there would not be a change in mass.
g Explain why plants growing in gardens near the coast wilt when they are flooded with sea water.

2.1 *Food for energy*

You eat food to give you energy, and to provide the substances you need for growth and for repairing damage to your body. Your body is composed of many complex substances such as **fats**, **proteins** and **carbohydrates**. The food you eat each day (your **diet**) must contain these materials so that you remain healthy.

Everyone eats food for energy and to provide building blocks for new growth.

Fuel for the body

Cells in the body obtain energy from carbohydrates, fats and proteins. Energy is needed:

- for muscle contraction in movement, eating and digestion
- for body maintenance, e.g. the heart pumps blood, the kidneys produce urine and the liver generates heat to keep the body warm
- to help body cells make the substances they need to work properly, e.g. some cells build glucose up into glycogen which is stored in the liver and the muscles as a reserve energy supply.

How much energy?

If you play a lot of sport, or have a job that involves much hard, physical work, then you need to eat more energy-containing foods than people who sit at a desk all day. The table shows how much energy is required by people of different ages and occupations. When women are pregnant or breast-feeding they need to increase the amount of energy-rich food they consume to provide for the fetus or for the baby.

Age/activity	Energy needed in kJ per day	
	male	female
Baby	2 000	2 000
Child	8 500	7 500
Teenager	11 000	8 800
20-year old office worker	10 700	8 100

How do you know how much to eat? The photographs opposite show how much energy someone might take in through his or her diet in a day.

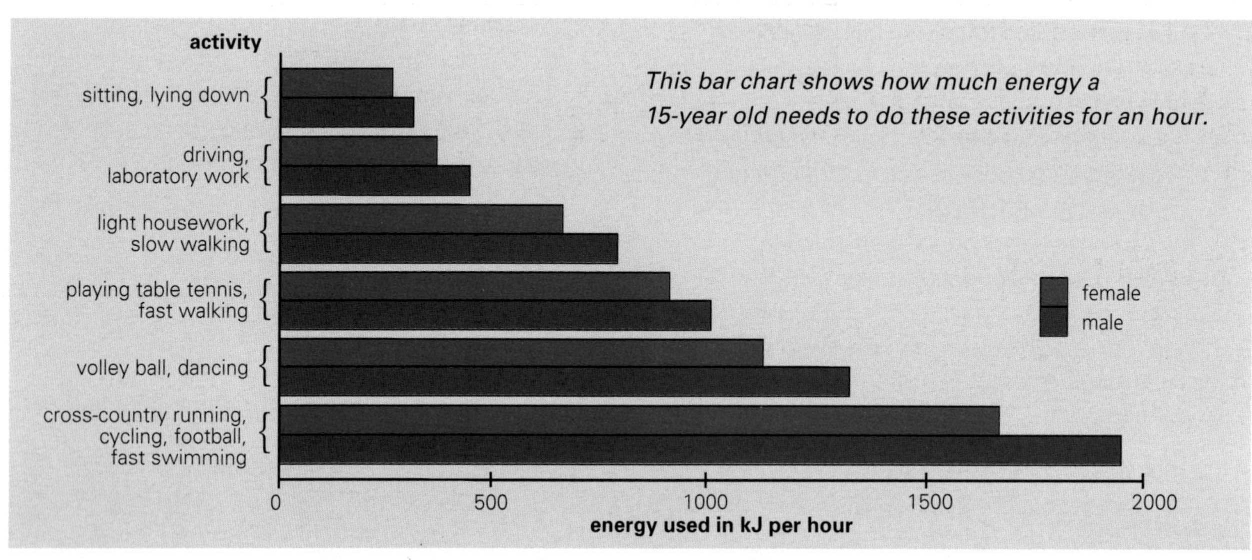

This bar chart shows how much energy a 15-year old needs to do these activities for an hour.

Carbohydrates

Carbohydrates are the most readily available form of energy as they are easily digested and absorbed. The two types of carbohydrates that provide energy are:

- those high in **sugars** – e.g. jams and sweet fruits
- those high in **starch** – e.g. bread, potatoes, chapatti, pasta and cereals.

Proteins

Foods rich in protein e.g. meat, fish and beans provide us with the raw material in the form of amino acids

- for growth
- for the repair of damaged tissues
- to help in the fight against disease.

Too little protein in the diet of children slows down their growth and development. The body makes many different types of protein to carry out different jobs.

Fats

Fats are found in milk, cheese, butter, margarine and vegetable oils. Eating the fats and oils in fatty foods gives us lots of energy and also provides a way of storing energy. In addition fat stored underneath the skin cuts down heat loss. The fatty acids contained in fats are also needed to make cell membranes.

breakfast 2400 kJ

mid-morning snack 2480 kJ

lunch 3850 kJ

dinner 2650 kJ

Total energy content = 11 380 kJ.
This is typical for an active 15–18 year old male.

	Energy in kJ per gram
Carbohydrate	16
Protein	17
Fat	37

The table shows the amount of energy you get from 1 gram of carbohydrate, protein and fat.

QUESTIONS

1 List the three nutrients that provide energy in the diet.

2 List three uses of the fat we eat.

3 List five foods high in energy.

4 Explain why protein is essential in the diet.

5 Explain why we must balance our energy intake with our energy needs.

6 Use the bar chart to calculate approximately how much energy you use in a typical day.

2.2 *Healthy eating*

Have you ever noticed the number of preparations of vitamins and minerals on supermarket shelves? Judging by this it would appear that we need lots of these substances to keep healthy. In fact every day only tiny quantities of vitamins are required but these small amounts are vital to our well-being.

Vitamins

Vitamins are complex chemicals which have little in common with each other except that, if they are missing from your diet, you become unhealthy.

Lack of vitamins (**deficiency**) can lead to disease and possible death. Vitamins A, C, D and E, K and the B group vitamins are all required in your diet.

Vitamin C (ascorbic acid) helps the cells in the skin and the mouth stay healthy. A lack of vitamin C can lead to a condition called scurvy whereby

- your skin does not repair itself
- you develop sores, your gums bleed and your teeth become loose
- your resistance to infection decreases making you susceptible to infectious diseases.

You can get a good supply of vitamin C from green vegetables and citrus fruits like oranges and lemons.

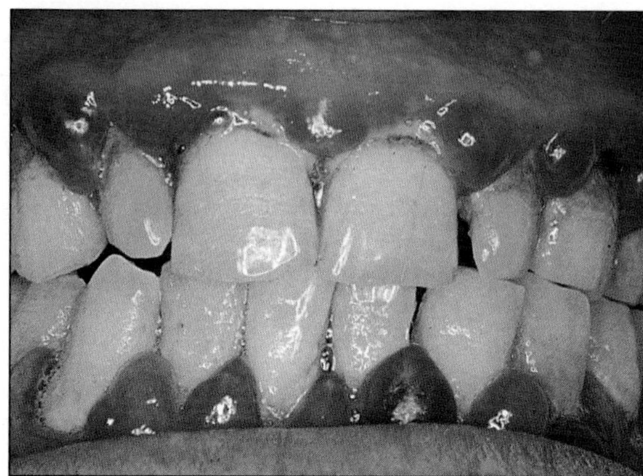

Scurvy is caused by not eating enough vitamin C. This person has inflamed gums.

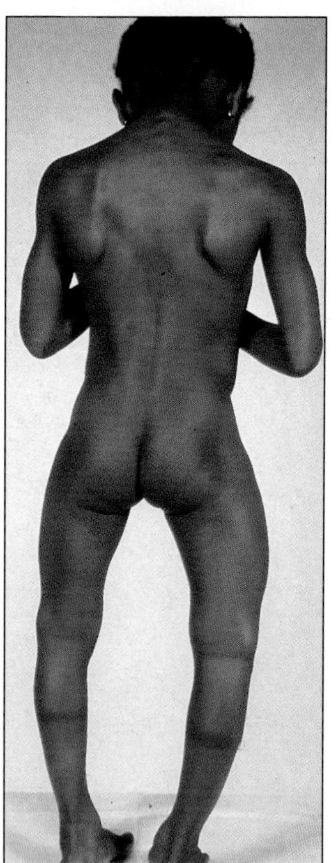

This child is suffering from rickets.

Vitamin D is essential in the formation of healthy, strong bones. Without enough vitamin D, the bones of children do not develop properly - the leg bones bow outwards as they are not strong enough to support the rest of the body. This deficiency disease is called **rickets**. The skin can make vitamin D if exposed to sunlight. However Britain's sunshine does not stimulate the skin to produce enough, so vitamin D must be present in the diet. Dairy products, liver and oily fish contain a good supply of vitamin D.

Vitamin A is used by retina cells in the eye to give good vision in dim light and to protect the front of the eye (see 3.9). Vitamin A deficiency causes the surface of the eye to dry out (known as 'dry eye') and causes poor vision in dim light. In severe cases it can lead to blindness.

Posters like this one from India remind people to take vitamin A supplements.

Mighty minerals

You also need small amounts of minerals such as iron, calcium and iodine. The table shows where they come from, what they do and what happens if you do not get enough of them.

Mineral ions	Main job	Deficiency disease	Good sources
Iron	used to make haemoglobin (see 2.9) in our red blood cells	in **anaemia**, the blood is able to carry less oxygen resulting in tiredness and lack of energy	green vegetables, liver, kidney, eggs or iron tablets to supplement the diet
Calcium	plays a part in making the bones hard and strong	weak bones and teeth: children may develop rickets	milk, cheese and fish
Iodine	used in the thyroid gland to make a hormone (see 3.3) called thyroxine	poor growth in children, and adults become slow and lacking in energy	fish, some brands of table salt have iodine added

Eat some fibre

Fibre in the diet is formed by indigestible material such as cellulose. It passes right through the gut and leaves the body as solid waste in the **faeces**. Fibre keeps the food in our gut soft and moist and so prevents **constipation**. It also lowers the risk of getting bowel cancer and of developing heart disease. Leafy vegetables, bran and brown bread are high in fibre.

Water

It is essential that you constantly replace the water lost in faeces, urine, sweat and breath by drinking between 5 and 7 litres every day – 70% of your body is water.

Getting the balance right

Your diet should contain just enough energy to meet your daily needs and a wide variety of foods rich in protein and fat to give you the amino acids and fatty acids that you need. Your diet should also provide you with all the vitamins, minerals and fibre that you require.

The way to keep healthy is to choose a variety of foods and in the right balance. The pyramid shows examples of four main food groups. The size of the parts of the pyramid gives you some idea of how much food of each group you should eat. Food from the two groups at the base of the pyramid should provide the main part of every meal. You should then add smaller amounts from the other two sections.

Eat food from all of the food groups but in different amounts.

QUESTIONS

1. Make a table showing the sources and functions of vitamins A, C and D. Include the names of the relevant deficiency diseases and the effects of these diseases.
2. Explain why calcium, iron and iodine are needed in the diet.
3. Explain why water and fibre are needed in the diet.
4. Write a leaflet for distribution in a supermarket explaining the need to eat a balanced diet.

2.3 *Digestion*

Why do we digest our food?

We need to break food down into tiny pieces. Then we change the large molecules of starch, protein and fat into small molecules which can be carried in the blood and used by the cells. Digestion involves the *mechanical* breakdown of food into small pieces followed by the *chemical* breakdown of large molecules into small ones.

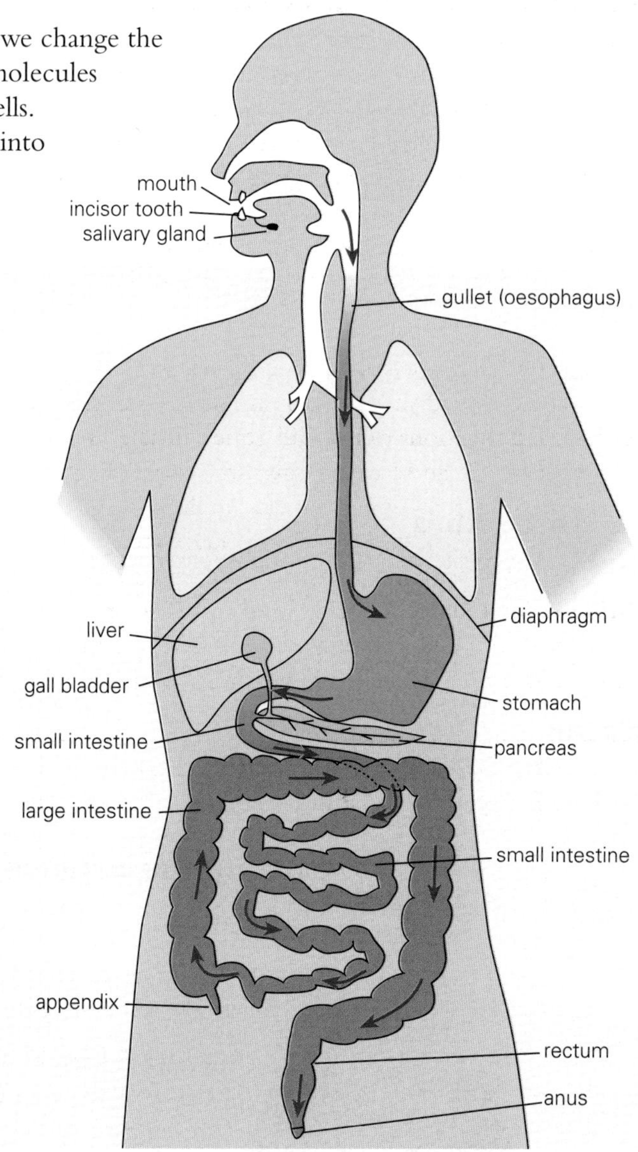

Food in a semi-digested and digested state moves along the gut following a path marked by the arrows.

In the mouth

Mechanical digestion starts in your mouth. An adult should have 32 teeth of four different types. Each type has a different job to do according to its shape. Sharp **incisor** and **canine** teeth at the front of your mouth bite and tear into food. The large, flat **premolar** and **molar** (cheek) teeth crush the large lumps of food into smaller pieces.

When your mouth 'waters', a juice called **saliva** is produced by the salivary glands in your head. Your tongue helps to mix the food and the saliva together making it easier to swallow and pass down the gullet (**oesophagus**) into your stomach.

The gut or digestive tract

The oesophagus is the start of a tube known as the gut or **digestive tract**. The gut is 5–12 metres long and as you can see from the diagram it is not a simple tube. The gut has many different parts. Each of these parts makes a contribution to converting food into a form that can be used by your body's cells.

In the stomach

The muscles in the stomach walls contract mixing the food with gastric juices, which include **hydrochloric acid**, made in the cells lining the stomach (see 1.2). The acid kills any bacteria in the food and also breaks up some of the particles of food especially meat. The stomach stores food until it has been partly broken up and then it is moved, in small amounts, into the small intestine.

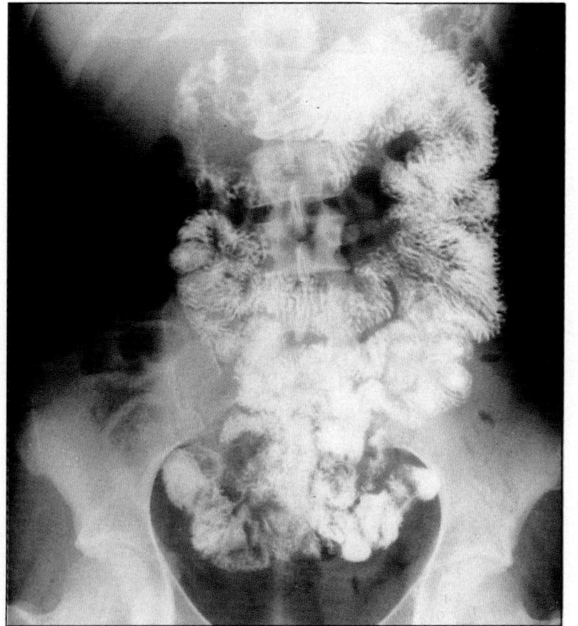

This X-ray photograph shows the stomach and intestines. Barium meal X-rays like these show if there is something wrong with the person's digestive tract.

Absorbtion in the small intestine

The food that enters the small intestine is highly acidic and here it is mixed with alkaline juices from the liver and the pancreas. This neutralises the acid and makes the pH of the small intestine slightly alkaline, about pH 8. Here the food is finally broken down into substances that are small enough to pass through the wall of the intestine into the blood where they can be transported to all parts of the body.

The small intestine is well adapted for absorption. The inside is folded and the folds are covered in small finger-like projections called **villi** (one **villus**). The villi are very thin and have a large surface area. Each villus has many small blood vessels, capillaries, to carry away absorbed sugars, amino acids, water, minerals and water-soluble vitamins like vitamin C. Once the food molecules have been absorbed and transported in the blood, they enter cells where they are used to make new cells and repair the body.

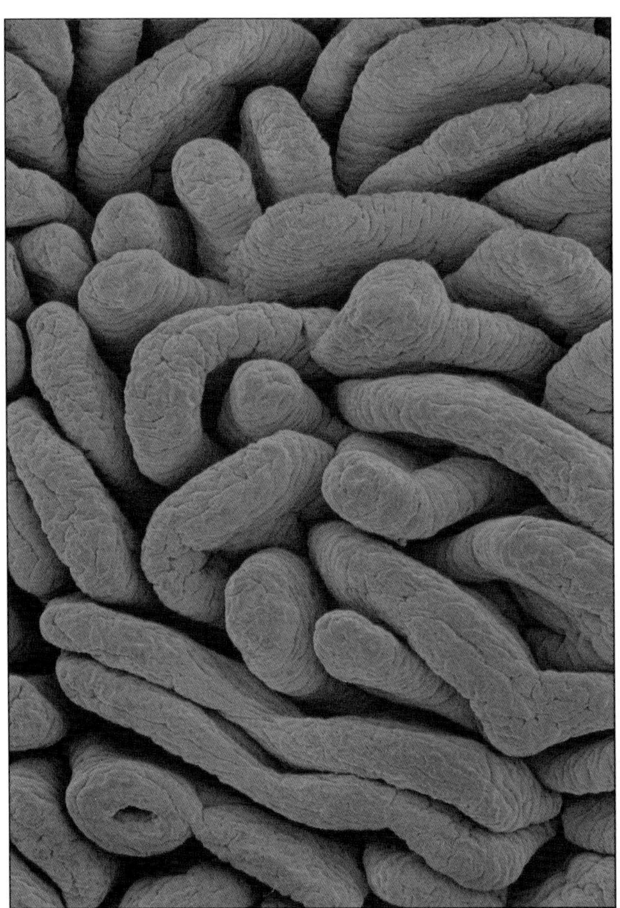

This scanning electron micrograph shows the villi of the small intestine (× 80).

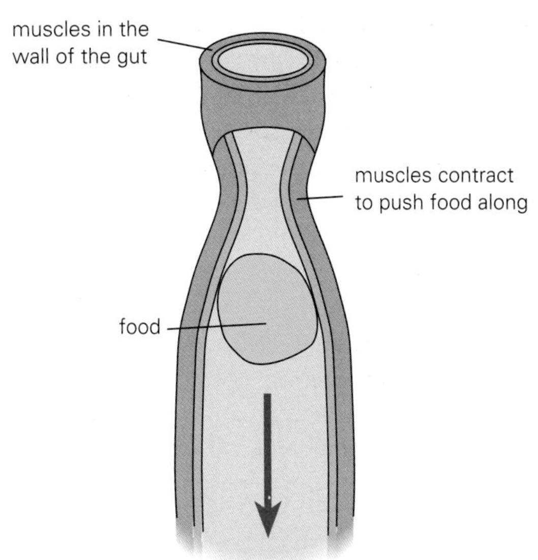

The muscles in the gut wall contract so that food is pushed forwards along the gut. This type of muscular contraction is called ***peristalsis.***

Undigested food

Cellulose present in plant foods such as cereals, fruit and vegetables provides fibre in your diet. Fibre provides bulk against which the muscles in the gut wall can squeeze and push food along. As humans cannot digest it, cellulose passes straight through the small intestine into the first part of the large intestine, the **colon**. Much of the remaining water in food is absorbed here. Cellulose and any other indigestible substances are stored as faeces in the **rectum**. The faeces are passed out at intervals through the **anus**.

QUESTIONS

1 Explain why digestion is necessary.

2 Make a list of the parts of the gut and state their functions.

3 List three ways in which the small intestine is adapted for absorption of food.

4 List two functions of the large intestine.

5 Explain why someone who has to have an X-ray of his or her stomach and intestines must not eat for eight hours beforehand.

2.4 *Enzymes and digestion*

Food

Starch, proteins and fats are large molecules that are insoluble in water. This means that they will not pass through the gut wall into the blood. To be of use to body cells, these large molecules must be changed into small, soluble molecules that can diffuse into the blood – glucose molecules from the breakdown of starch, amino acids from proteins and fatty acids and glycerol from fats. The main function of the digestive system is to bring about these changes.

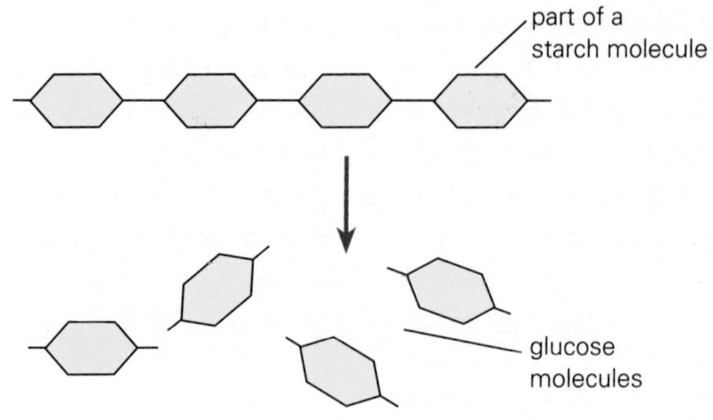

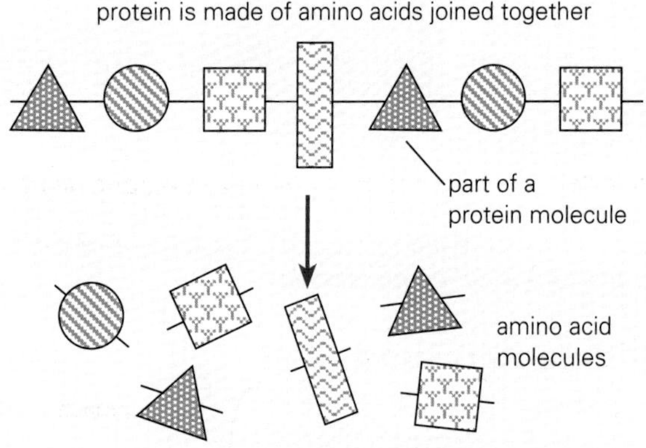

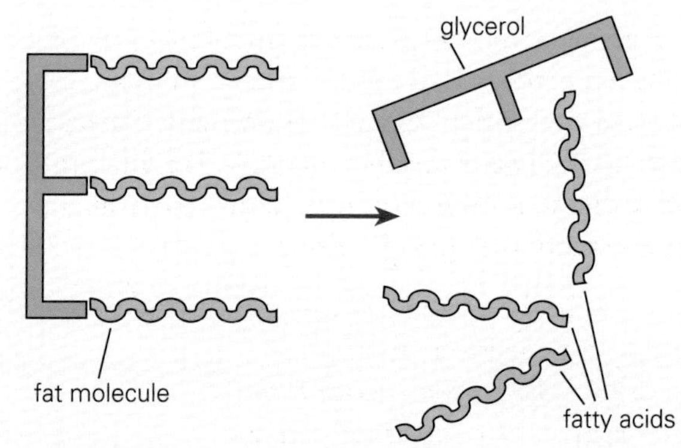

Each of these reactions takes place very slowly in the absence of an enzyme.

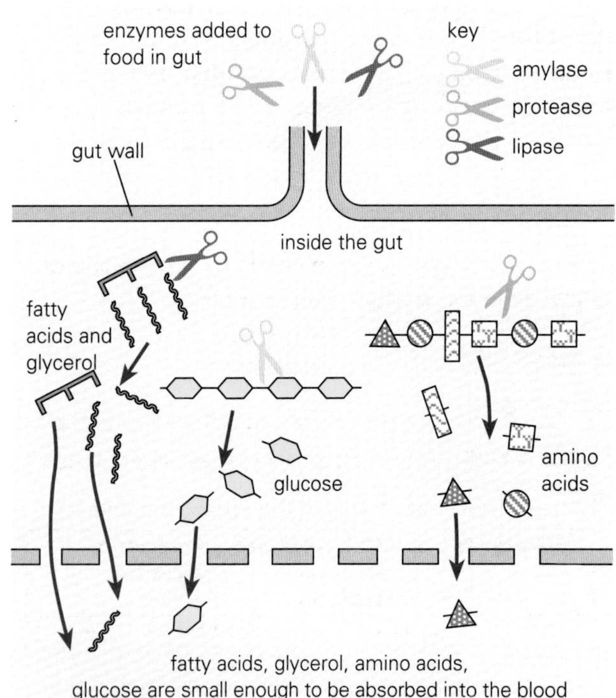

Enzymes catalyse the reactions of chemical digestion.

Biological catalysts

Catalysts are substances that increase the rate of chemical reactions. **Enzymes** are biological catalysts that speed up the reactions that go on inside living things. The enzymes of digestion move into the gut to speed up the breakdown of nutrients from our food. Without enzymes it might take you 20 years to digest a meal.

In common with all other enzymes, digestive enzymes show **specificity**. This means that each enzyme will only catalyse one reaction – it is *specific* to that reaction only. For example the carbohydrase enzyme **amylase** will only catalyse the breakdown of starch to sugar, it will not digest proteins or fats.

Enzyme	Reaction speeded up
carbohydrase, e.g. amylase	starch ⟶ sugars
protease	protein ⟶ amino acids
lipase	fat ⟶ fatty acids and glycerol

Enzyme activity

The activity of human enzymes increases between 0°C and 37°C. The best or **optimum temperature** is body temperature (37°C). Above this temperature, the enzymes lose their specific shape and do not function – they become **denatured**. This is a permanent change so it cannot be reversed. Enzyme activity also varies with pH. Enzymes need a particular pH to work well.

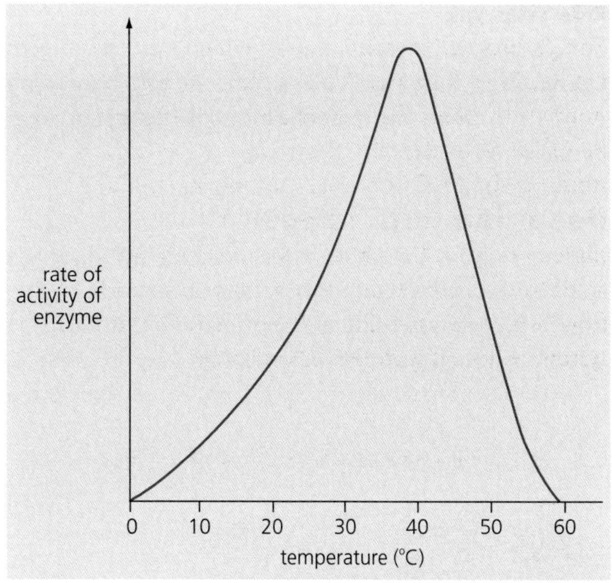

The effect of temperature on an enzyme-controlled reaction.

Digestive enzymes

Amylase is found in saliva in your mouth. This is where the digestion of starch to sugar begins.

Gastric juices in your stomach contain a protease enzyme called **pepsin**. This enzyme, unusual in that it works well in acid conditions, starts the breakdown of proteins. The stomach stores food until it has been partly digested. The food is then moved in small amounts into the small intestine.

Enzymes in the small intestine work most effectively in alkaline conditions. Digestion is completed here using enzymes (carbohydrase, protease and lipase) from the pancreas and some more produced in the small intestine. The products of these reactions are small enough to pass through the wall of the intestine. They are also soluble in water and so can enter the bloodstream for transport to other parts of the body.

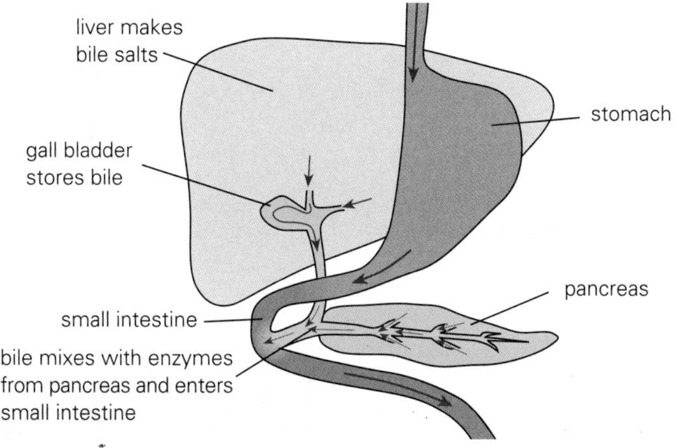

The liver and digestion

Bile is the digestive juice made by the liver. It contains **bile salts** which help with the digestion and absorption of fat. Bile salts are like detergents in that they break up, or **emulsify**, large globules of fats into smaller droplets making them water soluble. These smaller fat droplets provide a much larger surface area for the digestive enzyme lipase to work on. Any excess sugar from the diet is stored in the liver as **glycogen**. Glycogen provides a reserve energy supply during exercise and between meals.

QUESTIONS

1 Where in the gut do the following occur: **a** chewing, **b** digestion of protein, **c** emulsification of fat, **d** absorption of sugar?

2 Explain why digestion is necessary.

3 Explain the term enzyme.

4 Copy and complete this table showing the main digestive enzymes in the human gut.

Name of enzyme	Where made	What substance the enzyme works on	Products of digestion

5 Why do enzymes no longer work if they are boiled?

6 Describe the function of the liver in digestion.

2.5 *Respiration*

On the go

Food is full of chemical energy which the body needs. The process by which the energy from food molecules is released and transferred into other forms is called respiration. How much respiration takes place at any time depends on the body's demand for energy.

Respiring with oxygen

During respiration, glucose, amino acids and fatty acids are broken down by enzymes using oxygen to form carbon dioxide and water. This process takes place step by step transferring energy for use by the cell. This type of respiration using oxygen is called **aerobic respiration**. Aerobic respiration is the complete breakdown of food providing energy for all the activities in the cell.

$$\text{glucose} + \text{oxygen} \longrightarrow \text{carbon dioxide} + \text{water} + \text{energy released}$$

This equation summarises aerobic respiration in which glucose is completely broken down in the presence of oxygen and energy is released. Carbon dioxide is a waste product.

$$C_6H_{12}O_6 + 6O_2 \longrightarrow 6CO_2 + 6H_2O + \text{energy released}$$

This is a balanced chemical equation showing the number of molecules involved in aerobic respiration.

Any reaction where chemicals combine with oxygen, like respiration, is called an **oxidation reaction**.

Energy uses

Energy released in respiration is used for:

- movement
- keeping warm
- growth, repair and reproduction
- making large molecules from small ones.

Energy is needed to turn small molecules from food into large ones for growth and repair.

Muscles, including the heart and the muscles used in breathing, need energy to make them contract.

The bodies of mammals and birds need energy to maintain their temperature above that of their surroundings.

Respiration without oxygen

Sometimes your body cannot breathe fast enough to get enough oxygen to your muscles. This happens during demanding or exhausting activities. Your muscles use up all the available oxygen to release energy from glucose and then they still need more energy. If this happens glucose is broken down by **anaerobic respiration** to **lactic acid**.

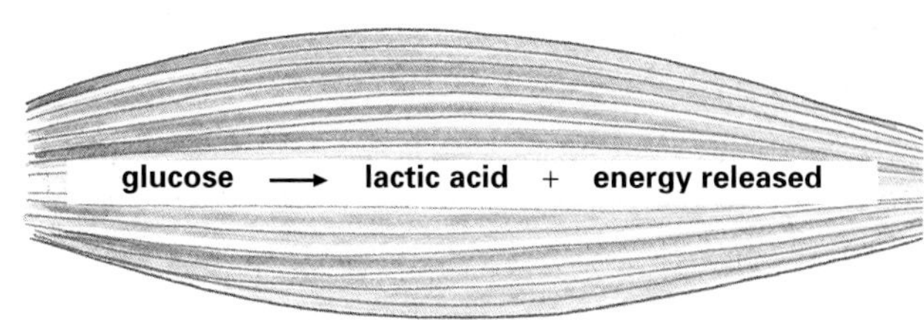

This equation summarises anaerobic respiration.

Anaerobic respiration is an inefficient way of obtaining energy from glucose because:

- the breakdown of glucose is incomplete as carbon dioxide and water are not produced
- molecules of lactic acid still contain a large amount of chemical energy
- after a short time lactic acid builds up in the muscles causing painful cramp and preventing the muscles from working.

Getting rid of lactic acid

Lactic acid has to be oxidised to carbon dioxide and water after exercise is completed but this needs oxygen. The extra oxygen is absorbed from the air you breathe in. If the physically demanding exercise or activity has caused a build up of lactic acid, then an **oxygen debt** is created which has to be repaid. This is why you breathe heavily *after* strenuous exercise.

Deep breathing supplies oxygen to pay off the oxygen debt. Sprinters can run 100 m without breathing.

Mitochondria in respiration

In cells the structures called mitochondria are sometimes called 'powerhouses' because it is here that aerobic respiration takes place. Mitochondria contain nearly all of the enzymes needed for respiration (see 1.3).

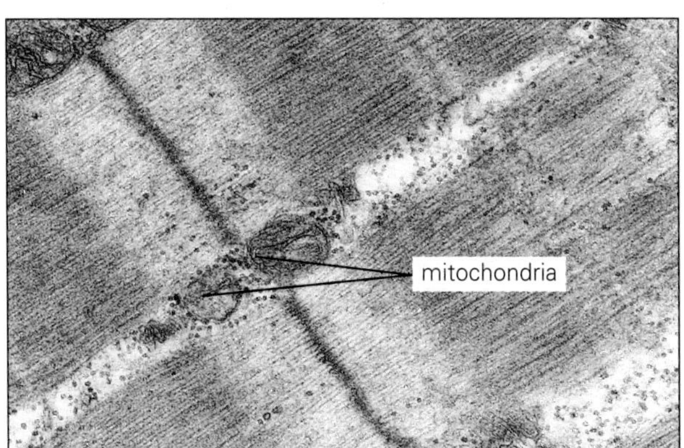

An electron micrograph of mitochondria in muscle. Much respiration takes place in muscle tissue as muscles have a lot of work to do.

QUESTIONS

1. What is the function of respiration?
2. What are the end products of aerobic respiration?
3. When happens to the energy released in respiration?
4. When you stop running you continue to breathe deeply. Explain the reasons for this.
5. Why are there many mitochondria in muscle cells?

2.6 *Breathing*

Filling the lungs

To survive your body needs a constant supply of oxygen for respiration. At the same time carbon dioxide, the waste product of respiration, must be removed since it becomes poisonous if it builds up in your body. **Breathing** provides your body with the constant supply of oxygen you require and removes unwanted carbon dioxide.

When you breathe in, air moves down your **windpipe** (or **trachea**) to fill your **lungs**. The windpipe splits into two parts, one for each lung, called the **bronchi**. The bronchi in turn split into many smaller tubes called **bronchioles**. At the end of each bronchiole there are many tiny air pockets called **alveoli** (singular, **alveolus**). Blood flows through lungs via a network of tiny **capillaries**. The alveoli and capillaries are in very close contact and an exchange of gases takes place between the air in the alveoli and the blood:

- oxygen diffuses from the air in the alveoli into the blood
- carbon dioxide diffuses out of the blood into the air in the alveoli.

Gas	air breathed	
	in %	out %
Oxygen	21	16
Nitrogen	79	79
Carbon dioxide	0.03	4

The table shows the concentration of gases in the air you breathe in and out.

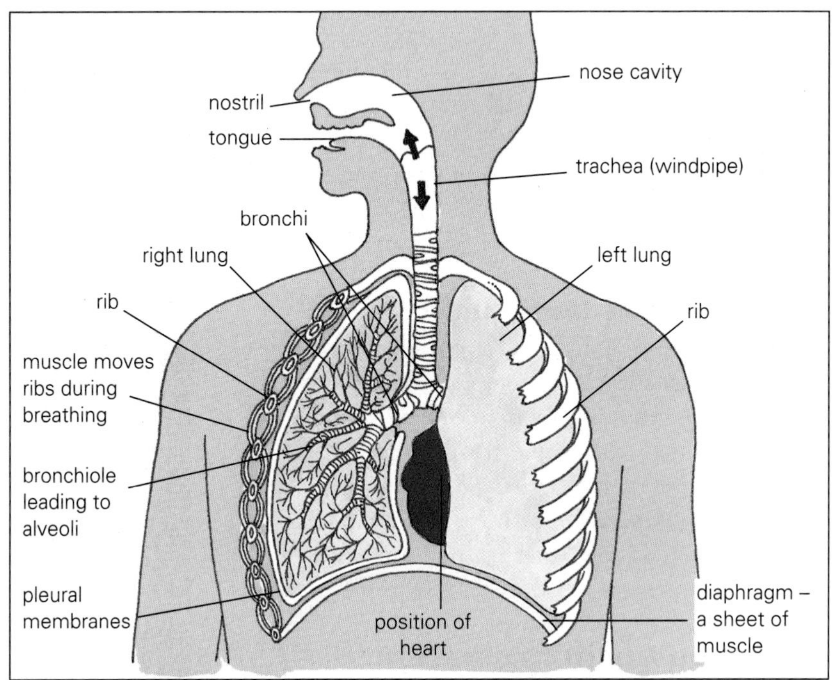

*Lungs are the main organs in your breathing system. They are situated in a cavity in the chest called the **thorax** and surrounded by the **rib cage**.*

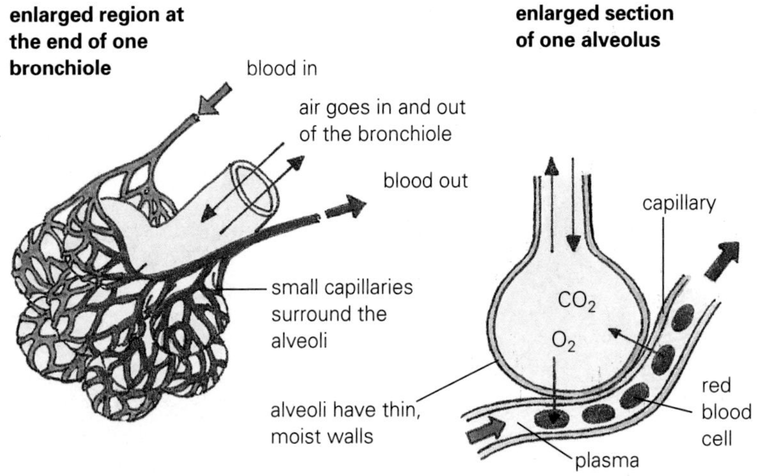

Alveoli are like tiny balloons, each smaller than the point of a pin. Each is surrounded by many capillaries to ensure a good blood supply.

Exchanging gases

There are 300 million alveoli in each lung which together give a very large, thin, damp surface and a good blood supply. This allows gases to pass readily between the air and the blood. Oxygen dissolves in the moist lining of the alveoli and diffuses into the blood because there is a higher concentration of oxygen in the alveoli than in the blood. The blood flowing through the lungs contains more carbon dioxide (from respiration) than the alveoli and so it diffuses out of the blood, into the air in the alveoli. Then it is breathed out from the body (see 1.5).

Breathing in

When you breathe in the muscles in the diaphragm contract so that it flattens and moves downwards. At the same time the muscles between the ribs contract to raise the ribcage and move it outwards. These movements increase the volume of the chest. As the volume of the lungs increases, the air pressure inside decreases to become less than atmospheric pressure. Air is forced into the lungs by the higher pressure outside the lungs.

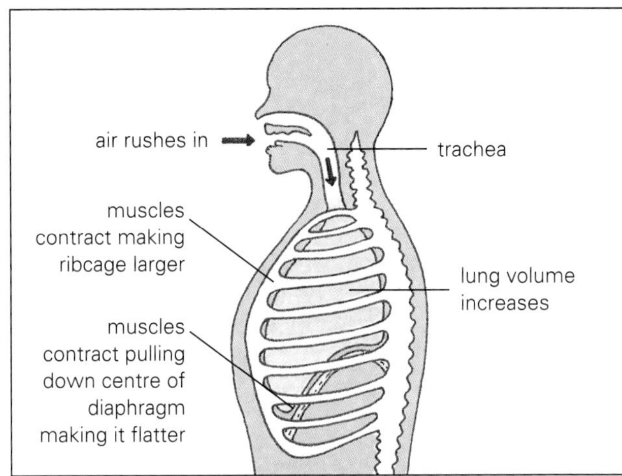

When breathing in the volume of the chest increases and so the lungs fill up with air.

Breathing out

When you breathe out the diaphragm muscles relax so that the diaphragm returns to its resting position arching up into the chest beneath the ribcage. The rib muscles relax and the ribs fall under their own weight. The volume of the chest decreases so that the air pressure in the lungs increases and is greater than atmospheric pressure. Air is forced out of the lungs though they do not empty completely. There is always air left in your lungs so that the exchange of gases goes on all the time.

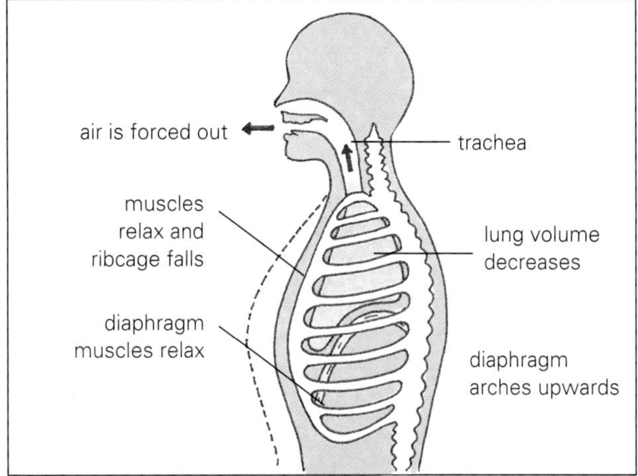

When breathing out the volume of the chest decreases thus raising the pressure in the chest and squeezing air out of the lungs.

Keeping the lungs clean

Dirt as well as air can get into the lungs. To make sure that the air passages and the alveoli do not become blocked or infected, the inhaled air is cleaned by:

- hairs in the nose which trap some dirt particles
- **mucus**, a kind of slime, in all the passageways which traps and removes dust and microbes
- **cilia**, that look like tiny hairs, which beat backwards and forwards, moving mucus from the depth of the lungs towards the nose and throat.

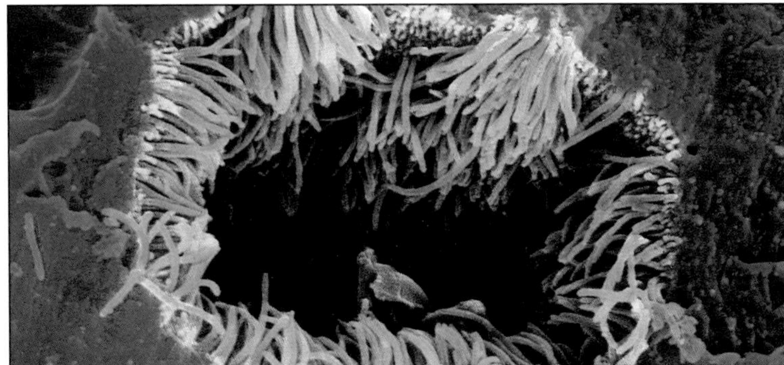

These are the cilia lining a bronchiole (× 1700). Their movement sweeps mucus out of the lung.

QUESTIONS

1. Describe the pathway taken by a molecule of oxygen from the atmosphere to the air in an alveolus.
2. Describe how you breathe air in and out.
3. Explain why it is important for the lungs to be continually supplied with fresh air.
4. Explain how the alveoli are specially adapted for the exchange of gases.
5. Describe how the lungs are kept clean.
6. Plan an investigation to find the effects of different types of exercise on the rate of breathing.

2.7 *The heart*

Transport

Blood supplies every cell in the body with food and oxygen and takes away waste such as carbon dioxide. The body transport system involved in this supply and removal consists of **blood**, **blood vessels** and a double pump, the **heart**.

The heart and circulation

There are four main compartments in the human heart. The top two are called **atria** (one **atrium**). The lower two are called **ventricles**. Much of the wall of the heart is made from muscle fibres. Blood is pumped by the heart to all parts of the body. This is called the **circulation**. **Veins** carry blood to the heart and **arteries** carry blood away from the heart.

On its way round blood passes through the heart twice. You have a double **circulatory system**: blood flows through the two circuits, one to the lungs from the heart and one to the rest of the body from the heart.

What happens to blood as it circulates?

Use the arrows in the diagram to help you follow this description.

1 Blood is pumped from the right ventricle to the lungs, where it gains oxygen and loses carbon dioxide. It becomes **oxygenated**.

2 The oxygenated blood from the lungs drains into the vein that returns blood to the left atrium of the heart. The blood is pumped into the left ventricle.

3 The heart then pumps blood at high pressure from the left ventricle through the arteries to the rest of the body. As the blood flows through all the other organs, it loses some oxygen and gains some carbon dioxide.

Glucose, amino acids and other food substances also pass from the blood to the cells. Water, urea and other wastes pass into the blood.

4 Blood that has lost some oxygen, **deoxygenated** blood, leaves the organs, drains into veins and returns to the right atrium of the heart.

organs above heart
lungs
1
2
right atrium
left atrium
4
3
heart
right ventricle
left ventricle
organs below heart

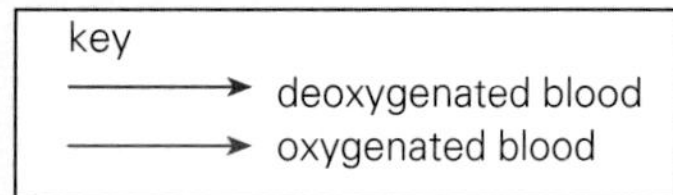

Blood is pumped to the lungs and then flows back to the heart. Blood is then pumped to all the other parts of the body and returns to the heart.

The heart cycle

During one heart beat the two atria are filled with blood. They then contract at the same time to force blood into the ventricles. When the two ventricles are full they contract together. The ventricles contract just after the atria. Our **heart rate** is usually about 70 beats every minute. During vigorous exercise is may rise to nearly 200 contractions a minute in young people. The heart rate is controlled by the brain and it responds to the demands of the body for more oxygen and the removal of excess carbon dioxide during exercise.

How blood flows through the heart

The atria that receive blood from the veins are thin walled since they do not pump blood any great distance. The ventricles are thick walled as they pump blood through the arteries at high pressure. The right ventricle has a thinner wall than the left ventricle as it only has to pump blood to the lungs, which do not offer much resistance to the flow of blood. The blood pressure in the artery going to the lungs, the **pulmonary artery**, is therefore much lower than that in the **aorta** (the artery going to the rest of the body).

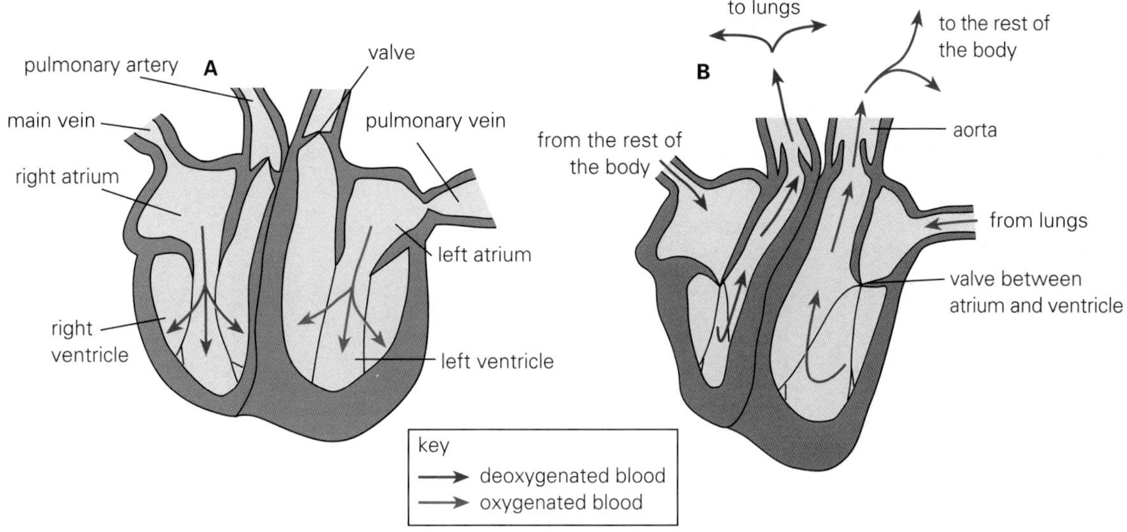

*In **A** the ventricles are relaxing and filling with blood from the atria. In **B** they are contracting to pump blood into the arteries.*

In part **A**, deoxygenated blood flows from the tissues through the main vein (vena cava) into the right atrium. Oxygenated blood from the lungs flows through the pulmonary vein into the left atrium. The atria contract forcing blood into the ventricles.

In part **B**, the ventricles contract forcing blood into the two main arteries. Deoxygenated blood flows through the pulmonary artery to the lungs. Oxygenated blood flows through the aorta to the rest of the body.

Heart valves

Valves in the heart ensure that blood moves in the correct direction. When the ventricles contract to pump blood out of the heart into the arteries it is important that blood is prevented from flowing back into the atria, since the thin walls of the atria would be damaged (see **B**).

To stop blood flowing back into the ventricles from the arteries there are valves at the base of the aorta and the pulmonary artery. These close to prevent backflow into the ventricles when the blood pressure in the ventricles is lower than that in the arteries (see **A**).

QUESTIONS

1. Describe the pathway taken by blood leaving the aorta to complete a circuit around the body returning to the aorta again. Include a simple labelled drawing of the heart in your answer.
2. State three differences between the blood in the pulmonary artery and blood in the pulmonary vein.
3. Why are the walls of the two ventricles much thicker than those of the two atria?
4. Why is the blood pressure in the aorta greater than that in the artery going to the lungs?
5. Explain the function of valves in the heart.

2.8 Circulation

Blood vessels

Blood flows from the heart around the body in three main types of vessel, arteries, veins and capillaries. The heart pumps blood into arteries to distribute it to the main organs. Blood in the arteries is at high pressure. As it flows through the capillaries and veins the pressure falls. Pressure is needed to push blood through a large number of small blood vessels much the same as pressure is needed to move water through the pipes in a house.

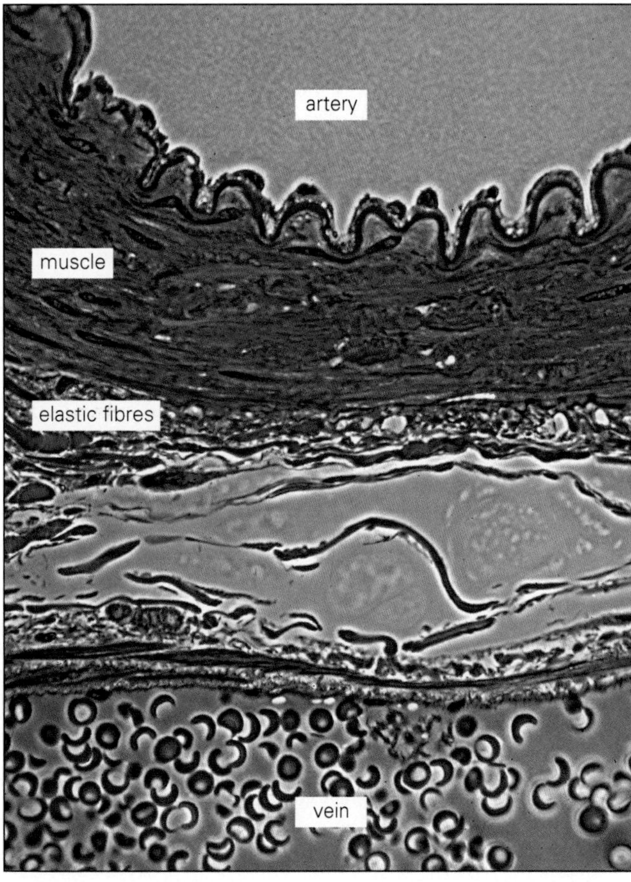

Arteries have thick walls containing muscle and elastic fibres. Veins have thinner walls and often have valves to ensure that blood flows in the correct direction.

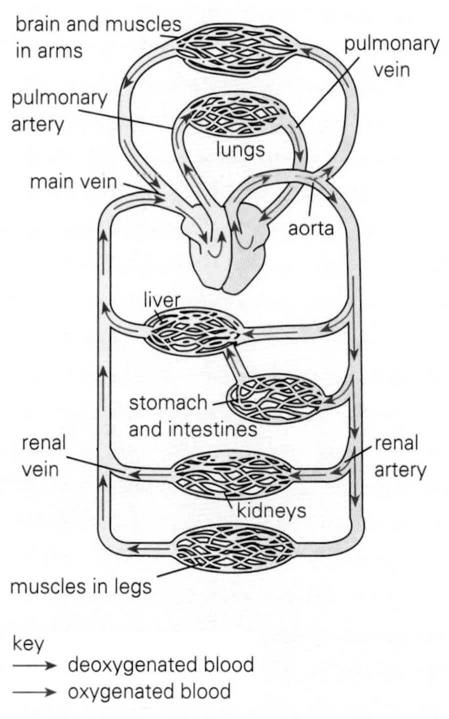

The main blood vessels in the body. Substances pass to and from the blood in the capillaries.

Arteries

Blood is forced out of the ventricles at high pressure. The arteries are thick walled and elastic to withstand this pressure. The elastic fibres in their walls help to push the blood along the arteries towards the organs. This makes sure that blood arrives at the organs at about the same pressure that it left the heart, maintaining a good supply of oxygen to the tissues.

Veins

Veins are much wider than arteries but have thin walls. The blood pressure is low so veins do not require thick layers of muscle or elastic tissue. Blood in the veins is squeezed along when muscles contract. This means that blood returns faster to the heart when you are taking exercise. Veins have valves inside them at intervals to stop blood flowing away from the heart and collecting in the veins.

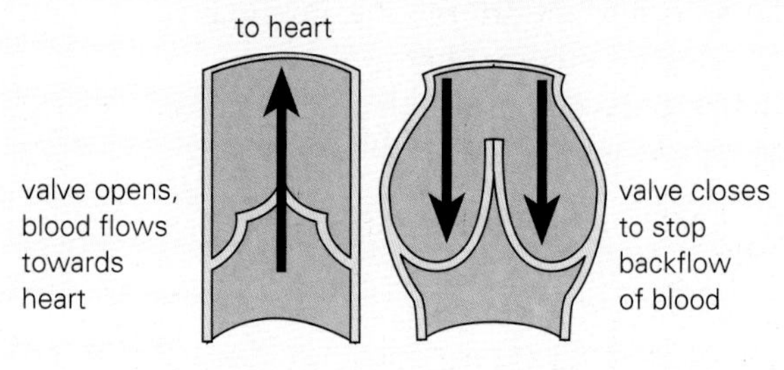

This diagram shows how valves in veins open and close.

Capillaries

Oxygen and food are supplied to cells and waste is removed from cells when blood flows through very fine blood vessels called capillaries. Capillaries are specially adapted for this exchange. These vessels are lined by a thin layer of cells with holes to allow small molecules to pass out of the blood to the cells. Small molecules can also pass out of the cells and into the blood.

Organ	From cells to blood	From blood to cells
Muscles	carbon dioxide lactic acid	oxygen, amino acids, glucose
Small intestine	glucose, amino acids, minerals, vitamins, water, some fat, CO_2	oxygen
Lungs	oxygen	carbon dioxide

The substances that move between cells and blood as it flows through the capillaries in muscle, small intestine and the lungs

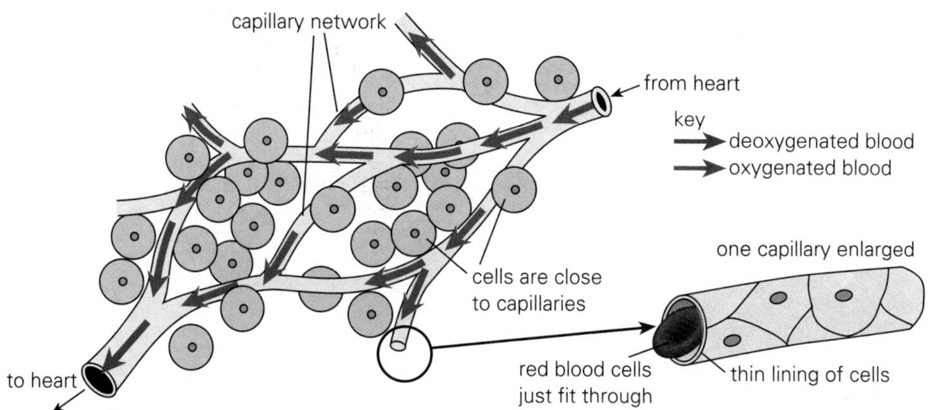

Large numbers of thin-walled capillaries provide a huge surface area for the exchange of substances between the blood and the tissues.

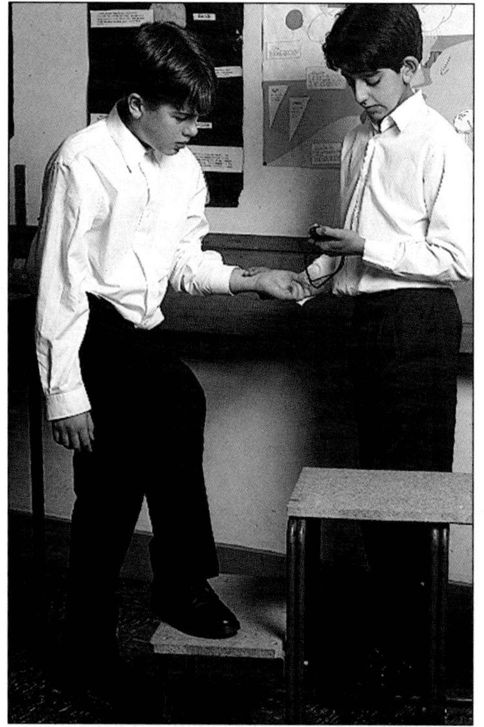

A low resting pulse rate which does not rise too high during exercise indicates that you have a healthy heart.

A finger on the pulse

Since the blood comes out of the heart in surges the arteries expand slightly with each heart beat. Where there is an artery present near the surface of your body (a pressure point) this slight expansion can be felt. This is your pulse. The pulse is a measure of the heart rate and is a good indication of your state of health and fitness.

QUESTIONS

1 Make a table to show four differences between the structures of arteries, veins and capillaries.

2 Explain how capillaries are adapted to allow easy exchange of substances between the blood and cells.

3 Explain how valves in veins ensure that blood flows only one way.

4 Explain what your pulse is and why it is often measured.

5 Plan an experiment to find the effects of different types of exercise on your pulse rate.

2.9 *Blood*

Essential to life

Blood moves substances rapidly from one part of the body to another. It also helps to prevent infections entering your body through injuries to the skin.

Adults have about 5 litres of blood. If you cut yourself the blood appears to be a red liquid but in fact it is made up of several types of cells suspended in a liquid. These are:

- **red blood cells**, which transport oxygen and some carbon dioxide
- **white blood cells**, which help to defend the body against disease
- **platelets** (small pieces of cells), which release chemicals which cause blood to clot
- **plasma** which is a pale yellow, straw-coloured solution of substances dissolved in water.

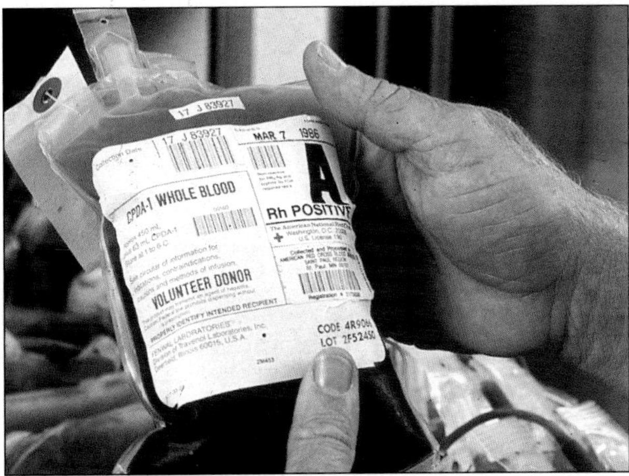

This pack contains whole blood as it is when taken from a blood donor.

If you spin whole blood in a centrifuge it separates into its constituents.

Red blood cells

Red blood cells are produced in the bone marrow. There are about 5000 million in every 1 cm^3 of blood. Red cells have no nucleus and they are packed with molecules of dark red **haemoglobin**. In the lungs haemoglobin combines with oxygen forming bright red **oxyhaemoglobin**. When blood reaches the capillaries in body tissues, oxyhaemoglobin readily gives up oxygen, which then passes through the capillary walls into the tissue.

Red cells have a distinctive disc shape that gives them a large surface area. This shape and the fact that they are very thin means that gases can pass easily in and out of the cells. Red cells are flexible and can change shape so can easily pass through capillaries (see 2.8).

Haemoglobin and carbon dioxide

In the tissues where the concentration of carbon dioxide is high red cells gain carbon dioxide. Some combines with haemoglobin after it has lost its oxygen. The rest of the waste carbon dioxide is transported in the plasma.

Each of these blood cells is only 0.007 mm in diameter. They last for only a few weeks before being destroyed in the liver. They are full of the iron-containing protein, haemoglobin.

White blood cells

White cells are larger than red cells and unlike them have a nucleus. There are far fewer of them in blood. There is one white cell for about every 700 red cells. White cells play a major part in the body's defence against disease-causing microbes like viruses and bacteria. White cells move from the blood to the tissues where they help fight disease.

In this electron micrograph you can see white blood cells which search out and destroy disease-causing microbes (× 4400).

Platelets

Platelets, which are fragments of cells with no nucleus, play a major part in the thickening of the blood called **clotting**. When a break, caused by a cut or a graze, occurs in a blood vessel it is sealed up very quickly to stop loss of blood. Platelets become sticky and plug the wound. They then release compounds which trigger off a series of reactions to form a **clot** to seal the wound. The area then dries to form a scab.

Formation of a clot stops too much blood loss and prevents bacteria entering your body.

Plasma

The straw-coloured fluid part of blood is called plasma. It transports cells and platelets and also soluble substances around the body from one tissue to another such as:

- digested food substances from the site of absorption, the small intestine, to all parts of the body
- hormones from the glands, e.g. adrenal gland, to all parts of the body (see 3.3)
- waste carbon dioxide to be expelled in the lungs
- urea, a waste product containing nitrogen, from the liver, where it is made, to the kidneys to be excreted in the urine
- proteins including antibodies and antitoxins (see 4.1)
- dissolved minerals such as calcium, phosphate, sodium, chloride and potassium.

QUESTIONS

1. List the constituents of the blood and describe what they do in the body.
2. Describe the appearance of red cells and explain how they are adapted to carry oxygen.
3. List the soluble substances present in the plasma and explain why each is a necessary part of the blood.
4. Describe how platelets are involved in blood clotting.
5. Describe how carbon dioxide is carried in the blood.

2.10 *Removing waste*

Excretion

Excretion is the removal of waste material from the many chemical reactions that go on in your body. You can be poisoned by your own waste and so it is important that waste chemicals are removed keeping conditions inside your body steady or *constant*. For example, carbon dioxide and water are the waste products of respiration and if either of these builds up in your body it can be dangerous. Carbon dioxide is removed, or excreted, in the lungs (see 2.6).

Organ	Excretory function or waste product
lungs	carbon dioxide
kidneys	remove urea from the blood and make urine
bladder	stores urine
liver	makes urea from amino acids

Different parts of your body excrete different waste products.

Waste from protein

Another important waste product is **urea**. You may eat more protein than you need for growth and repair. Amino acids from this excess protein are broken down into smaller molecules in the liver forming ammonia. Ammonia is very poisonous so it is then converted into the less poisonous urea. The liver then releases this urea into the blood stream. The **kidneys** make **urine** by taking urea and water from the blood.

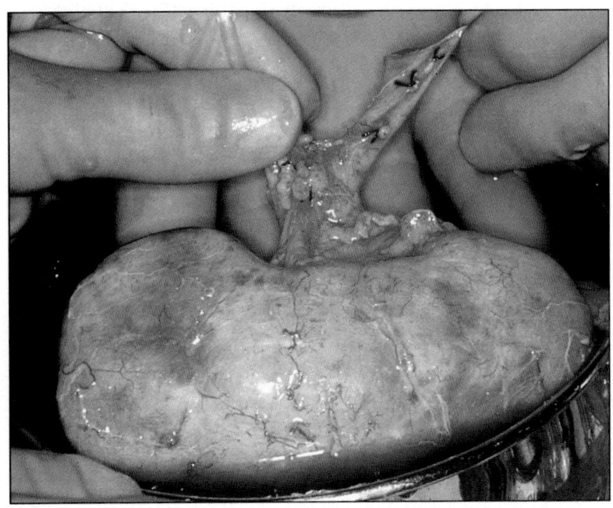

This photograph shows a whole kidney.

The urinary system

The kidneys are two dark red organs found on either side of the spine about level with your waist. Urine is made in the kidneys. It contains urea, and the salts and water that your body no longer needs. Your kidneys filter your blood to remove harmful substances. The urine that forms in the kidneys flows down the ureters into the bladder where it is temporarily stored. Urine passes out of the body through the urethra when a feeling of fullness reminds you it is time to empty the bladder (**urinate**).

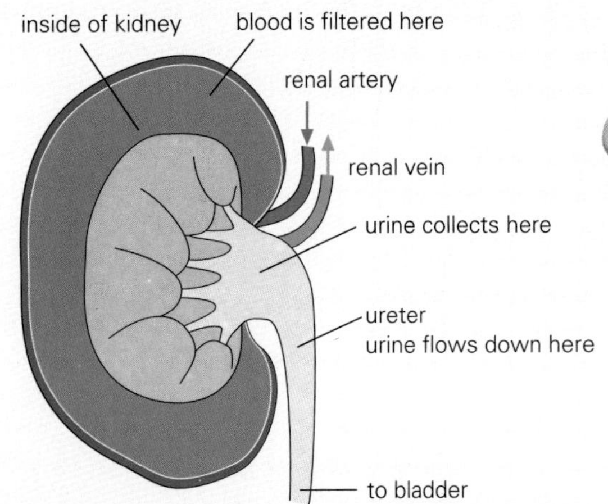

Here the kidney is sliced in half.

This girl is resting her fingers over the approximate position of her kidneys.

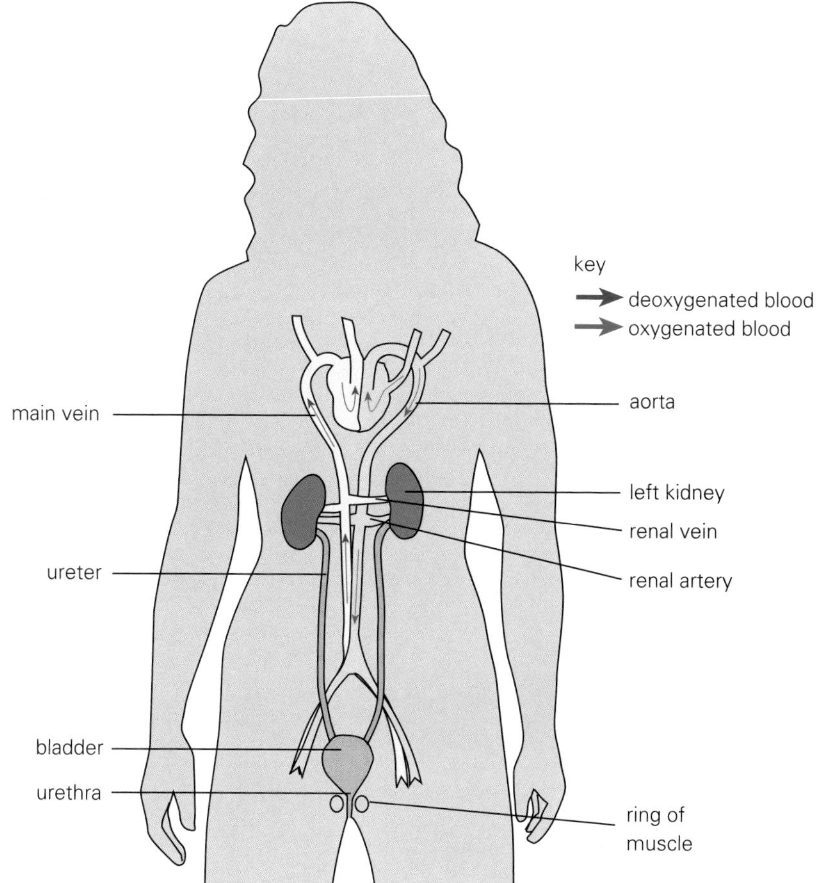

Blood flows into each kidney along the renal artery and leaves along the renal vein. (Anything relating to the kidney is described as ***renal****.)*

Filtration and reabsorption

Blood flows into the kidney capillaries from the renal artery at high pressure. Here it is filtered. The small molecules in the blood plasma such as water, ions, glucose and urea are forced out of the blood. This solution flows through the many tiny tubules in the kidney where all the useful substances such as glucose are reabsorbed (taken back) into the blood. This process prevents the loss of substances that the body cannot afford to lose. The rest of the solution that is not reabsorbed flows down the ureters and collects in the bladder.

Water control

You may have noticed that drinking large amounts of fluids results in more frequent visits to the lavatory. You go less often if you have been losing water by sweating more than usual. If you have a day when you either sweat a lot or do not drink much your urine is a dark yellow, concentrated solution. The body has been short of water and the kidney has reabsorbed it to keep the blood concentration normal. Having lots of drinks or cups of tea results in a dilute, pale yellow urine. Your body does not have a water shortage and plenty of water is lost in urine.

The kidneys make adjustments all the time to the water content of the blood so that it remains nearly constant. Any excess water in the blood is lost in the urine.

Constant flow

Blood leaving the kidneys in the renal vein will have lost some of its waste materials but not all. The blood in the renal vein has less urea, ions and water than that in the renal artery.

Blood passing through the kidneys once is not completely cleaned of waste so there must be a constant flow of blood through the kidneys whatever you are doing.

QUESTIONS

1 Explain the term excretion.

2 Describe the position of the kidneys in the body.

3 State the function of the kidneys, the ureter and the bladder.

4 How does the blood in the renal artery differ from blood in the renal vein?

5 Explain why blood flows continuously through the kidneys.

2.11 *Inside the kidney*

Under the microscope

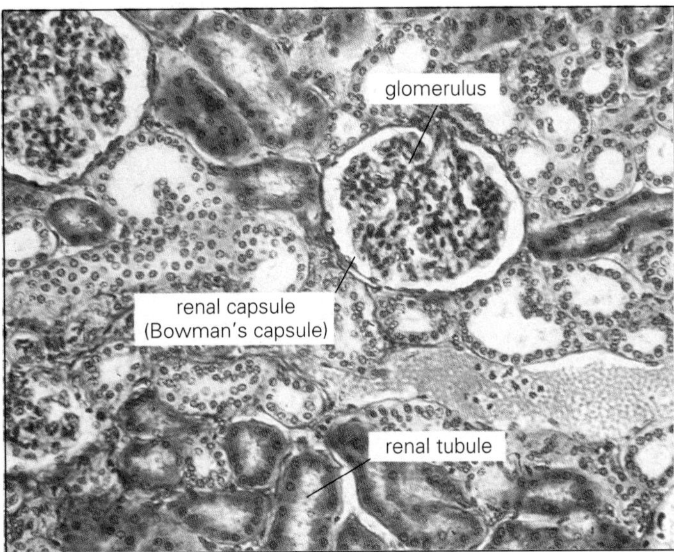

The photograph shows part of the kidney where filtration occurs (× 200).

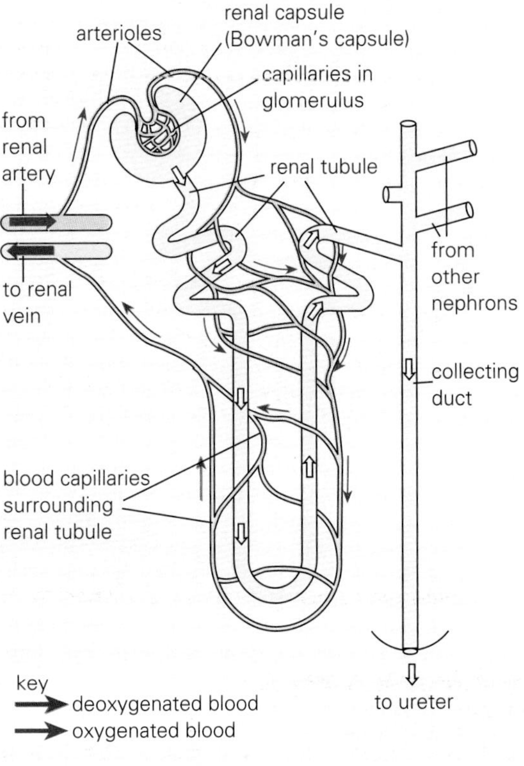

Each kidney contains about a million of these small tubes called nephrons.

When you look at the kidney in more detail under a microscope you see many blood capillaries and small tubes or **nephrons**. Each of these consists of a **glomerulus**, a **renal capsule** and a tube called the **renal tubule**. In each nephron the renal tubule loops round joining the renal capsule to a collecting duct that leads to the ureter. The number of nephrons in each kidney may decrease with age. The nephrons filter 60 litres of blood every hour and so all your blood passes through the kidneys every five minutes.

Pressure filtration

Blood flows along the renal artery, through the arteriole and enters the glomerulus under pressure. The blood is filtered under high pressure as it flows through the tight group of capillaries in the glomerulus. After being filtered the blood flows through the capillaries which are wrapped round the tubules and then out of the kidney in the renal vein.

As the blood in the capillaries of the glomerulus is under high pressure, small molecules like glucose, ions and urea are forced with water out of the blood. Poisonous substances like alcohol and drugs are forced out at the same time. Red and white cells, platelets and other blood proteins are too large to be filtered out and so remain in the blood. The capillaries in the glomerulus act as a molecular sieve letting through small molecules but not large ones. The solution formed in the capsule is called the **filtrate**.

Size of blood constituents	
Too large to be filtered	**Small, can be filtered**
red cells	water
white cells	glucose
platelets	urea
plasma proteins	ions spent hormones

This table shows the substances in blood plasma that are filtered out of the blood into the capsule and the cells and other substances that are too large to get through the filter.

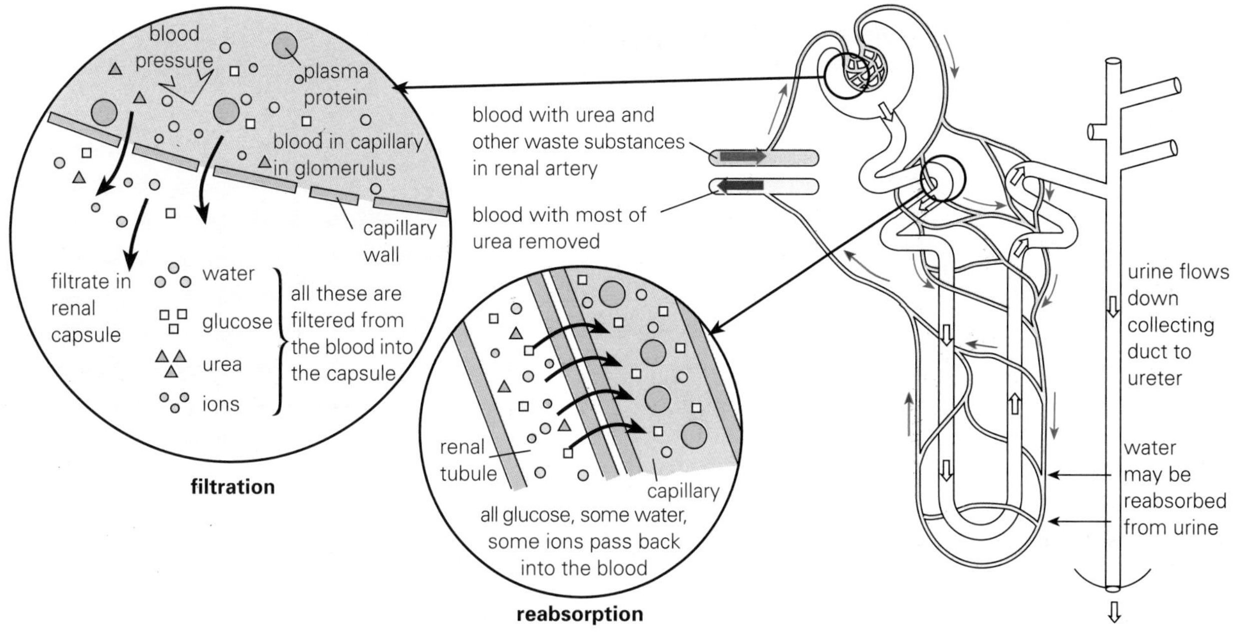

These diagrams show how urine is formed from blood plasma in a nephron.

Inside a kidney tubule

The filtrate from the capsule flows down the nephron, inside the renal tubule. Here useful substances like glucose and some salts are reabsorbed by active transport back into the blood along with enough water to keep the blood concentration constant (see 1.5). The rest of the filtrate, containing urea, ions and water, passes down the nephron into the ureter and into the bladder. The kidney can adjust the amount of water it reabsorbs depending on the circumstances in the body (see 3.5).

As you can see from the table, very little of the material that is filtered is excreted in the urine. Almost all of it is taken back into the blood. This is called **selective reabsorption**. It is rather like spring cleaning; imagine taking everything, apart from the heavy furniture, out of a room and then putting back all the things you wanted to keep. The rest is thrown away.

Selective reabsorption		
	Mass in grams per day	
Substance	**filtrate**	**urine**
Sodium	600.0	6.0
Potassium	35.0	2.0
Calcium	5.0	0.2
Glucose	200.0	0
Urea	60.0	35.0
Water	180 litres	1.5 litres

This table shows the comparison between the filtrate in the nephron and the urine.

QUESTIONS

1 Make a labelled drawing of a kidney nephron. On your drawing show where pressure filtration and selective reabsorption occur.

2 Explain why some constituents of the blood are filtered in the kidney but others are not.

3 Describe how the kidney is adapted to filter the blood.

4 Every day large quantities of ions, sugar and water are filtered from the blood in the kidney and yet very little is excreted in the urine. Explain why.

2.12 *Kidney problems*

Kidney failure

Kidneys can fail because of an infection, a bad case of poisoning, an injury with severe loss of blood or very high blood pressure. Fortunately kidney failure is uncommon. It is possible to live with just one kidney, but if both fail then **kidney dialysis** is necessary.

Kidney dialysis can be done using a machine which reproduces some of the functions of the kidney. Blood is taken from an artery and is pumped through tubes with very thin walls made of a partially permeable membrane (like Visking tubing).

The blood flows into the machine at high pressure (just as it enters the kidney). It then passes through the tubes which are surrounded by a solution of glucose and ions in water – the **dialysing solution**. This solution is kept flowing all the time so that it is constantly replaced by fresh solution. There is no urea in the dialysing solution, so urea passes from the blood into the solution on the other side of the membrane. Cells and larger molecules like protein are held back in the blood.

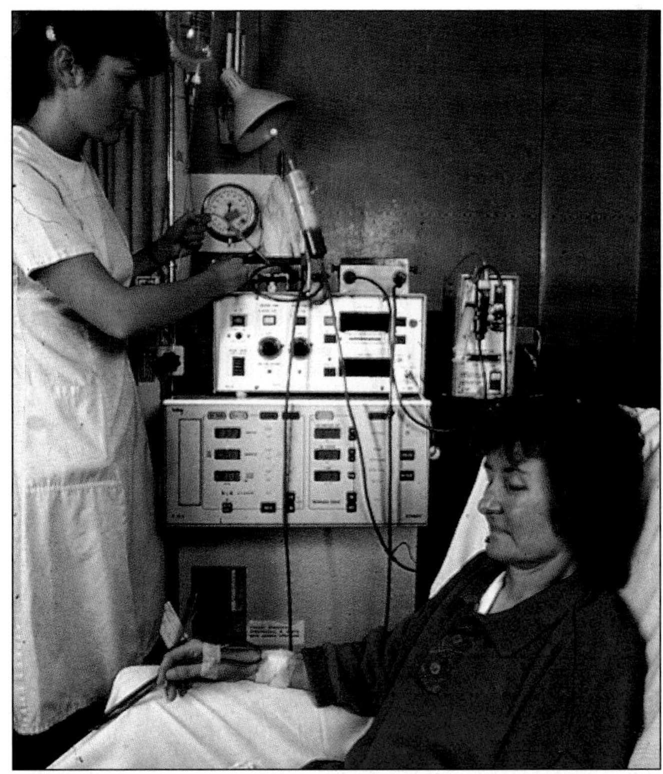

An artificial kidney – a dialysis machine – does the job of the kidney. Dialysis can be done in hospital or, if someone in the family is trained to help, at home.

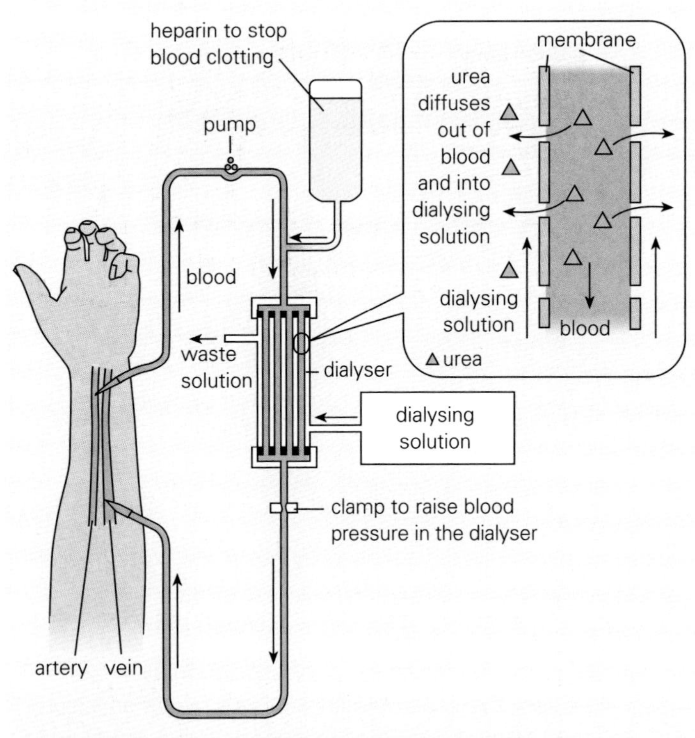

The membrane in the dialyser has an enormous surface area.

The kidney machine must be able to remove waste from the blood but not useful substances like glucose and some ions like sodium and chloride. However, these small particles can pass through the membrane. To prevent losing glucose and useful ions the dialysing solution has exactly the concentration of water, glucose and ions that is correct for the blood. So as blood flows through the machine these substances pass in and out of the blood maintaining constant levels in the blood. Someone with kidney disease is usually on the dialysis machine for 3 to 4 hours, and this is repeated three times a week.

People who have kidney failure have to keep to a very strict diet and avoid too much salt and protein. In between visits to hospital, the urea concentration of the blood gradually increases. During dialysis it falls to near zero. People on dialysis must also be careful that they do not drink too much fluid as the dialysis machine, unlike the kidney, does not regulate the amount of water in the blood.

Kidney transplants

A long-term solution to kidney failure is to transplant at least one kidney from a suitable donor. The transplanted kidney must be matched very carefully so that the organ (the kidney) is accepted by the recipient's body and is not rejected. A family member is most likely to be able to provide a matching kidney. If this is not possible an accident victim could be a donor.

People who have just received a transplant are treated with drugs that suppress their immune system. This is to try to stop the body rejecting the new kidney but has the disadvantage that the person is more susceptible to catching infectious diseases.

Donor kidneys are preserved (cold) in this machine until they can be transplanted into the patient.

Dialysis on the move

CAPD is a newer approach to treating kidney failure. The **C** stands for continuous because the blood is being cleaned all the time. The **A** is for ambulatory (walking) because the person can get on with everyday life while **D** for dialysis is going on. The **P** is for **peritoneal**. The **peritoneum**, the lining of your body cavity, is a kind of bag holding the organs in your abdomen. The peritoneum is used as a dialysis membrane. Dialysis solution from a bag is run into the body with tubes running into the space around the body organs – the peritoneal space. The used solution is run out again using gravity by placing the bag on the floor.

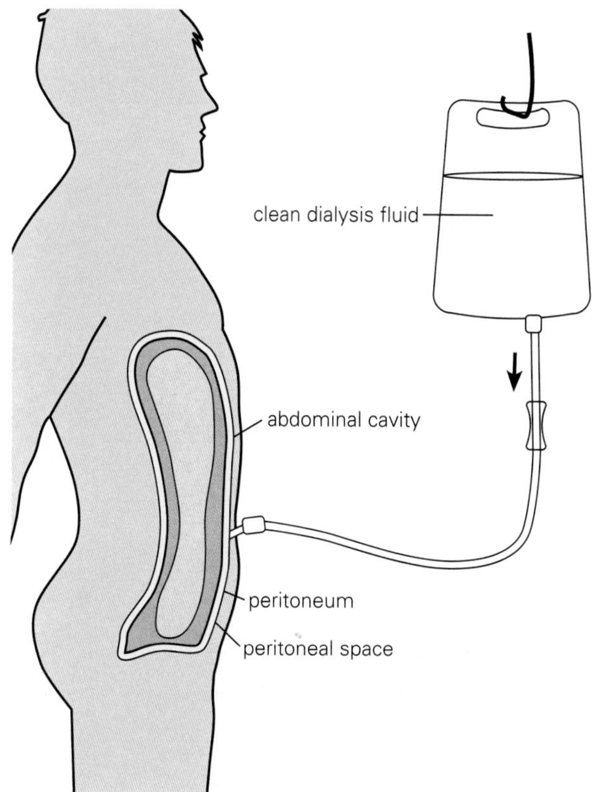

This diagram shows a man undergoing CAPD. The bag contains the solution for dialysis that is going on inside his body.

Carrying this card could give someone a chance of living a normal life.

QUESTIONS

1. Explain why people with kidney failure have to be careful about their diet.
2. Describe what happens to blood as it passes through a kidney dialysis machine.
3. What are the advantages and disadvantages of **a** kidney dialysis and **b** kidney transplants?
4. Discuss the factors for and against a system, used in some other countries, in which people have to opt out if they do not wish to donate their organs for transplants.

3.1 *Homeostasis*

This marathon runner reaches out for a drink.

Staying steady

To work efficiently your body needs to keep conditions inside roughly the same or constant. When you get hot you begin to sweat. When you have too much water in your body you urinate more often. When you suddenly need more energy you breathe faster. All these changes happen because you are making demands on your body and it responds to keep everything inside working efficiently. Even though you do all sorts of things which could change these internal conditions, your body detects the changes and takes steps to restore constant conditions. Therefore your body under normal conditions never becomes too hot or too cold; you do not become dehydrated or swell up with too much water.

All activity can lead to changes inside the body. For example

- when you take a sauna you become very hot
- when you take a swim in winter you may feel cold and shiver
- you might drink vast quantities of cold drinks in very hot weather.

Counteracting these changes and keeping everything about the same is called **homeostasis**. This happens automatically, you do not have to think about it.

Constant conditions

Conditions within your body must be kept steady or constant for your cells to work correctly. *Body temperature*, the *pH of the blood* and the *concentration of the blood* are internal conditions which must be kept constant.

Body temperature is important because chemical reactions inside human cells are catalysed by enzymes which only function well at 37°C. Most also only work efficiently at a pH of about 7. Blood controls both the pH and temperature in cells. Finally, the concentration of blood, that is how much water and solutes it contains, is important because this affects the way substances like food, oxygen and waste move between blood and the cells.

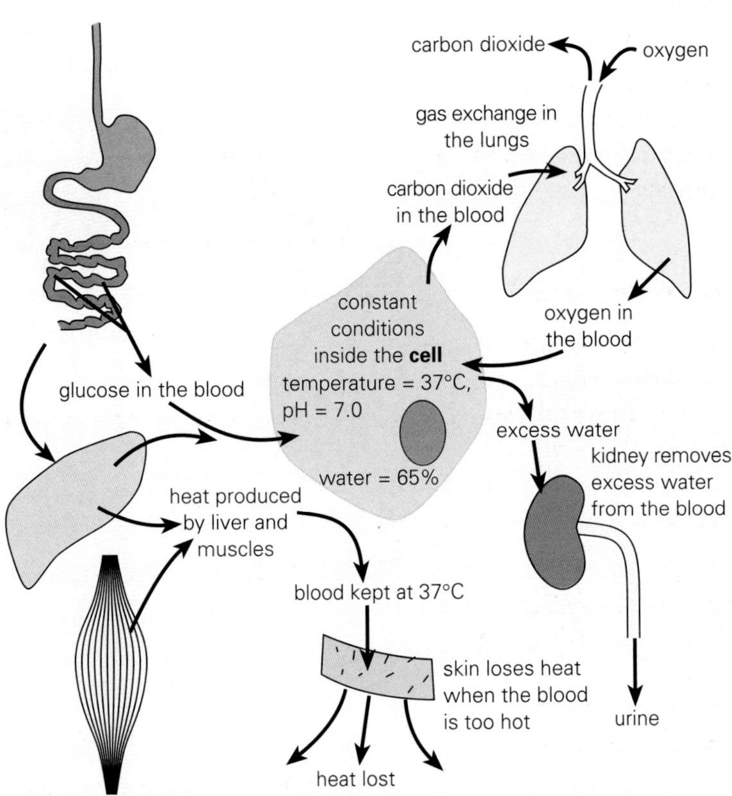

Cells function efficiently when they are kept in constant conditions.

Responding to change

- Drinking increases the quantity of water in your blood.
- When you run your muscles use up glucose from the blood, and they produce heat causing a rise in body temperature. During strenuous exercise muscles respire anaerobically producing lactic acid which can cause a decrease in blood pH.
- When you sweat you lose salt and water.

Your body takes counter measures to prevent these changes going too far and upsetting the balance within the body. The liver, kidneys and lungs help to maintain internal conditions by regulating what is contained in the blood. When you eat, drink and take exercise internal conditions begin to change.

Organ	Regulatory action
Lungs	absorb oxygen and remove waste carbon dioxide along with some water when you breathe out
Liver	makes and stores glycogen for extra energy supplies when required produces urea from excess amino acids that cannot be stored in the body
Kidneys	remove urea, excess water and ions in the urine

The skin

The skin is an important organ of homeostasis. It is the first part of the body to detect decreases in temperature in the air. It helps us to keep cool by losing heat in the form of sweat, and it protects us against disease.

Skin is made from different tissues. The outer tissue is full of cells packed with a tough water-proofing protein, which protects the body against puncture and stops us losing water by evaporation. These cells eventually die and are rubbed off.

Opening on to the surface of the skin are the sweat ducts which carry sweat from the sweat glands. When the body is too hot sweat pours on to the surface of the skin as a way of losing heat.

The deeper layer of the skin contains blood capillaries, sweat glands, nerves for detecting temperature, pressure and pain. Beneath is a layer of fat which acts as a thermal insulator.

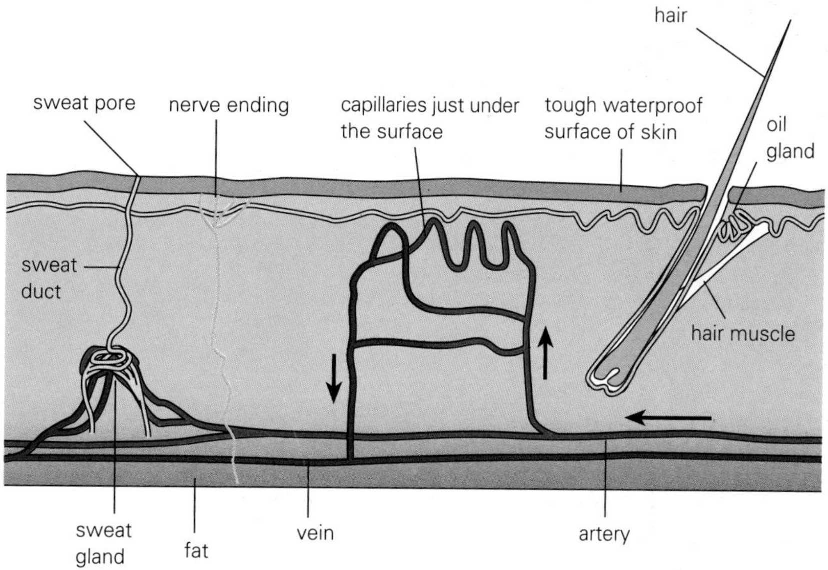

The diagram shows the structure of the skin.

QUESTIONS

1 Give a brief explanation of homeostasis.

2 State three internal conditions in the body that are kept constant.

3 Explain the advantages of keeping cells in constant conditions.

4 State three functions of human skin.

5 Describe the changes that occur in the body when you go for a run. What does the body do to keep internal conditions constant during this exercise?

3.2 *Hot and cold*

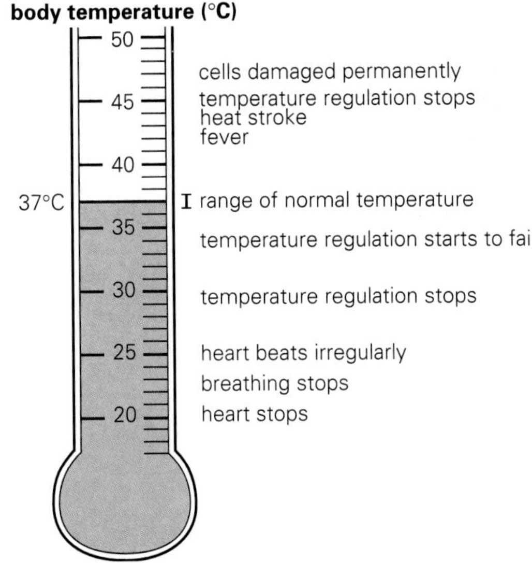

Cells do not work properly if your body temperature varies. If there is a change of more than 1°C you can be in severe danger.

Temperature regulation

Have you ever put a jumper on and taken it off again later in the day? Have you ever considered why you wear warm jumpers and fleecy jackets in winter? You, in common with other mammals and birds, produce your own body heat. You do not rely on absorbing heat from your surroundings, but your surroundings can affect your body temperature.

Your normal body temperature is 37°C. This is the temperature of the central part of the body (the **core**) containing the main organs like the heart, kidneys and brain. The temperature of the skin – your outer layer – is often at the temperature of your surroundings. To keep the core temperature at or near 37°C body temperature is constantly monitored and controlled. Keeping the body temperature constant is part of homeostasis.

In hot climates people often wear loose, thin clothing which allows convection currents to transfer heat away.

Controlling body temperature

Heat is produced when cells respire. When you are not exercising most of the heat in the body is produced by the liver. During exercise much more heat is produced by the muscles. Blood flowing through these organs absorbs the heat and distributes it around the rest of the body.

When it is cold, blood is diverted away from the skin so it does not lose heat. This conserves body heat and reduces heat loss. When you begin to overheat you can lose heat by sweating and letting more blood flow close to the skin's surface. Heat is lost from the blood to our surroundings. We can also lose heat if we sit on something that is cold, or eat or drink something cold.

Mammals have a layer of fat beneath their skin which serves as a thermal insulator. As we do not have much body hair like other mammals, we use clothes instead to keep in the heat. Layers of warm clothing trap air which insulates the body.

The body's thermostat

Your thermostat (or **thermoregulatory centre**) is in the brain. This centre receives information about the temperature of your body from the blood that flows through the brain. It also receives information about the temperature outside your body from receptors in the skin.

The thermoregulatory centre regulates body temperature by controlling

- the conservation of heat
- the production of heat
- heat loss.

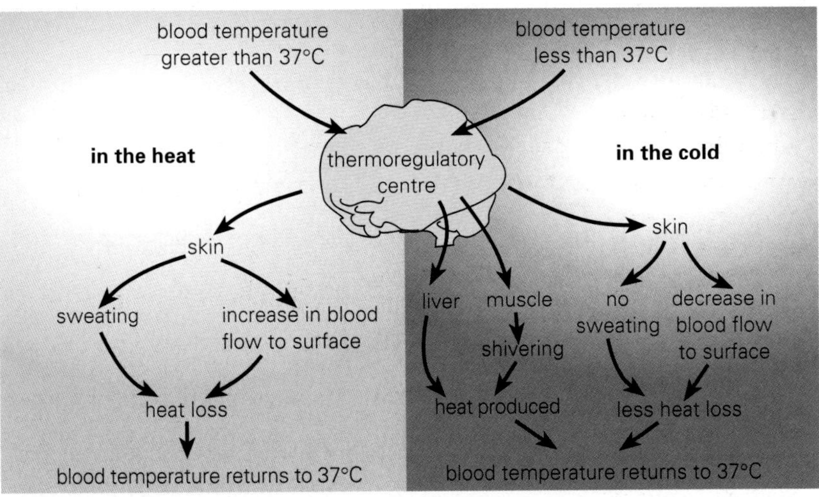

The control centre in the brain keeps the body temperature more or less constant.

Conserving heat

When you start to feel cold, the thermoregulatory centre does its best to retain heat already in the body, without using up any energy in keeping warm. It does this by stimulating muscles in the walls of small blood vessels (**arterioles**) in the skin to contract (**vasoconstriction**). This reduces the flow of blood to the capillaries just beneath the skin surface keeping blood away from the skin's surface so little heat is lost. The production of sweat also stops so that heat is not lost by evaporation (see diagram **A**).

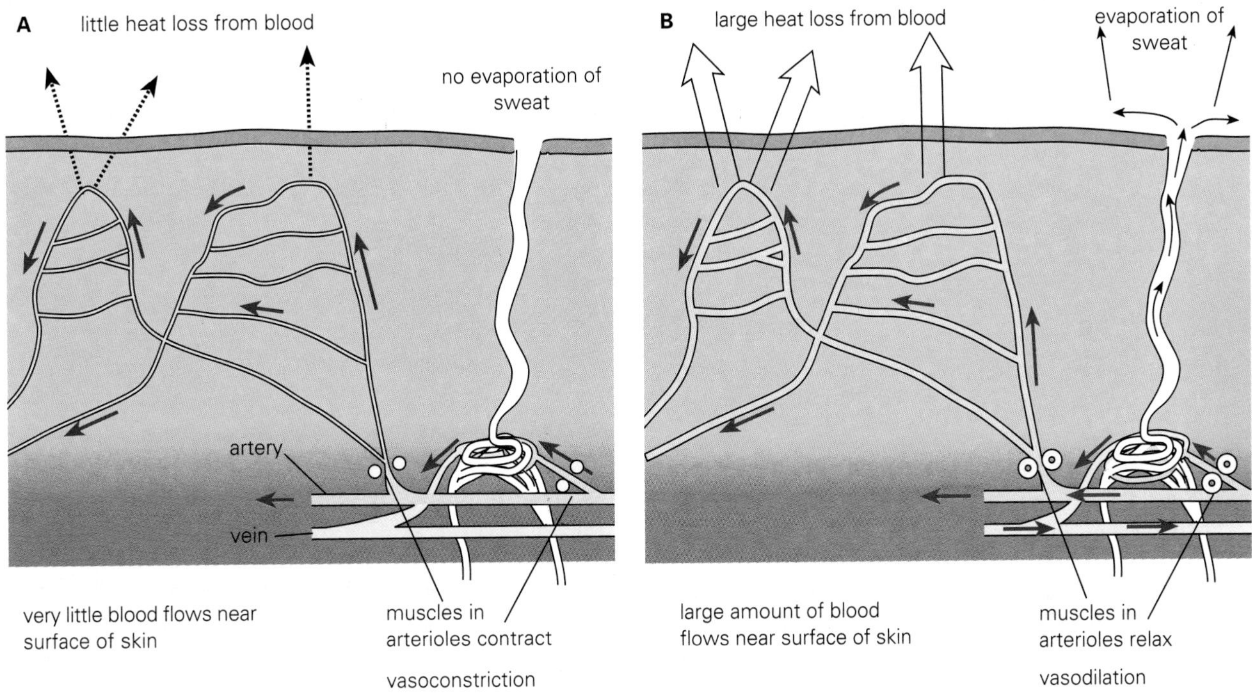

*The flow of blood through the capillaries in the skin is controlled so that heat can be kept in the body when it is cold (**A**) or lost when it is hot (**B**).*

Producing heat

If the temperature of the body still decreases the muscles in the arms, back and legs 'shiver'. Muscles respire during shivering and so generate some heat.

Losing heat

When the body's temperature starts to increase (for example during exercise), the thermoregulatory centre stimulates the arterioles in the skin to widen (**vasodilation**) to allow more blood through the capillaries so heat is lost. Sweat glands produce more sweat which evaporates when it reaches the surface of the skin (see diagram **B**). Sweating is an effective way of losing heat as 1 cm^3 water transfers 2.45 kJ of energy to the surroundings when it evaporates.

QUESTIONS

1 State four ways in which the body loses heat.

2 Explain how humans keep warm in cold climates.

3 Explain how humans keep cool in hot climates.

4 Make a table to summarise the changes that take place in the body when the air temperature becomes too hot or too cold.

5 Explain how the thermoregulatory centre controls body temperature.

3.3 *Communication in the body*

Keeping in touch

When we feel cold we either put on warm clothing or turn on the heating. All this is coordinated by the brain. To maintain constant conditions in the body different cells, tissues and organs must be able to communicate with each other so that they can coordinate the body's responses to change.

Feedback

All homeostatic systems rely on the principle of **feedback** which is also used in domestic central heating systems. These systems have a control centre, the thermostat, which is set at the temperature you want for a room (**the set point**). The thermostat controls the central heating to keep the room at the temperature you set.

The set point for your body temperature is 37°C. **Sensors** in the control centre in your brain continually monitor your temperature and compare it with the set point (37°C). If there is a difference, sensors activate the control centre to instruct parts of the body (skin or liver for example) to take action to restore the body temperature to 37°C.

Negative feedback

The corrective action taken to restore body temperature to 37°C is called **feedback control**; because the changes that the control centre orders are immediately detected by sensors so that further adjustments can be made when the temperature changes again.

This type of control is called **negative feedback** because the control centre is always *reducing the difference* between the actual temperature and the set point of 37°C. This happens when body temperature is either too high or too low.

An example of negative feedback is shown in the graph. If the temperature of the body rises or falls below 37°C the control centre in the brain initiates appropriate action to reduce or raise the body temperature. The body temperature may rise or fall 0.5°C above normal temperature and still be within safe limits.

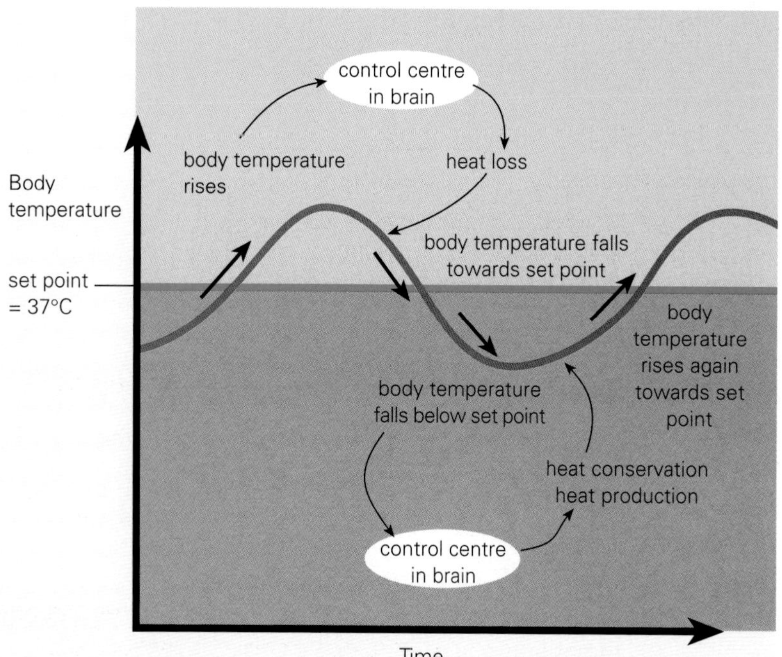

This graph shows how negative feedback is used in homeostatic systems like temperature control.

Fast and direct

Nerve endings in sensors communicate with the control centre by using **nerves**. If the control centre requires a fast response from a muscle or a gland, nerves are usually used to communicate with specific cells in the organ taking the corrective action. These are target cells. Communicating using nerves is a bit like using the telephone. It is fast and the information is passed on to one specific place.

Slow and general

When a slower response is required or many cells scattered all over the body are involved, chemicals released into the blood are used. These chemicals are **hormones**. The areas of the body that respond to the hormones are called **target organs**. Hormones do not go just to one place. The blood carries them everywhere. Communicating using hormones is like broadcasting. Only cells which can receive and recognise the hormones will respond. These are the target cells. Their response is usually slower as hormones take time to circulate in the blood.

Hormones are used in the body to control long-term processes such as reproduction (see 3.6) and growth, and some activities which occur quite quickly such as controlling our response to danger.

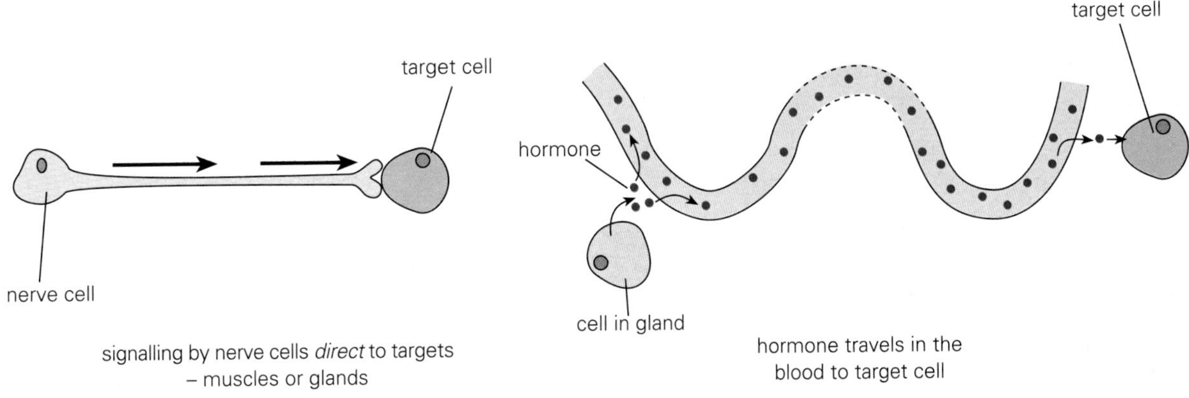

Nerves send signals direct to muscles or glands.
Hormones travel round the body in the blood before reaching their target cells.

Adrenaline – the action hormone

Adrenaline is made in the adrenal glands which are near the kidneys. Adrenaline is made in times of stress, anger, during exercise or when we see approaching danger. Adrenaline generally tones up the whole body to help it respond. It acts on muscles, liver, lungs and blood vessels. The release of adrenaline stimulates the following:

- an increase in blood glucose concentration
- the heart beats faster with greater force
- the rate of breathing increases
- blood vessels in the muscles widen
- blood vessels in the skin and gut constrict.

The body becomes more alert and better able to take sudden action because blood is diverted to flow through the muscles. The blood also contains plenty of oxygen and glucose to supply respiration to generate energy.

QUESTIONS

1 Give an example of a condition controlled in the body by negative feedback.

2 Explain the principle of negative feedback.

3 Why is it important for cells to communicate with one another?

4 List three differences between the way nerves and hormones are used to communicate between cells.

3.4 *Controlling blood sugar*

Glucose – fuel for life

Glucose is one of the main sources of energy for cells (see 2.5), and the only one that the brain can use, so the blood glucose concentration cannot be allowed to fall too low.

Glucose comes from digesting food so its concentration in the blood rises after a meal. We need glucose to provide energy all the time, but we only have two or three meals a day. The blood cannot hold enough to last us all day so something must be done to store glucose so that it is available at all times.

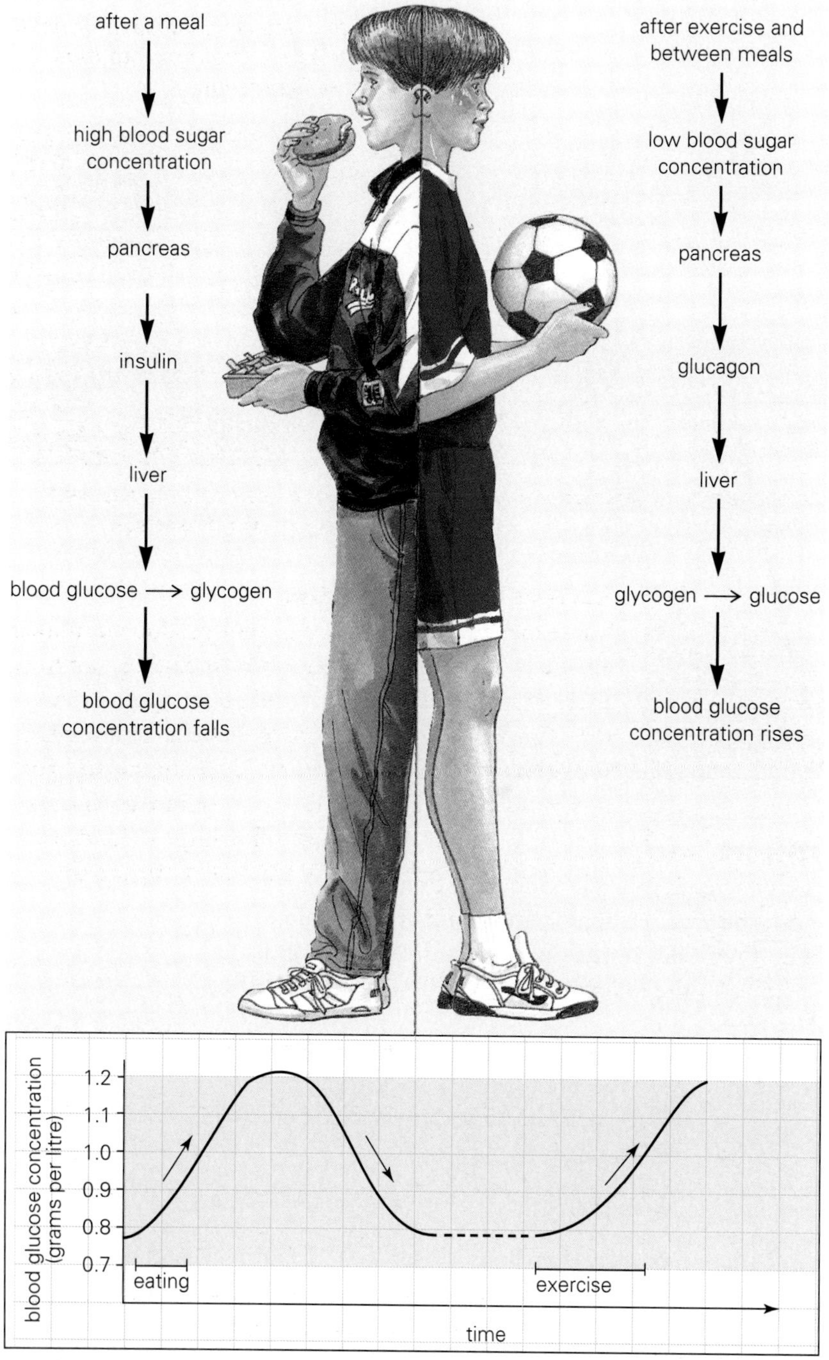

A balance between the production of insulin and glucagon brings about the small changes that keep blood glucose concentration within safe limits.

Homeostasis

Blood glucose concentration fluctuates between about 0.7 to 1.2 grams per litre of blood – these are the safe limits. If the glucose concentration is greater than 1.8 grams per litre the kidney tubules cannot reabsorb it and glucose appears in the urine. If blood glucose is lower that 0.6 grams per litre a person becomes unconscious and enters a coma.

The pancreas

The **pancreas** makes two hormones that help to keep the concentration of glucose within safe limits. It releases **insulin** when it detects a rise in blood glucose. Insulin stimulates liver and muscle cells to absorb glucose and convert it to glycogen so stopping the concentration in the blood going too high.

When the concentration of glucose falls the pancreas detects this and releases **glucagon**. Glucagon makes the liver break down glycogen into glucose and release it into the blood. Together these two hormones continuously control the blood concentration of glucose. This is an example of negative feedback. The pancreas acts as both sensor and control centre.

Glucose and diabetes

People who have **diabetes** cannot control the concentration of glucose in their blood. They may first become aware of this when they become irritable, lethargic and thirsty. They may lose weight. These symptoms are caused by the blood glucose concentrations rising too high after meals followed by very low concentrations between meals. This is happening because insulin is not being released by the pancreas therefore glucose is not being stored. One of the signs of diabetes is when glucose starts to appear in the urine as the kidneys cannot cope with all the glucose in the blood.

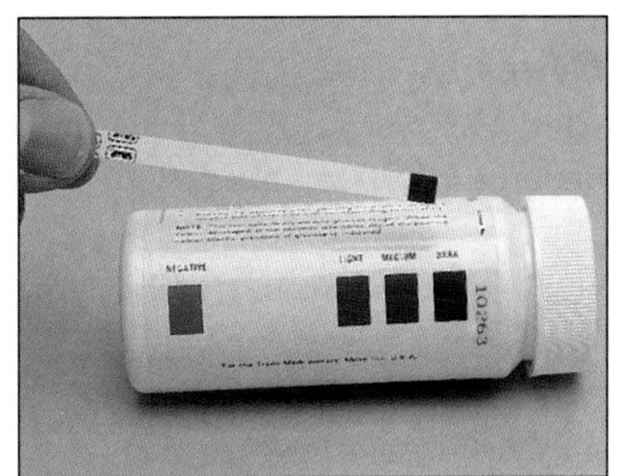

This test detects glucose in urine. If the strip turns from pink to blue glucose is present.

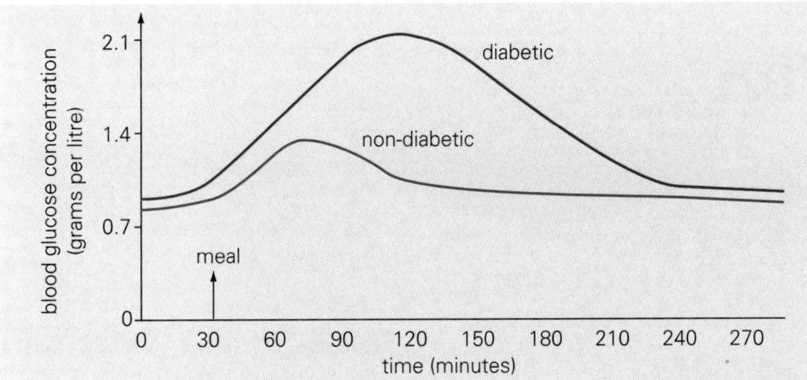

This shows how much the glucose concentration can rise in someone with diabetes compared with a non-diabetic.

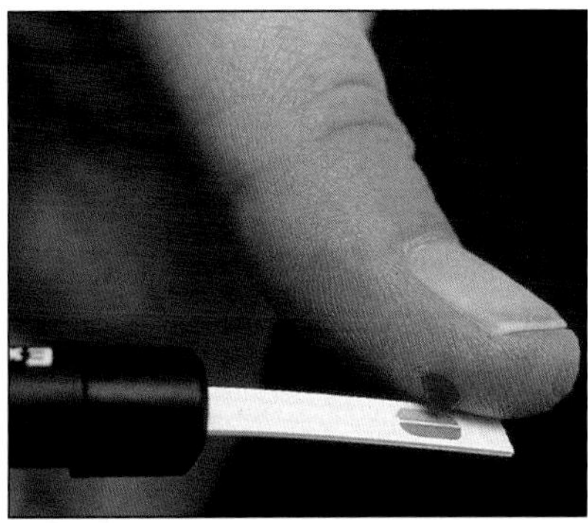

Blood glucose can be measured using a glucose biosensor.

Diabetics learn how to cope with their problem and can lead full and active lives.

Living with diabetes

Some diabetics (about 20%) cannot produce insulin at all. They learn to treat themselves by finding out how much insulin they will need and injecting it under the skin. The remaining 80% of diabetics still produce insulin but the target cells in the liver and muscle fail to respond. These people do not take insulin as they can control their diabetes by following a strict diet which involves taking a low amount of sugar and frequent exercise.

QUESTIONS

1. Why is blood glucose important?
2. Describe how the pancreas controls blood sugar concentrations.
3. Explain why this is an example of homeostasis.
4. Describe the symptoms of diabetes.
5. Explain why the blood sugar level of a diabetic rises very steeply after a meal.
6. How is diabetes treated?

3.5 *Controlling water*

Water, water everywhere

Water is very important to us. You can survive for weeks without food, but only days without water. Water is vital for the following reasons:

- it is an important constituent of cells and makes up most of the blood
- it is a solvent, dissolving glucose, gases such as oxygen and carbon dioxide and wastes such as urea
- it is essential for enzyme action, e.g. in digestion
- it has a high heat capacity which is important in temperature regulation (see 3.2).

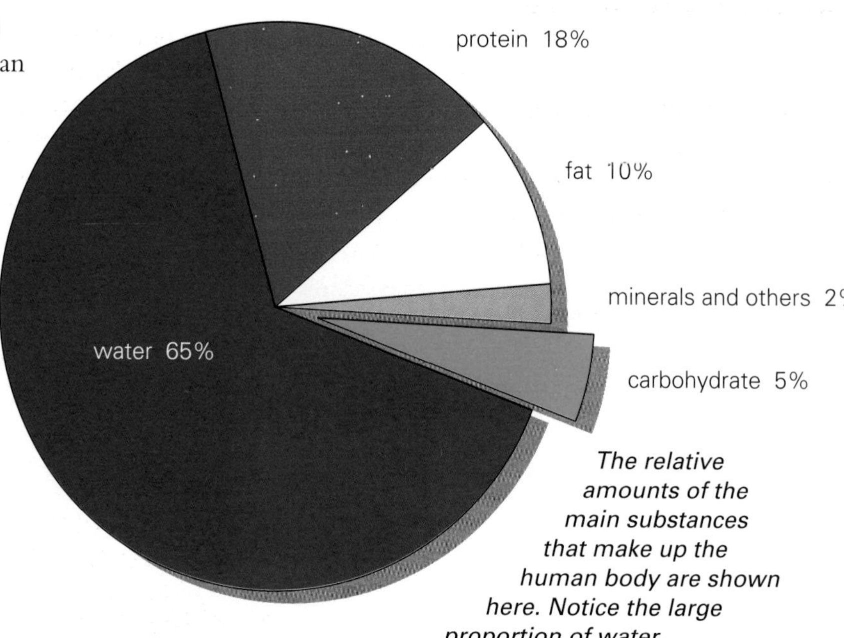

The relative amounts of the main substances that make up the human body are shown here. Notice the large proportion of water.

Volume of water (cm^3)			
daily input		**daily output**	
drink	1050	urine	1000
food	600	exhaled air	350
respiration	250	skin	400
		faeces	150
total	1900		1900

The volume of water you take in each day is balanced by the volume you lose.

Water in and water out

If your blood becomes too concentrated water is drawn out of the cells and tissues and they become dehydrated. Under these conditions the enzymes cease to work efficiently and so do the cells. If the blood becomes too dilute the reverse happens. Water collects in the tissues and the cells swell up. So it is essential that the water content of the body fluids is kept within very narrow limits.

The water content of the blood is continually influenced by the temperature of our surroundings, our diet and the amount of water we lose. Our waterproof skin keeps water in the body, but we lose it in our urine, faeces, breath and sweat. Water is also made when we respire. We can increase the amount of water in our bodies by drinking. We have no control over the amount of water lost in our breath but the amount of sweat lost depends on the air temperature and how active we are.

Homeostatic control

The control centre in the brain monitors the concentration of the blood. If the blood starts to become more concentrated it makes us feel thirsty and also instructs the **pituitary gland** to release **antidiuretic hormone** (**ADH**). This hormone stimulates the kidneys to reabsorb water into the blood from the urine. This causes the volume of urine to decrease and makes it more concentrated. When this happens it becomes dark yellow in colour. Reducing water loss in the urine helps to conserve water and reduce the likelihood of dehydration.

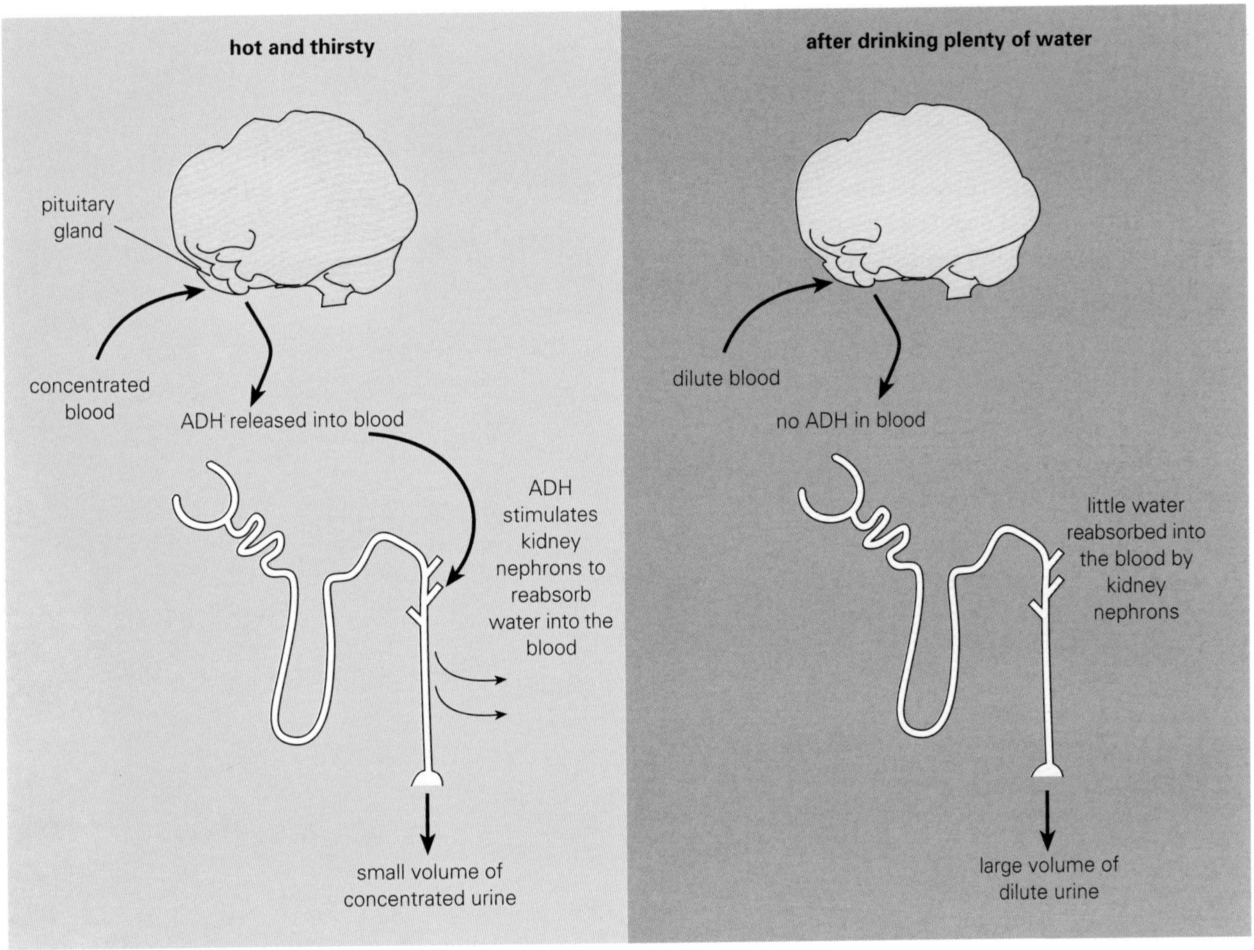

hot and thirsty

pituitary gland

concentrated blood

ADH released into blood

ADH stimulates kidney nephrons to reabsorb water into the blood

small volume of concentrated urine

after drinking plenty of water

dilute blood

no ADH in blood

little water reabsorbed into the blood by kidney nephrons

large volume of dilute urine

ADH controls the amount of water reabsorbed in the kidney.

Drinking a lot of water can dilute the blood. When this is likely to happen less ADH is released into the blood. As a result less water is reabsorbed in the kidney and more water passes through the tubules producing large volumes of dilute, pale yellow urine. Drinking alcohol also inhibits the production of ADH and so increases the likelihood of producing dilute urine. The large quantities of water in alcoholic drinks like beer have the same effect.

QUESTIONS

1 State five functions of water in the human body.

2 Explain why the amount of water in the blood must be kept constant.

3 Explain why some water must be present in urine.

4 Explain how blood could become **a** dilute and **b** concentrated.

5 Which gland produces ADH? Describe how ADH helps the body to conserve water.

3.6 *Hormones and fertility*

Hormones control development

Your body grows as cells enlarge and divide. However, growth is accompanied by changes in the cells as they develop to form tissues and organs. You not only have to grow physically in order to have a healthy life, but also have to develop emotionally at the same time.

Adolescence is an important stage in human development. It is the time which roughly coincides with the teenage years when emotional and physical changes occur. This stage is known as **puberty**. In boys during puberty the testes start to produce sperm and the male hormone, **testosterone**. In girls the ovaries begin to release eggs and also the female hormones **oestrogen** and **progesterone**, which together control the female's monthly menstrual cycle.

Development means all the changes that go on in sequence throughout a lifetime.

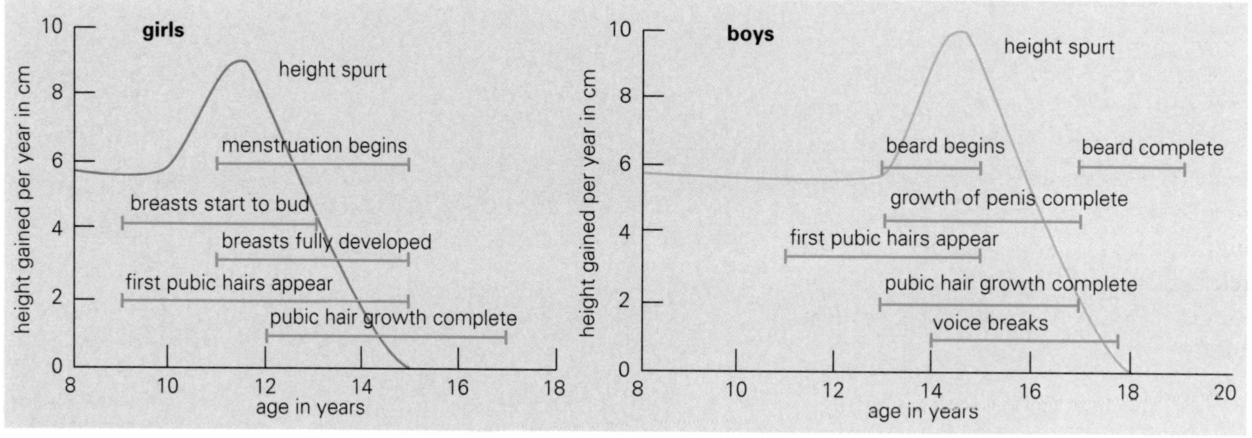

The normal range of physical development in boys and girls.

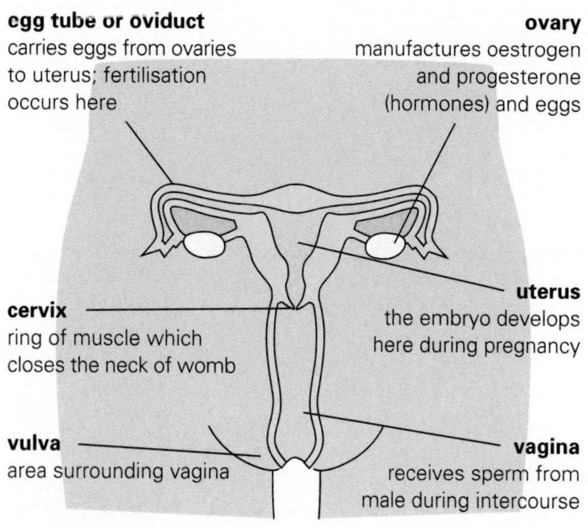

The female reproductive organs.

Physical development

The signs of sexual development shown in the graphs appear in boys and girls during their adolescence. These are called the **secondary sexual characteristics** and as you can see there is no 'normal' time for it all to happen. It starts at different ages for different people and takes several years to complete.

Menstruation

In women, about every 28 days, one egg is released from an ovary at ovulation. The egg then travels down the oviduct where it may be fertilised. If it is fertilised it beds into the lining of the uterus and develops into a fetus. If it is not fertilised the lining of the uterus breaks up and leaves the body as a monthly period (**menstruation**).

Hormonal control

At the beginning of the menstrual cycle the pituitary gland releases **follicle stimulating hormone** (**FSH**), which stimulates one of the follicles in the ovary to start growing and developing. The follicle cells also produce and release the hormone oestrogen which stimulates the wall of the uterus to repair itself and start growing, ready to receive the egg if it is fertilised.

The **hypothalamus** in the brain monitors the level of hormones in the blood and controls those released by the pituitary gland. The pituitary gland responds to increasing concentrations of oestrogen in the blood by releasing less FSH and releasing **luteinising hormone** (**LH**). LH stimulates the follicle to burst releasing the egg into the oviduct at ovulation.

After ovulation the follicle cells continue to grow and release another hormone called **progesterone**. This maintains the uterus in a state ready to accept the egg if it is fertilised. The release of progesterone continues for two weeks but, in that time, the pituitary responds by releasing less and less LH. This causes the progesterone level to fall with the result that the lining of the uterus is shed at menstruation, and FSH is released again by the pituitary. This marks the end of one cycle and the beginning of another.

If the egg is fertilised and a pregnancy begins, the placenta takes over the production of progesterone to prevent the uterus shedding its lining.

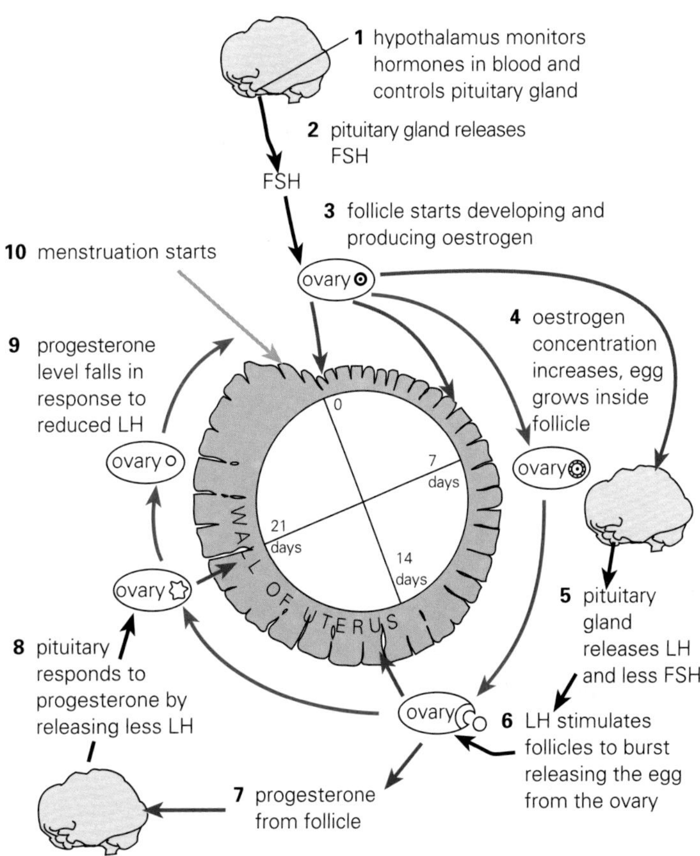

The changes that occur during a menstrual cycle.

Controlling fertility

One method of controlling fertility is the contraceptive pill. The combined contraceptive pill contains both oestrogen and progesterone which prevent ovulation. Taking the pill regularly as directed keeps the concentration of these hormones in the blood at a high level. The hypothalamus responds to these high levels by inhibiting the release of FSH and LH from the pituitary gland and this prevents the release of eggs from the ovaries.

Treating infertility

Some women have difficulty in becoming pregnant because eggs are not often released from their ovaries. Hormones can be used to treat this form of infertility. FSH is given to help stimulate the ovaries to release eggs.

QUESTIONS

1. Describe the changes that take place at puberty.
2. Describe the changes that occur in the ovary and the uterus during the menstrual cycle.
3. Explain how these changes are controlled by the hypothalamus, the pituitary gland and the hormones FSH, LH, oestrogen and progesterone.
4. Explain how hormones are used **a** to treat infertility in women and **b** in contraception.

3.7 *The nervous system*

Reacting to stimuli

All organs of the body have **sensory receptors** which send a continuous stream of information about what is going on outside and inside the body to the **central nervous system** (**CNS**). The **brain** and the **spinal cord** make up the central nervous system.

These people are using their senses to maintain their balance.

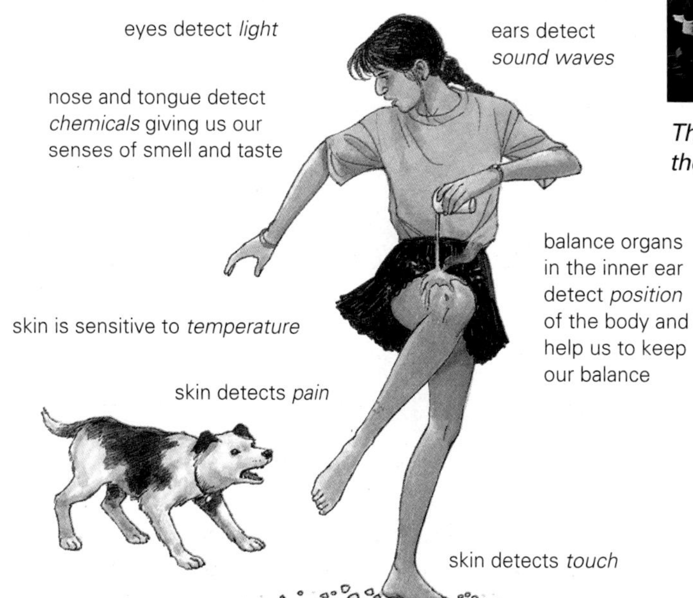

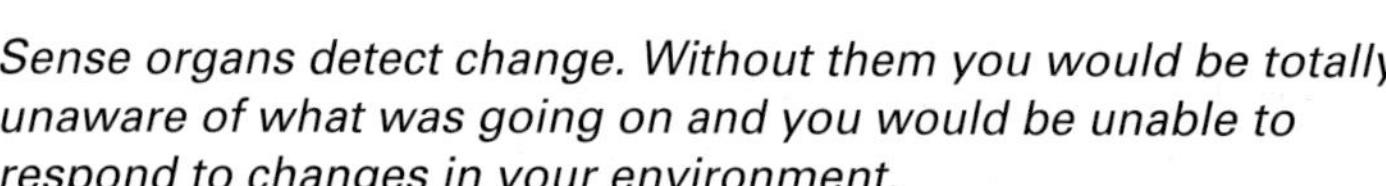

Sense organs detect change. Without them you would be totally unaware of what was going on and you would be unable to respond to changes in your environment.

Receptors in the skin are stimulated if you touch something hot. They are sensitive to temperature – and pain. Other receptors in different parts of the body are sensitive to touch, smell, taste and light. Information about changes, called stimuli, enable you to be aware of and react to your surroundings.

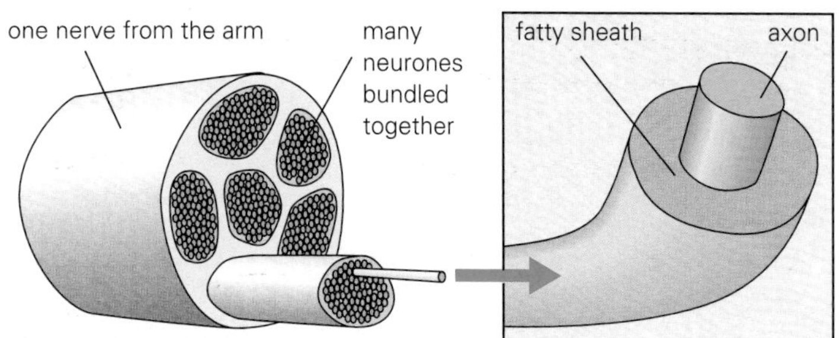

Within each nerve there are thousands of neurones. One is shown magnified on the right.

Neurones (or nerve cells) are the basic units of the nervous system. Many bundles of neurones make up a nerve. Neurones can have different structures depending on where they are located in the body.

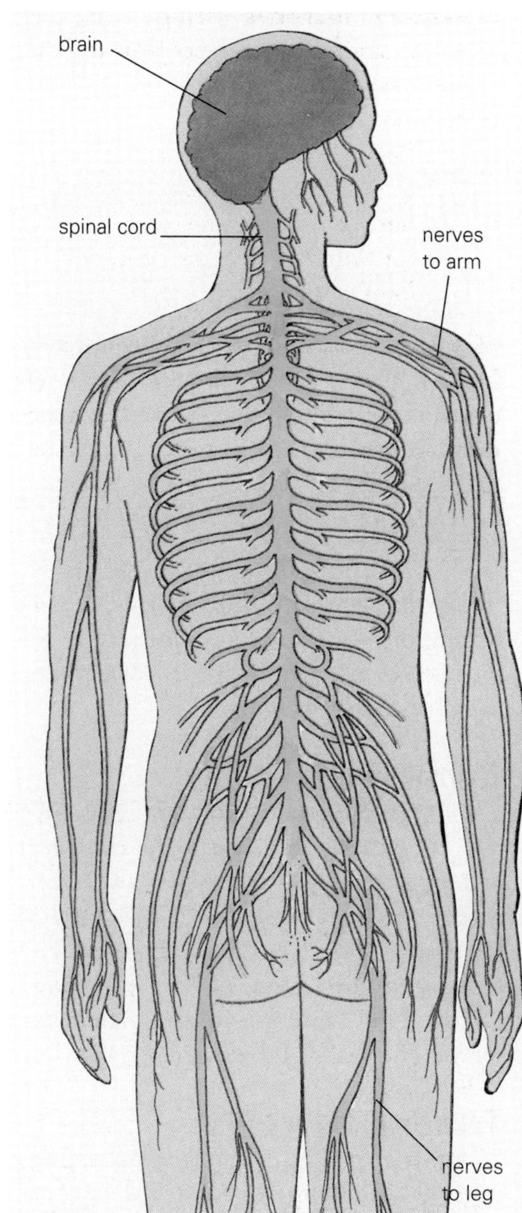

The brain and spinal cord make up the nervous system.

The response

Receptors respond to stimuli by sending brief electrical pulses (called **nerve impulses**) to the CNS. The degree of stimulation is indicated not by the size of the impulse, but by the frequency with which impulses are sent along sensory neurones. The stronger the stimulus the higher the frequency of impulses.

The brain sends nerve impulses to **effectors** (muscles and glands) along motor neurones. The effectors are where the actual response to the stimuli are carried out. Muscles respond by contracting or relaxing, glands respond by releasing hormones.

More about neurones

The diagram shows three types of neurone whose functions are as follows:

- **sensory neurones** – send information from the receptors to the CNS
- **motor neurones** – send information from the CNS to organs (effectors) such as muscles and glands
- **connector neurones** – relay information from sensory neurones to motor neurones.

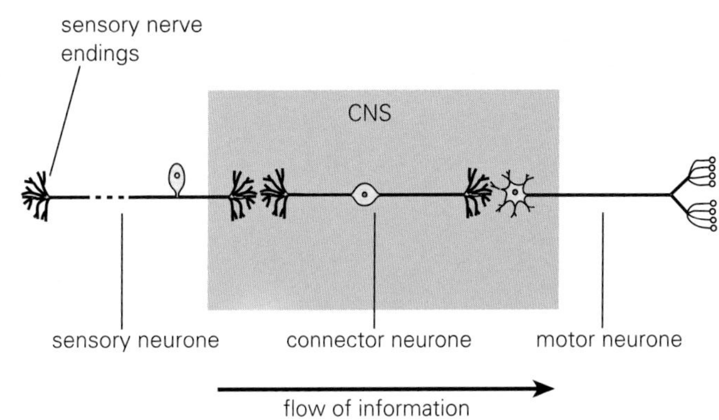

Motor neurones that transmit impulses from the brain or spinal cord to the muscles are very long, thin cells. The largest part of the neurone is the **cell body** which is in the CNS. This contains the cell's nucleus. Covering the cell body are many small, fine processes called **dendrites** which allow connections to be made with many other neurones.

The **axon** is a long thin extension which may be very long (up to half a metre). It is surrounded by a fatty sheath made up of cells which insulate the axon and make sure that the impulses pass at high speed (about 100 metres per second). The gaps in the insulation act like miniature booster stations helping the impulses pass along the axon.

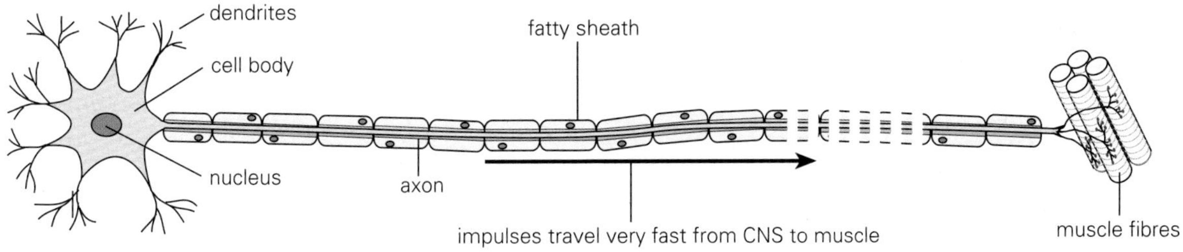

In motor neurones impulses travel rapidly along the axon to the muscle fibres.

QUESTIONS

1. Make a table to show all the sense organs in humans and the types of stimuli they receive.
2. State the functions of the three different types of neurone.
3. Explain how a motor neurone is adapted to its functions of sending nerve impulses quickly over long distances.

3.8 *Reflexes*

A simple reflex

Behaviour is a mixture of **reflexes**, which you are born with, and learned behaviour. Your response to a sharp, unexpected pin prick on the hand is an example of a simple reflex which is an inherited response to this stimulus.

The thorn prick is a stimulus. The response – jerking the hand away is automatic, fast and unlearned. This behaviour is coordinated (organised) by the nervous system. It happens very fast and you do not have to learn how to do it or even think about it. It does not involve the brain only the spinal cord.

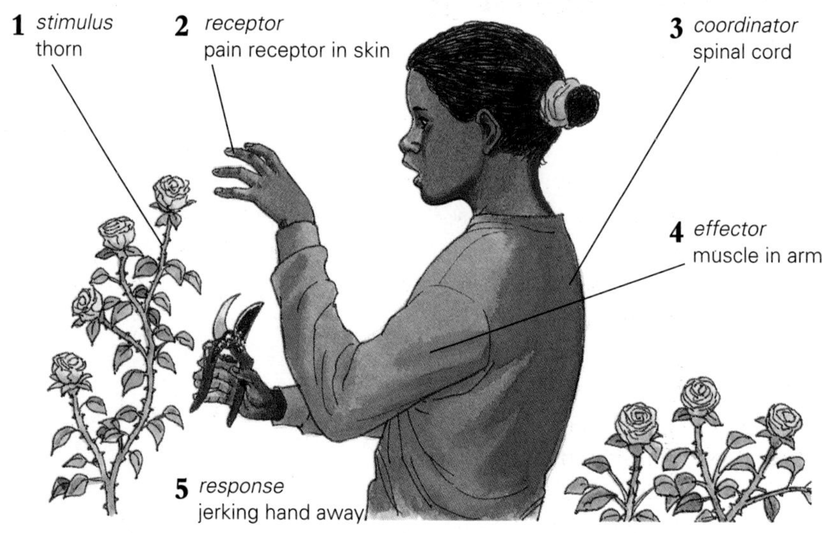

Reflex actions can be summarised as shown in the diagram. The effector could be a muscle that responds by contracting or a gland that responds by producing a hormone.

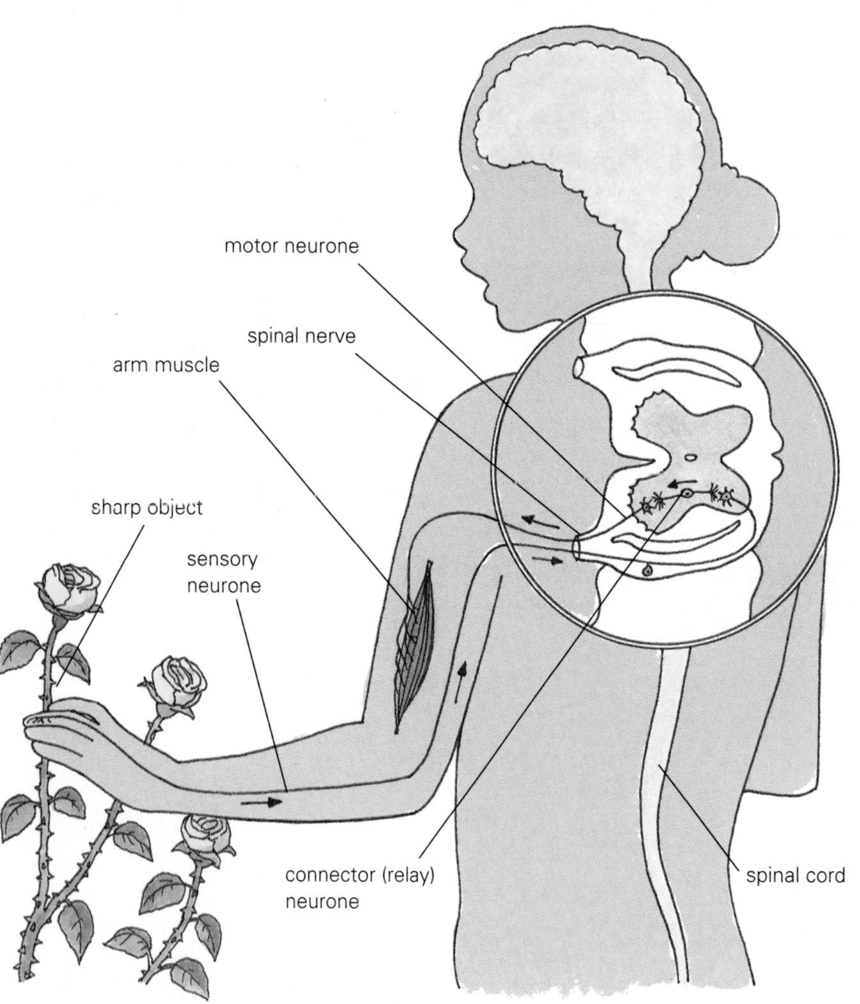

*The arrangement of the neurones in series like this is called a **reflex arc**.*

A reflex arc

The reflex action is controlled by three neurones acting in series. A sensory cell in the skin is stimulated by a sharp object and sends a stream of impulses along the sensory neurone which is inside a spinal nerve. The sensory neurone transmits the impulses into the spinal cord.

Inside the spinal cord the sensory neurone meets a connector (or relay) neurone which stimulates a motor (effector) neurone. Impulses pass along the motor neurone to the muscle, and stimulate it to contract so moving the hand away from the painful object. This reflex helps us to survive because a sharp object is likely to pierce the skin allowing bacteria to enter and cause disease.

The diagram shows the three neurones in the spinal cord. The spinal cord is shown on its side for simplification.

Chemicals bridge the gap

There are small gaps or junctions known as **synapses** between the neurones in any reflex arc. The stream of electrical impulses cannot cross the synapse so a chemical is released when the impulses reach the end of the sensory neurone. The chemical stimulates the next neurone in the series (the connector) and this transmits the impulse to the next synapse. More chemical is released here to stimulate the motor neurone. There are synapses between all neurones and at the nerve endings in muscles. Synapses slow down the passage of impulses in the nervous system, but they ensure that impulses only travel in one direction. (This is because the chemical produced to carry the impulse through the synapse is produced at only one side of the gap.)

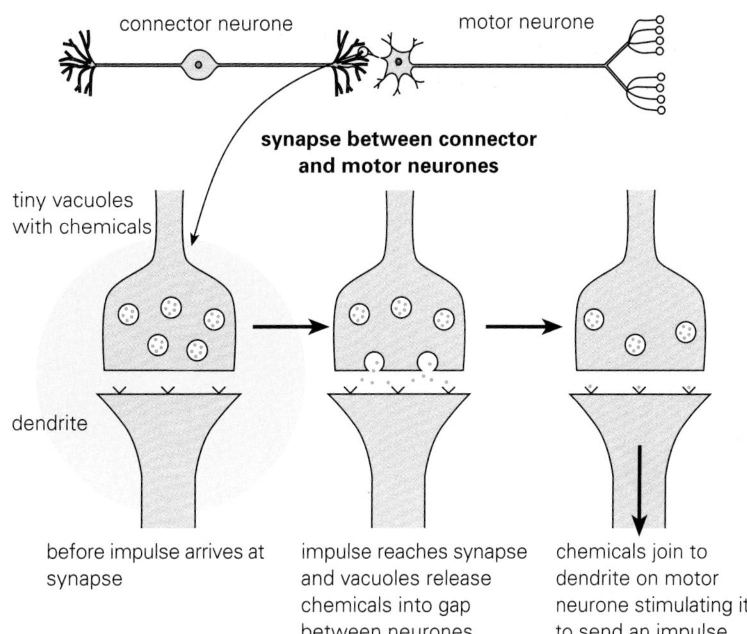

There are synapses between all neurones. To communicate they send chemicals across these tiny gaps.

More about reflexes

We are born with the patterns of behaviour known as reflexes. For example, a new born baby will grasp a finger placed in its palm. Doctors can check a baby's nervous system by testing this and other reflexes. Some of the new born baby's reflexes disappear as the nervous system develops and becomes more complex. Other inborn reflexes remain with us for life although they may change. The knee-jerk reflex is a simple one to demonstrate and is used by doctors when checking an adult's nervous system.

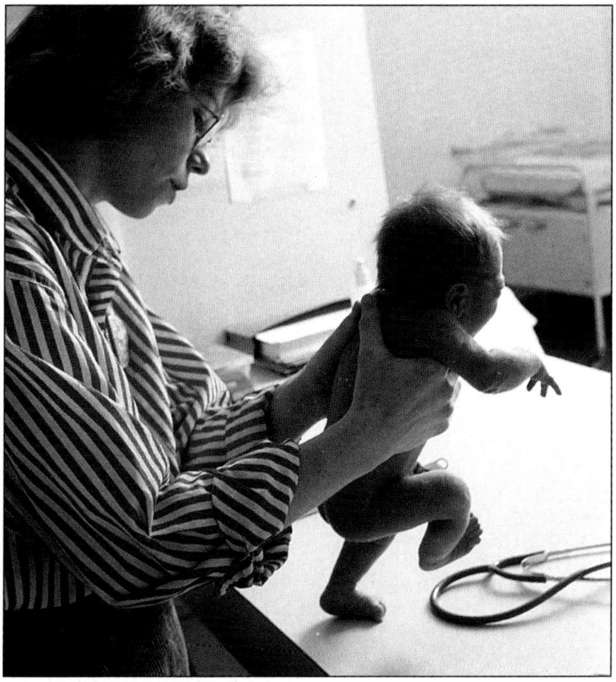

This doctor is checking the baby's nervous system by testing its reflexes.

Reflexes are vital to our survival. When a bright light is shone into the eyes the pupils decrease in size to protect the eye from damage (see 3.9). This is a reflex that occurs through the brain. Other inborn reflexes are just as important to our survival: shivering when cold, increasing the rate of breathing when we are exercising and need oxygen, the contractions of the bladder and rectum when they are full to expel urine and faeces.

QUESTIONS

1 Explain what is meant by a simple reflex. Give three examples of simple reflexes.

2 How do simple reflexes helps us to survive?

3 Describe the events that occur when the hand is removed quickly from a sharp object.

3.9 The eye

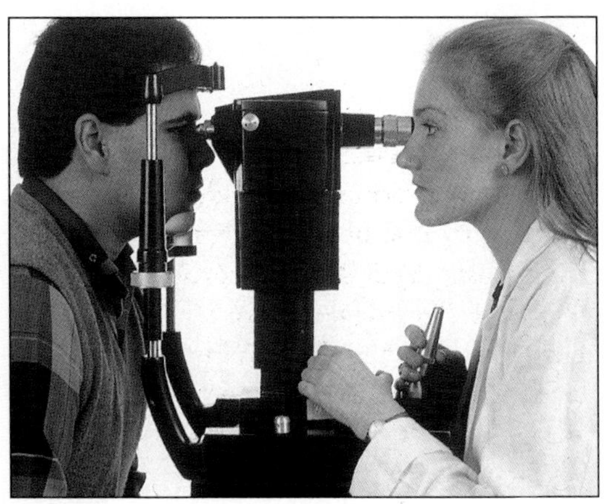
Eyesight is precious – look after your eyes!

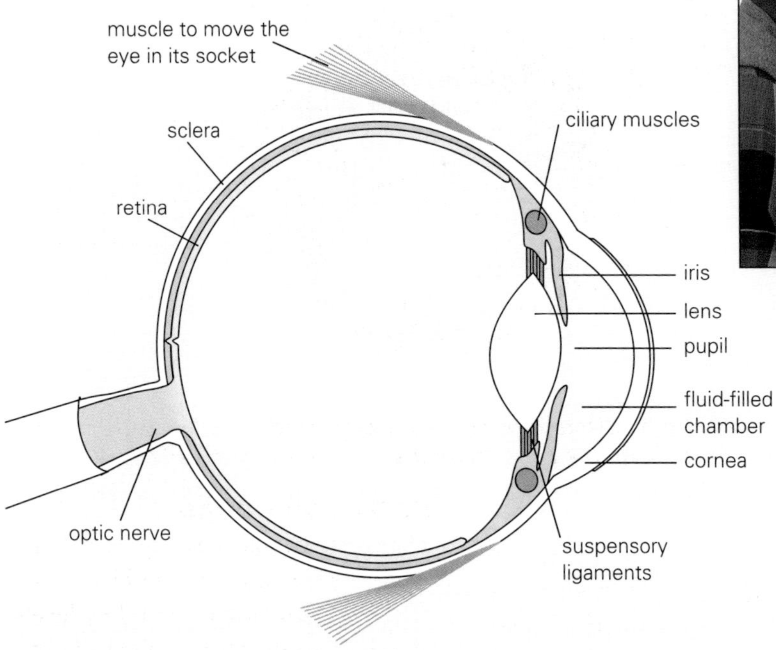

Here is the eye. An image of this picture is now on your retina.

The eye is a very special sensory organ which responds to the presence of light rays by sending nerve impulses to the brain. The **retina** at the back of the eye is full of light-sensitive receptor cells which send impulses to the brain along sensory neurones in the **optic nerve**. The brain then interprets this information to give us a constantly changing image of the world within our vision.

Several changes have to be made to the light as it enters the eye. Light has to be focused so a sharp image forms on the retina. Two parts of the eye focus light, the **cornea** and the **lens**. The focusing power of the lens changes as the shape of the lens changes so that you can see objects that are close to you and those at a distance.

The tough white fibrous capsule around the eye is the **sclera**. The front of the sclera is the transparent cornea. The cornea does about 60% of the focusing. Between the fluid-filled chamber and the lens is the **iris**. This is a muscular tissue which controls the size of the **pupil** and so the amount of light reaching the retina. The lens is held in place by **suspensory ligaments** which are delicate fibres. Running around the lens like a series of hoops are the **ciliary muscles** which control the shape of the lens.

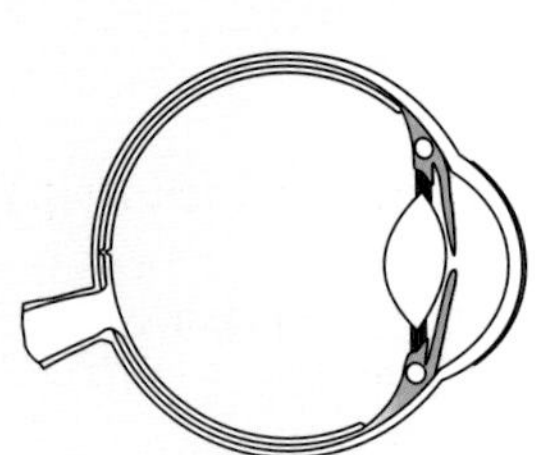

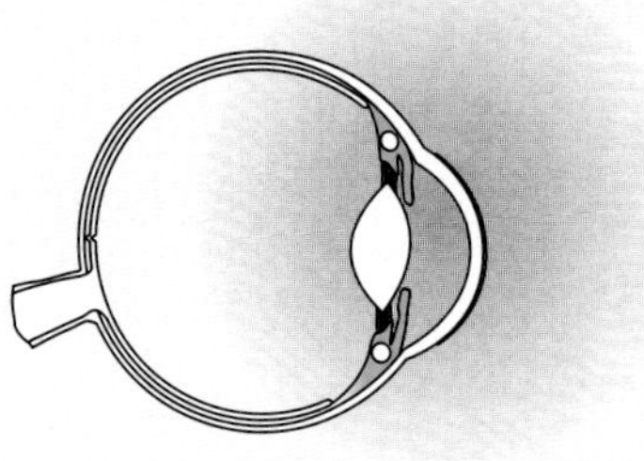

In bright light the iris reduces the size of the pupil so reducing the amount of light reaching the retina. In dull light the iris widens increasing the size of the pupil and letting in more light. These are reflex actions to protect the retina from being damaged by bright light.

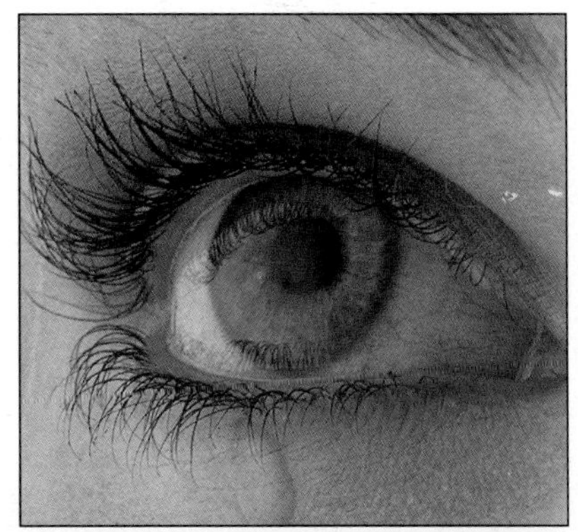

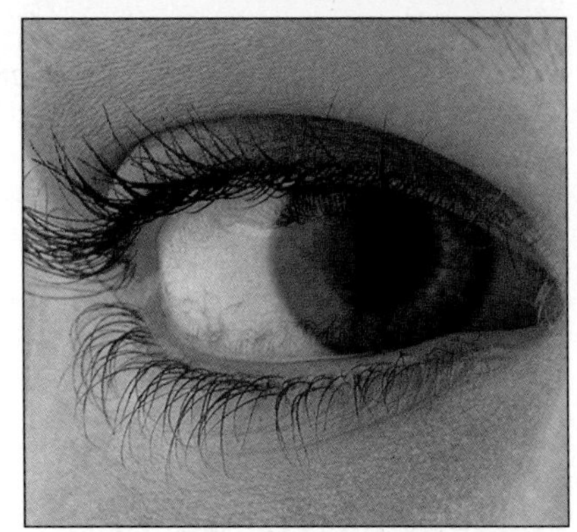

This is what happens in your eye when you are in very bright (above) and very dim light.

Image formation

Light rays entering the eye are brought to a point on the retina by the focusing action of the cornea and lens. The cornea is like a coarse focus while the lens gives us a fine focus so that the image is sharp. The diagram shows how light rays are refracted (change direction) in the eye:

- as they pass from the air into the cornea, and
- when they enter the lens from the fluid in the front chamber of the eye.

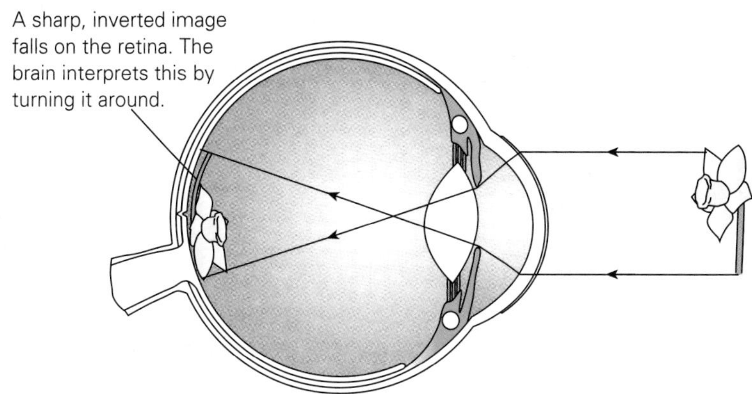

Light rays from objects in our field of vision need to be focused so that they form a sharp image on the retina in order to see clearly.

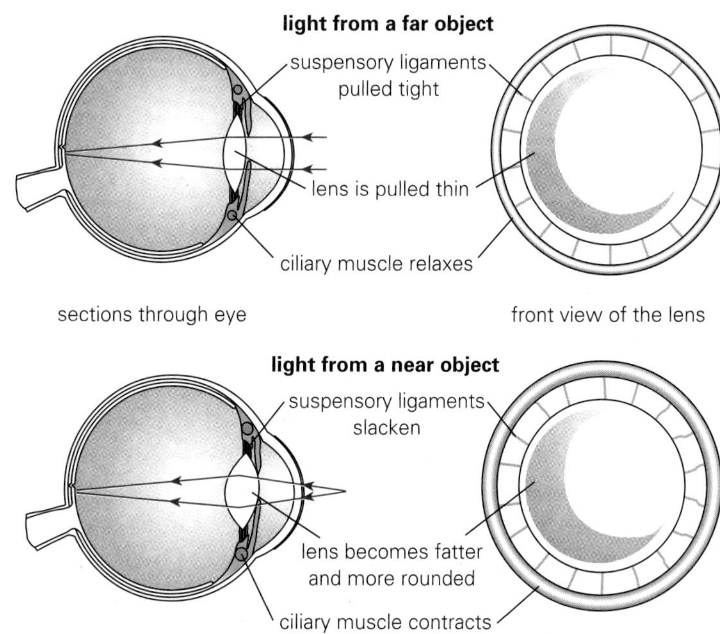

The lens does not have a fixed focusing ability. It changes shape as you look at near and far objects.

Rods and cones

The retina contains two types of cell. **Rods** enable you to see in black and white and function even in low levels of light. **Cones** work at higher light intensities and are the cells that allow you to see in colour.

Focusing near and far

In a camera the lens is moved backwards and forwards in order to change its focus. In the human eye the shape of the lens is changed – it is thin for far objects and thicker for near objects. When you want to look at something close to, like reading the pages of this book, your eye at first sees a blurred image. Immediately a reflex action occurs to change the shape of the lens and make it fatter. The ciliary muscle contracts to reduce the tension in the ligaments so the lens automatically becomes thicker.

QUESTIONS

1 Make an outline drawing of the eye and label the following structures:
sclera, cornea, iris, pupil, lens, ciliary muscles, suspensory ligaments, retina, optic nerve.

2 State the functions of the parts of the eye you have labelled.

3 Explain how an image is formed in the eye.

4 Explain how the eye changes when focusing from near to far objects.

5 Explain how the iris controls the amount of light entering the eye.

6 Plan an investigation to test people's eyesight.

4.1 *Disease*

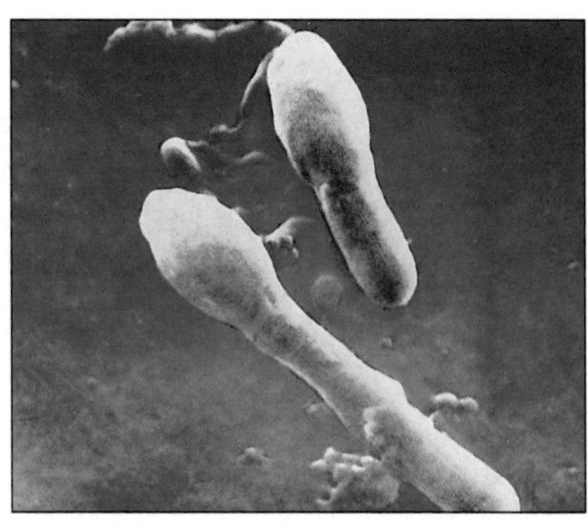

Tetanus bacteria like these release a toxin after they have entered the body through a cut or wound (× 9800).

The invaders

Diseases that are caused by invading microbes such as bacteria and viruses are called **infectious diseases**. When you cut or graze yourself bacteria and viruses can enter the wound and infect your tissues. Sometimes they will enter the blood and will travel throughout the body. Microbes can also enter your tissues by passing through the lining of the lungs, gut or reproductive system.

After bacteria enter the body they may reproduce rapidly and spread. Bacterial cells contain cytoplasm and have a cell wall, but they do not have a distinct nucleus. As they divide and grow, they release poisons called **toxins** which can make us feel ill.

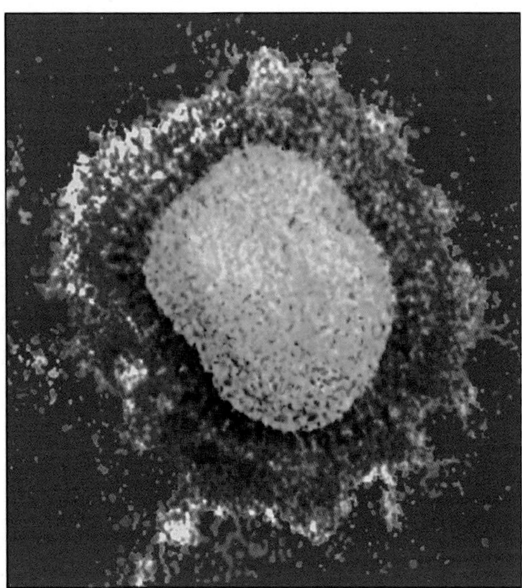

This is the virus that causes 'flu – the influenza virus (× 100 000).

Viruses are smaller than bacteria and cannot reproduce themselves. They consist only of a protein coat surrounding a few genes and so viruses are completely dependent on the cells they invade. They take over body cells and, once inside, direct them to make new virus particles.

First line of defence

The skin provides a *physical barrier* to most bacteria, viruses and fungi. The surface is composed of layers of dead cells that microbes cannot penetrate. The only way in for microbes is through breaks in the skin.

Chemical defences also exist to prevent the growth of harmful microbes in a number of ways:

- hydrochloric acid in our stomach destroys bacteria in food
- the trachea and bronchi are lined with cells that produce a sticky liquid mucus to trap microbes and protect the lungs (see 2.6)
- the blood produces clots that seal breaks in the skin (see 2.9).

Once inside the body

When invading microbes enter our tissues white cells form the next line of defence. There are two types – **phagocytes** and **lymphocytes**.

Phagocytes are made and stored in **bone marrow**, a soft tissue at the centre of some bones. When an infection happens they are released and travel in the blood to the place where bacteria have entered the body. Phagocytes surround bacteria and then destroy them using enzymes. When a large number of phagocytes do this at the site of an infection they often die and form **pus**.

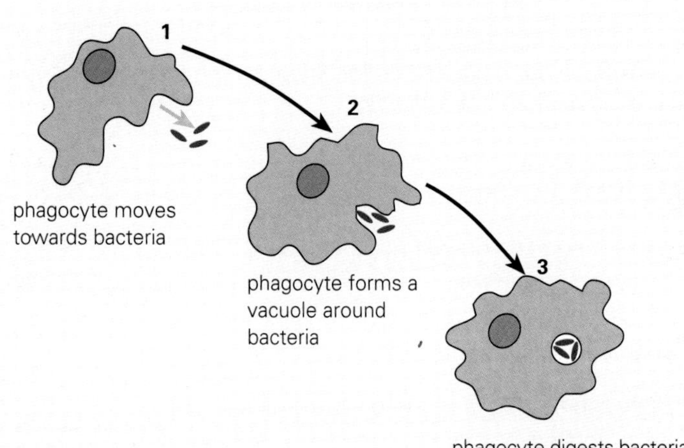

*Phagocytes **ingest** microbes. (They surround and destroy them.)*

Lymphocytes and antibodies

Our bodies contain very large numbers of lymphocytes which recognise different types of bacteria and viruses. They produce proteins called **antibodies** which destroy specific bacteria and viruses. For example, the antibody for the measles virus is different from the antibody for chickenpox. Antibodies often work by causing bacteria to clump together making it easy for phagocytes to find and ingest them. Some antibodies combine with the poisonous waste products (toxins) of bacteria and render them harmless. Such antibodies are called **antitoxins**.

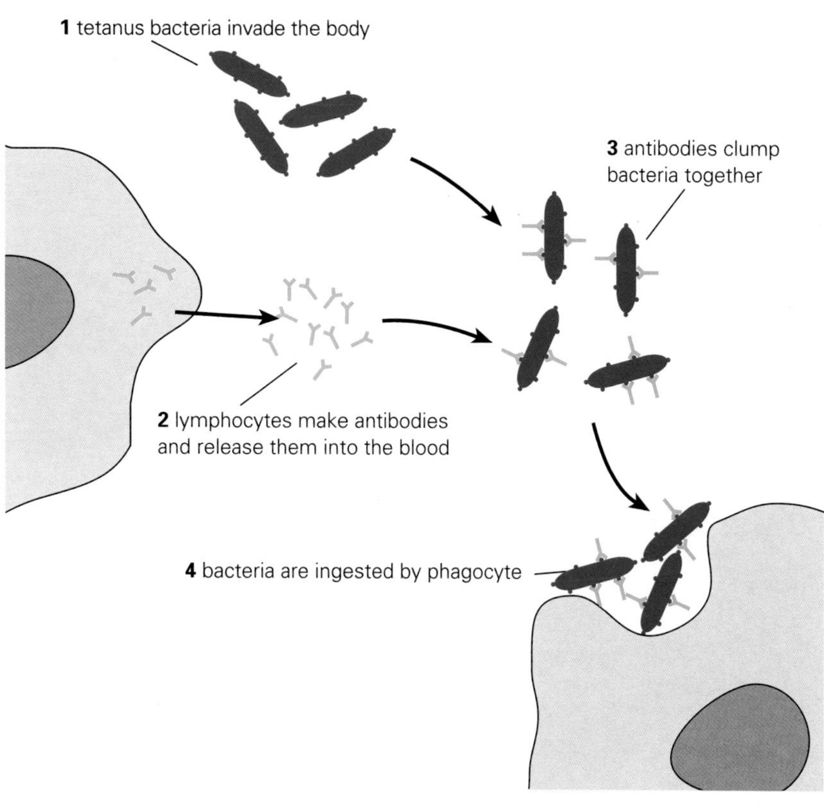

Lymphocytes produce antibodies against invading antigens – in this diagram it is tetanus bacteria.

Antigens

Bacteria or viruses which cause the lymphocytes to produce antibodies are **antigens**. When an antigen enters the body for the first time lymphocytes respond quite slowly and you suffer the symptoms of a disease.

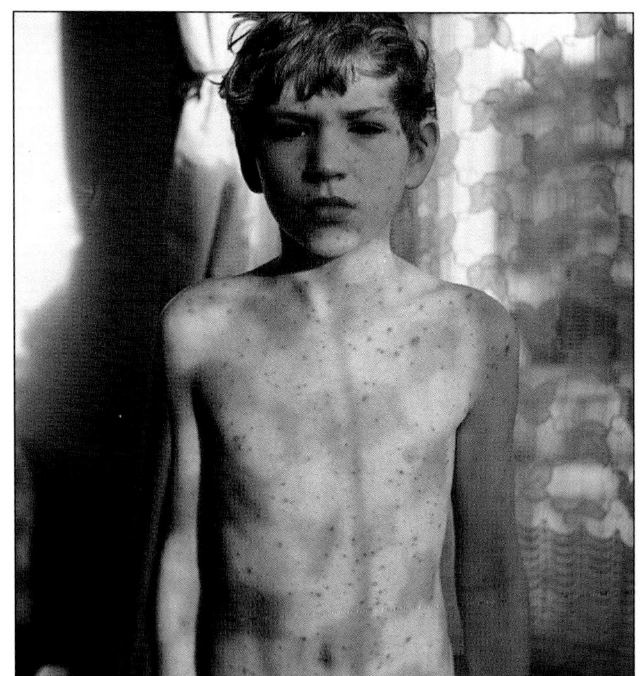

Once you have had chickenpox you are protected from catching it again.

The immune response

The production of antibodies by the body in recognition of foreign material is called the **immune response**. After white cells have made an antibody in response to a particular infection they can easily recognise the microbe and produce the same antibody again so that you do not usually catch the same disease twice.

QUESTIONS

1 Explain the term infectious disease.

2 Summarise the differences between bacteria and viruses.

3 What is the difference between antibodies and antigens?

4 Describe the roles of phagocytes and lymphocytes in fighting disease.

4.2 *Lifestyle and disease*

Spreading disease

Infectious diseases are spread from person to person in a number of different ways. This spread is known as **disease transmission**. Diseases can be passed or transmitted from infected people to uninfected people in the following ways:

- Insects, e.g. a mosquito feeds on the blood of a person who has malaria. The mosquito picks up the organisms which cause malaria and transmits them when it feeds on an uninfected person.
- Water, e.g. the hookworm lives in the gut. Its eggs leave the body of infected people in their faeces. The eggs hatch in water and the hook worm bores its way through the skin.
- Through the air, e.g. transmission can take place in droplets of water. Bacteria that cause tuberculosis (TB) are spread in droplets of water from the lungs. People infected with TB spread large numbers of bacteria when they sneeze.
- Food poisoning is caused by bacteria such as *Salmonella*. It is spread when food is not prepared hygienically.

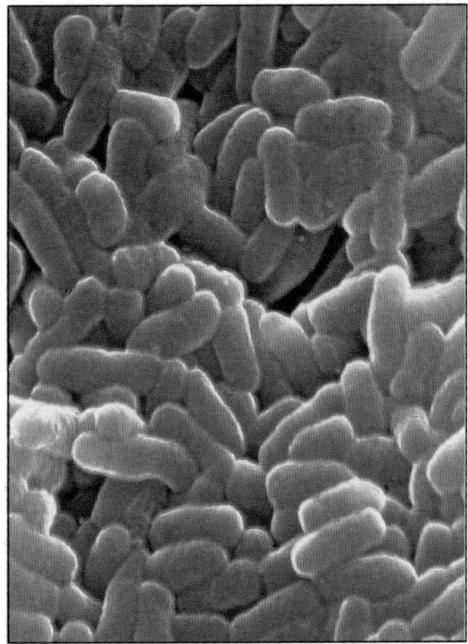

These bacteria cause TB (× 2000).

A mosquito taking a blood meal.

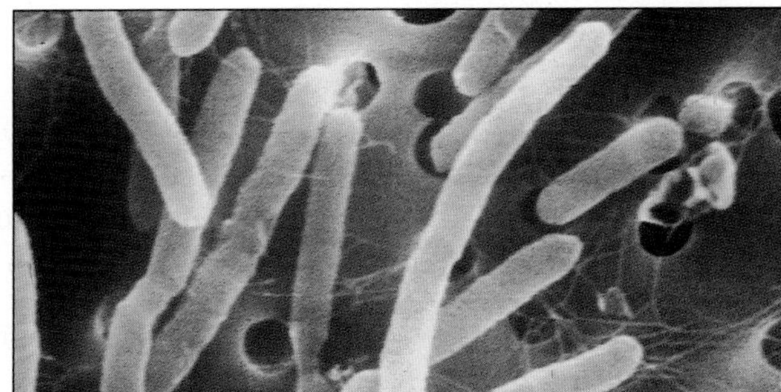

Salmonella *causes food poisoning (× 7000).*

Many children and adults who live in conditions such as those shown in the photograph suffer from diarrhoea and other diseases that are spread through drinking contaminated water. The bacteria which cause these diseases pass out in people's faeces. As there is no treatment of sewage, or treatment of drinking water, children pick up these microbes very easily. Many die of these diseases every year in Africa, Asia and South America. The only way to prevent this happening is to break the transmission from one person to another. This is done by treating human waste in sewage works and providing clean, piped water which is first chlorinated to kill all bacteria.

Living conditions favour the spread of some diseases. People who live in the difficult conditions shown are at great risk every day of catching deadly infectious diseases such as tuberculosis (TB), cholera, typhoid, tetanus and many others.

Immunity protects against disease

One way to protect people against disease is to immunise them. This gives you immunity to a disease before you catch it. This can be done in two ways. You can either be given a **vaccine** (which gives you a permanent form of immunity) or you can be given some antibodies which will last a few weeks or months.

Vaccination

This is done by injecting, or taking by mouth, a small quantity of dead or weakened microbes of the disease as a vaccine. The microbes still carry antigens and so this stimulates the production of antibodies but, because the microbe has been altered, you do not get any of the symptoms of the disease concerned.

A common vaccine is MMR for mumps, measles and rubella (German measles) which is given to children in their first year of life or later. Other examples include polio, influenza and whooping cough. It is important to have the long-term immunity provided by this treatment even though these diseases are rare in Britain because the microbes that cause them are still around and cause occasional outbreaks of the disease.

Temporary immunity

Injecting serum containing ready-made antibodies to a disease provides short-term immunity. This is used after a person has caught a disease or if he or she is thought to be at risk of catching it. For example anti-tetanus serum contains antibodies to fight the tetanus toxin. This helps fight the disease until the body makes enough of its own antibodies. Protection against diphtheria is also provided in this way.

Success and failure

Smallpox is a disease that has been eradicated from the world. The virus that caused it was very stable – it did not change. It was therefore quite easy to make a vaccine against smallpox that could be used all over the world. In 1980 the world was declared free of the disease.

Similar campaigns have been tried since against other diseases, e.g. measles, but these diseases are caused by microbes that change their antigens. It is impossible therefore to develop a vaccine that will protect against all strains of the disease. This means that we cannot rely on medicine to control the spread of disease. People's living conditions and diet must also be improved at the same time.

QUESTIONS

1 Make a list of ways in which infectious diseases are transmitted from person to person.

2 Explain how poor living conditions favour the spread of disease.

3 Write a leaflet for an aid organisation that wants to raise money to provide clean, piped water in villages that have no running water.

4 Explain the benefits of vaccination.

5 Explain why we become immune to a disease after being vaccinated.

4.3 *Drug use and abuse*

What are drugs?

A **drug** is any chemical substance that affects the way the body functions. Throughout history different types of drugs have been popular; tea and coffee became common in England in the 17th and 18th centuries. Cocaine was used in medicines and in drinks in the last century. During the Second World War drugs called amphetamines were given to pilots to keep them awake. We use drugs to change our moods, to treat and cure all types of ailments and to change the way we view the world. Some drugs, such as aspirin and penicillin, are extremely useful and safe.

For one reason or another people in different societies have taken drugs.

People take drugs for different reasons. No one completely understands why they do this.

Drugs as medicines

Drugs affect us in many ways, for example:

- Aspirin relieves pain by stopping the production of certain chemicals in the body which stimulate our sensory nerves and cause pain. It also thins down the blood, an extremely important effect for those with heart problems.
- Antibiotics such as penicillin are used to control and cure infections produced by bacteria. Bacterial cell walls are weakened by antibiotics. The cell then swells and bursts.

Most drugs taken as medicines to treat or prevent disease are beneficial and not harmful. However drugs should be taken with caution and only when they are needed. All drugs have some side effects. For example a drug taken to relieve a headache might produce an upset to the digestive system.

Group of drugs	Names of drugs	Effects on the body
hallucinogens	LSD magic mushrooms	produce hallucinations
intoxicants	alcohol solvents	drunkeness
hypnotics, anti-anxiety drugs	sedatives, tranquillisers, e.g. Valium, barbiturates	causes sleep, reduces anxiety
stimulants	nicotine, cocaine, amphetamines, caffeine (in tea and coffee)	increases the ability to concentrate, makes people energetic and confident
opiates	heroin, morphine, codeine	pain killer, feeling of relaxation and euphoria

Only some of these drugs have medical uses.

Drugs can be abused

Drugs can be taken for reasons other than medical ones. Drugs like tranquillisers and stimulants are substances that can be prescibed as medicines but they can be misused or abused. Others, such as LSD and cocaine, are drugs that are not used as medicines. The table shows the types of drugs which can be abused.

Solvent abuse

A **volatile** substance is one that easily changes from a liquid into a gas. Dry cleaning fluids, perfumes and alcohol are volatile liquids. **Solvents** are liquids that allow other substances to dissolve in them. A large number of common substances like household cleaners and glues contain volatile liquids as solvents. When inhaled these substances can produce an intoxicated state similar to that produced by drinking too much alcohol. 'Glue sniffing' or inhaling these substances can produce hallucinations but at the same time does serious damage to the lungs, liver, brain and kidney.

Talking with others often helps people overcome their dependence on drugs.

Young people have been maimed or killed, often suffocating by inhaling their own vomit, after inhaling solvents.

Addiction

Taking drugs regularly over a period of time and in large doses can cause **addiction**. The person taking the drug comes to rely on its effects. Often the body comes to need more and more of the drug to produce the same desired effect. The person is **dependent** on the drug. In the end they are unable function without it.

The long-term effects of addiction include character changes and health hazards like blood infections from using contaminated needles for injecting drugs. Making and carrying out the decision to stop taking drugs is extremely difficult. It requires great motivation from the person and also much support from relatives and friends. When giving up the drug the addicted person often suffers from painful and uncomfortable **withdrawal symptoms** like raised temperatures, sickness and severe cramp.

QUESTIONS

1 Explain the term drug.

2 Explain to someone the difference between a drug and a medicine.

3 Design a poster for a doctors' waiting room on the safe use of medicines.

4 What is solvent abuse? What are the dangers and why do you think it is more common among younger people than among adults?

5 Explain why it is diificult for some people to give up a drug on which they are dependent.

4.4 *Alcohol*

Alcohol (proper name ethanol) is a part of a whole range of drinks including beer, wine, cider and spirits like gin and whisky. These drinks line supermarket and off-licence shelves and are available for purchase in public houses that are open for most of the day. Alcohol is one of the world's commonest drugs.

Celebrations in many countries include drinking alcohol.

How much alcohol?

The amount of alcohol in alcoholic drinks is measured in different ways. Sometimes it is given as a percentage by volume (for example whisky is 37.5% vol. and some beers are 3.5% vol.).

Another way is to give the units of alcohol. One unit is equivalent to the amount in half a pint of ordinary beer or lager. This is about 8g alcohol which is approximately the amount that we can remove from our bodies in one hour.

Knowing how much alcohol is present in drinks is important as it enables you to make sensible decisions about drinking considering:

- health reasons, as only a certain quantity can safely be consumed per week
- safety reasons, as if you are a driver, and you do decide to drink, your own and the safety of others is important
- social reasons, as nobody likes people who drink to excess and behave in unreasonable ways.

These ordinary pub measures each contain 1 unit of alcohol. Notice how much alcohol some drinks contain compared to others.

Alcohol absorption

Alcohol is absorbed into the blood very quickly through the lining of the stomach. It is slower if you have just had a meal or if you drink while you are eating. Alcohol then circulates around the body in the blood. As it is a small molecule it passes through the cell membranes very easily and quickly enters the cells. It mainly affects the liver and the nervous system.

A depressant drug

Alcohol affects brain functions by slowing down the passage of nerve impulses along neurones. It acts as a depressant drug. As the amount of alcohol in the blood rises, our behaviour changes and the time taken for us to respond to any stimulus lengthens. At quite low levels alcohol reduces the power of coordination, judgement and self-control. Drinking alcohol affects a car driver's ability to judge speed and distance, and react quickly in an emergency.

Prolonged drinking may even lead to unconsciousness and a coma. As well as reducing the efficiency of the nervous system alcohol tends to increase self-confidence. This is a dangerous combination behind the wheel of a car or a motorcycle. Heavy drinkers often become confused and have poor short-term memories. They also suffer from depression and poor self-esteem.

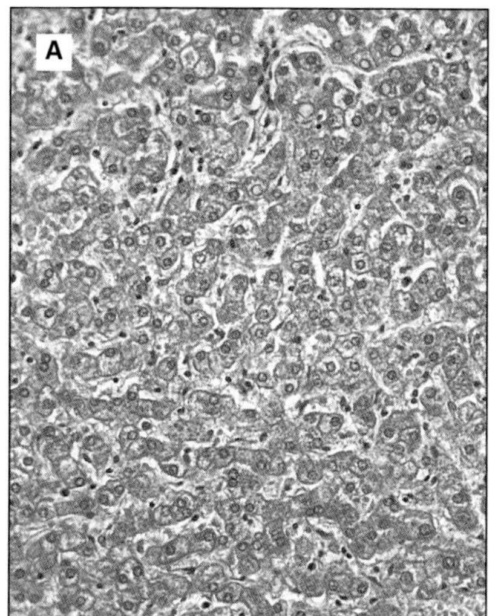

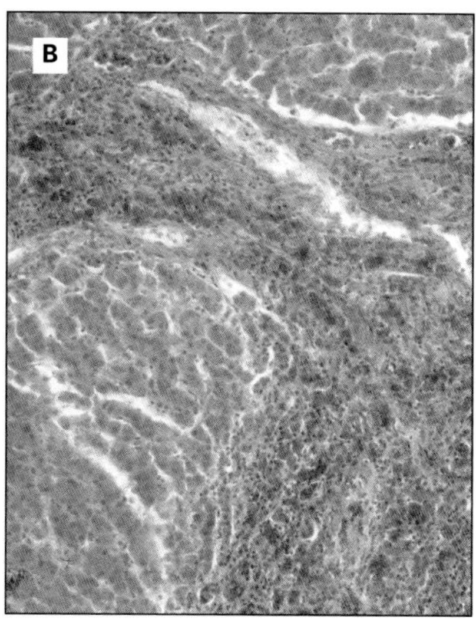

*Photograph **A** shows a healthy liver under the microscope. Compare it with brown scar tissue in the liver of someone with cirrhosis (**B**).*

Liver damage

Some alcohol passes out of your body in urine, sweat and breath but most of it is metabolised (changed into other substances) in the liver. Alcohol destroys liver cells. Dead cells are replaced by fibrous tissue. This is called **alcoholic hepatitis**. If heavy drinking continues the liver becomes hard and full of nodules. This is an irreversible condition called **cirrhosis**. The liver becomes less and less efficient and the metabolism of the whole body suffers. Cirrhosis can be fatal if the person continues to drink alcohol.

Withdrawal symptoms

Some people become addicted to alcohol. These alcoholics have severe withdrawal symptoms when days pass without an alcoholic drink. They shake, feel sick, sweat a lot and feel weak. They may also have hallucinations. Delirium tremens (DTs) is a severe form of this. The only real cure is to give up drinking.

In Britain in 1993, 540 people died in 9480 road accidents where a driver was under the influence of alcohol. The legal limit for driving in Britain is 80 mg of alcohol in every 100 cm³ blood.

Moderate drinking

When alcohol is drunk in moderate quantities it makes people feel relaxed, inhibitions are removed and conversation becomes easier. Unlike cigarette smoking moderate drinking does no harm. It may even be beneficial in reducing the risks of heart disease. However alcohol is easily abused by some who get drunk. As the blood alcohol level rises they become more and more irresponsible in their actions. The police spend a good deal of their time dealing with alcohol-related problems such as violence.

Alcohol, like most other drugs, can also cause problems for babies if their mothers drink while they are pregnant. It can cause babies to have a low weight at birth. In the worst cases babies are born already addicted to alcohol and suffer withdrawal symptoms.

QUESTIONS

1 Describe ways of measuring the alcohol content of drinks.

2 Describe the effects of drinking alcohol on the liver.

3 Explain to a new driver the dangers of drinking and driving. What advice would you offer?

4 Devise an advertising campaign to stop alcoholic abuse by young people.

4.5 *Tobacco*

Stars in popular films were rarely seen without a cigarette.

Social habit

Books and advertisements from the 1920s and 1930s show that then many people smoked cigarettes. Even fashion photographs show models with cigarette holders. At that time smoking was not thought to be harmful. In the 1950s the relationship between smoking and lung cancer was discovered and people first became aware of the possible dangers of smoking cigarettes. People who smoked developed lung cancer more often than those who did not. Nowadays we know much more about how smoking affects your body and yet many people still smoke.

Nicotine

Smokers crave and become addicted to **nicotine**. Nicotine is found in the leaves of the tobacco plant. Inhaled cigarette smoke containing nicotine passes down the trachea and into the lungs. Nicotine then passes through the alveoli and enters the blood stream. It is transported to the brain, reaching it in about 7 seconds, where it stimulates the central nervous sytem and relaxes the muscles.

Harmful effects

Smoking can produce the following serious, harmful effects.

- Nicotine in cigarette smoke makes arteries narrow which increases blood pressure. Nicotine also increases the stickiness of the platelets in the blood so increasing the chance that a clot will form.
- Carbon monoxide gas in the smoke combines irreversibly with haemoglobin in red cells. This reduces the amount of oxygen the blood can carry and so starves the tissues of oxygen.
- Both smoking tobacco and drinking alcohol increase the chance that fat will be deposited in the artery walls leading to angina (chest pain) and a possible heart attack.

Tar

Tar in cigarette smoke prevents the cilia in the trachea from working efficiently. Tar is a mixture of over 4000 substances that, when breathed in, does not pass into the blood but remains in the lungs. Tar irritates the lining of the air passages stimulating it to increase the amount of mucus released. This extra mucus collects and narrows the passages and smokers cough to move it out from the lungs where it builds up, hence the term 'smokers' cough'.

This irritation makes smokers much more susceptible to lung disease. The small airways, the bronchioles, are narrowed making breathing difficult, and if they become infected **bronchitis** develops. Tobacco smoke can also cause a disease called **emphysema**. In this case constant coughing damages and destroys the alveoli reducing the surface area for gaseous exchange. Sufferers cannot absorb enough oxygen and are often short of breath.

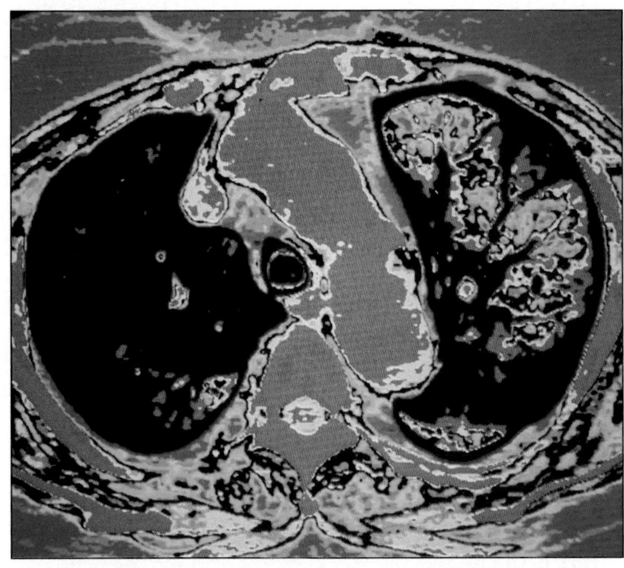
This horizontal section through the chest shows lung damage (blue/green) on the right due to emphysema.

Lung cancer

Scientists have shown that there are substances in the tar in cigarette smoke that damage lung cells and cause cancer. Lung cancer used to be a rare disease, but the incidence has increased considerably throughout the 20th century. The rise is correlated with the increase in cigarette smoking.

The risk of developing lung cancer increases if you:

- smoke a large number of cigarettes per day
- start smoking at an early age
- inhale smoke
- live in areas of high atmospheric pollution
- live in the same house as someone who smokes.

Damage to others

It has now been established that smoking is a health risk not only to the smokers but also to those around them. Non-smokers have to suffer the effects of breathing in exhaled smoke, known as **passive smoking**.

Unborn babies are affected badly if their mothers smoke. The amount of oxygen carried by the mother's blood is reduced and so less is passed across the placenta to the baby.

Babies before and after they are born are particularly susceptible to damage.

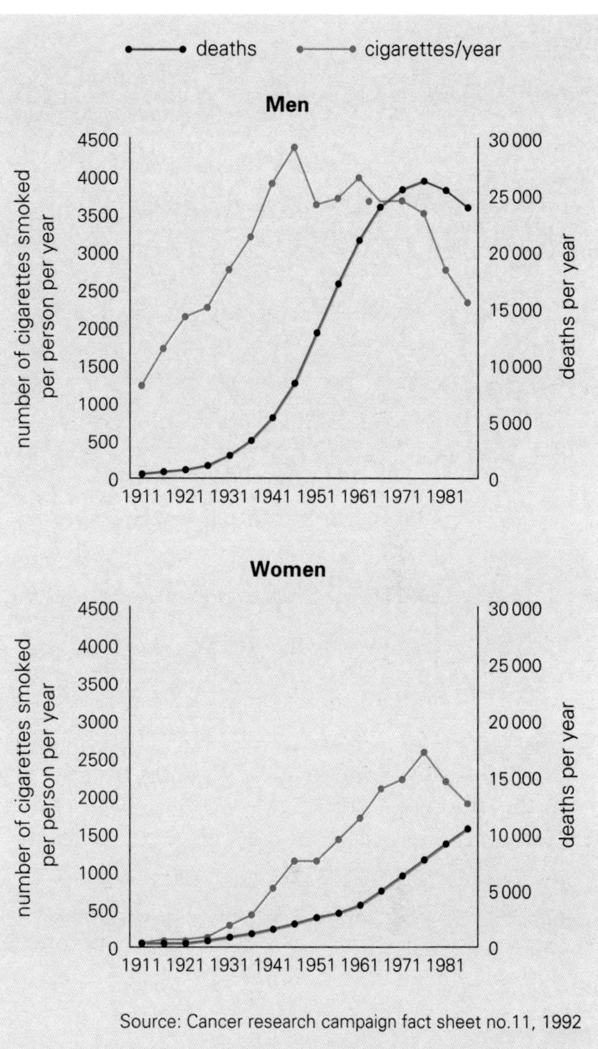

These graphs compare the number of cigarettes smoked per person per year with the deaths from lung cancer over the same period, in the UK.

QUESTIONS

1 What effects on the body do each of the following have **a** nicotine **b** carbon monoxide and **c** tar?

2 Should smoking be allowed in public places? List the reasons for and against.

3 Write a letter of advice to a friend who is being encouraged to start smoking.

4 Construct an information leaflet outlining the options available to smokers wishing to give up the habit.

SECTION B: QUESTIONS

1a Describe the functions of vitamins A and C in the body.

b A shortage of iron in the diet can make people feel tired and lack energy. Explain why.

c **i** Why is it recommended that children have more calcium in their diet than adults?

ii When should women increase their intake of calcium? Explain your answer.

2 The energy available from proteins is 17 kJ per gram and carbohydrates 16 kJ per gram. Fats provide 37 kJ per gram. The table below shows the composition of four types of nut.

Nut	Mass (g per 100 grams)			
	fat	carbohydrate	protein	water
peanut	57	10	28	5
walnut	57	6	12	25
Brazil nut	67	9	16	8
chestnut	6	37	2	55

a Use the information above to calculate the energy content in kJ per 100 gram of each type of nut. Show your working.

b Explain why chestnuts have less energy than the others.

c Describe the consequences of having a diet that provides:

i too much energy

ii too little energy.

3 Catalase is an enzyme found in many plant and animal tissues. It breaks down hydrogen peroxide (H_2O_2) into water and oxygen. Hydrogen peroxide is a toxic waste product of chemical reactions inside cells. When uncooked foods are put into hydrogen peroxide the oxygen and water form a froth. With meat (muscle tissue) there is a vigorous reaction.

a What is an enzyme?

b No frothing occurs if cooked meat is added to hydrogen peroxide. Why is this?

c Describe how you would carry out experiments to investigate:

i the levels of activity of catalase in different animal and plant tissues

ii the effect of temperature on the activity of catalase.

In your answers give full experimental details including lists of the factors that need to be kept constant. Explain how to collect quantitative measurements enabling you to plot graphs of your results.

4a Where in the digestive system is amylase produced?

Some apparatus was set up as shown.

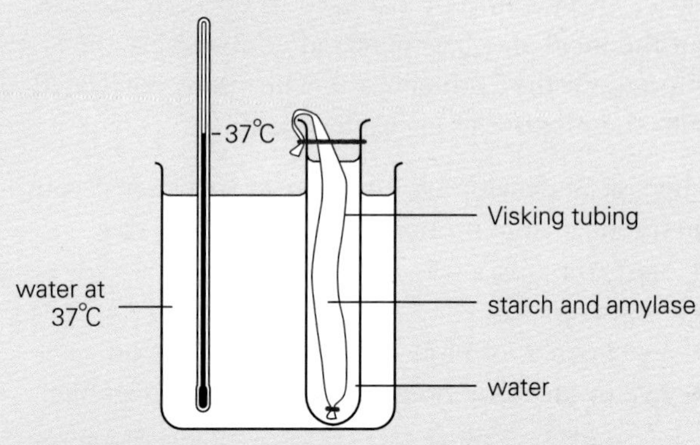

The water in the test-tube was sampled at three time intervals and tested for the presence of starch and sugar. The results are shown in the table.

Time (minutes)	Starch test	Sugar test
0	negative	negative
5	negative	positive
10	negative	positive

b Why was the test-tube kept at 37°C?

c Describe how the tests for starch and sugar are carried out.

d Explain fully what happens to the starch in the bag to give the results shown in the table.

5a Make a table to show four differences between red and white blood cells.

Study the table below which shows five substances that are transported in the plasma.

Substance	Organ
urea	kidney
glucose	small intestine – after a meal
adrenaline	adrenal gland – during exercise
carbon dioxide	muscles – during exercise
sodium ions	skin – on a hot day

b **i** State whether the concentration of each substance in the plasma would increase or decrease as blood flows through the organs indicated above.

ii Explain each of your answers.

6 A student measured the thickness of the walls of three different blood vessels.

The results are shown in the table.

Blood vessel	Thickness of wall (mm)
A	0.7
B	1.5
C	0.001

a Identify **A**, **B** and **C**.

b Explain why:

i the wall of **C** is much thinner than **A** and **B**

ii B is thicker than **A**.

7a Humans have a double circulation. What does this mean?

b Make a labelled drawing of a vertical section through the heart. Label the blood vessels through which blood enters and leaves the heart. Label the position of the four valves and the direction taken by blood through the heart.

8a i What causes your pulse?

ii How can your pulse rate be measured?

Recordings were taken of a student's pulse rate, breathing rate and the volume of each breath while he pedalled on an exercise bicycle. He pedalled slowly to begin with and then very fast for three minutes and then slowed down. The results are in the table.

Time (min)	Pulse rate (beats per min)	Breathing rate (breaths per min)	Average volume of each breath (cm^3)
1	64	12	500
2	65	11	520
3	80	20	1500
4	112	25	1750
5	120	35	2000
6	90	15	1500
7	84	12	750

b Calculate the total volume of air he breathed in during each minute.

c Plot a graph to show the changes over seven minutes to:

i his pulse rate

ii the volume of air he breathed each minute.

d Mark on the graph when the exercise began and when it ended.

e Use the information in the graph and the table to describe the changes that occurred during exercise.

f Explain why these changes occurred.

g Explain why breathing did not return to pre-exercise levels immediately exercise stopped.

9a Name the process in the body that makes carbon dioxide.

b Explain why the body excretes carbon dioxide.

c Describe how carbon dioxide is excreted.

10 The table shows some data about one human kidney.

Fluid	Volume (cm^3 per min)
blood in renal artery	600.0
plasma in renal artery	350.0
filtrate in Bowman's capsules	64.0
urine in ureter	0.6

a Calculate:

i the percentage of plasma in the blood

ii the volume of plasma entering the kidney every hour

iii the volume of filtrate formed every hour

iv the percentage of the plasma entering the kidney that forms filtrate

v the percentage of the filtrate that is reabsorbed

vi the volume of urine produced per hour.

b i Where is urea produced?

ii Explain how it is produced and why it is excreted.

The table shows the contents of blood plasma and urine.

Substance	Concentration (g per 100 cm^3) plasma	urine
water	90.00	95.00
protein	7.00	0.00
urea	0.03	2.00
glucose	0.10	0.00
sodium ions	0.32	0.60
chloride ions	0.37	1.80

c Explain why these substances are not in urine:

i protein

ii glucose.

d Describe how the following processes in the kidney are involved in forming urine:

i filtration

ii selective reabsorption

iii reabsorption of water.

SECTION B: QUESTIONS

e Calculate the urine:plasma ratios for urea, sodium and chloride by dividing each urine concentration by the relevant plasma concentration.

f Explain the significance of a high urine:plasma ratio.

11a Explain why someone may need kidney dialysis treatment.

The diagram below shows the dialyser unit in a kidney dialysis machine.

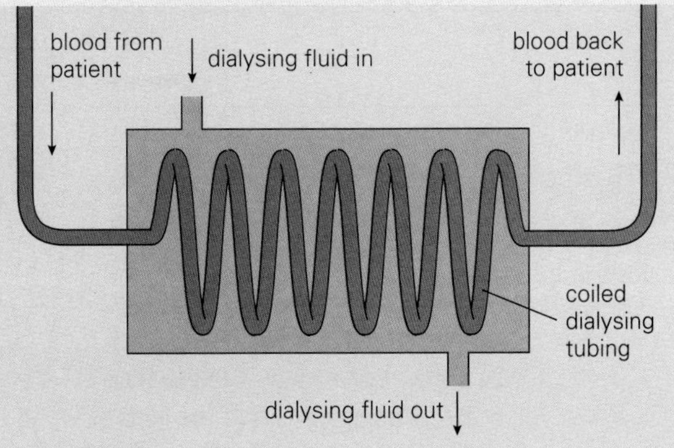

b Why does the dialysis tubing have a large surface area?

c Describe what happens to blood as it flows through a dialyser unit.

d A person on kidney dialysis has dialysis three times a week. The maximum urea concentration when dialysis starts each time is 3 g per litre. Sketch a graph to show the expected changes in blood urea concentration over a week.

e How does the person prevent the urea concentration rising too quickly between treatments?

12a Describe the position of the liver in the body.

b Describe how the liver is involved in the following body processes: excretion, digestion, control of glucose concentration in the blood, temperature control, destroying poisonous substances.

13 Jonathan felt very tired and lacked energy. A medical check-up revealed that he had glucose in his urine.

a Describe how a urine test for glucose is carried out. What would indicate a positive result?

Jonathan was then given the following test. He drank a glucose solution and the glucose concentration of his blood was tested at intervals for a few hours. The results are shown below together with those of the same test from Sarah who tested negative for glucose in urine.

Time (h)	Blood glucose concentration (g per litre)	
	Jonathan	**Sarah**
0.0	1.50	0.70
0.5	2.90	1.20
1.0	3.45	0.95
1.5	3.50	0.70
2.0	3.40	0.70
3.0	2.85	0.65
4.0	1.80	0.65

b Draw a graph of these results.

c Describe briefly how the blood might be tested for glucose.

d Suggest what Jonathan is suffering from. Give a full explanation of your answer.

e What treatment would a doctor be likely to prescribe?

14 If you put your hand into very hot water, you are likely to remove it very quickly. This is a reflex action.

a List the parts of the nervous system that are involved in coordinating this reflex action.

b Draw a flow chart to show the sequence of events that occurs between touching the hot water and removing the hand.

c Explain the benefit of reflex actions like this to our survival.

d Explain how a motor neurone is adapted to conduct nerve impulses.

15 Various internal conditions are kept constant by homeostasis.

a Explain the advantages of keeping the following conditions constant:

i concentration of the blood

ii body temperature

iii blood glucose concentration.

b Explain how the body is made aware that the skin temperature is decreasing.

c Describe the changes that occur to prevent a decrease in body temperature.

d Explain how the body is made aware that there is not enough water in the blood.

e Describe how the body reduces the loss of water in the urine.

16a Make a table to show the hormones that control the menstrual cycle. Include the following information: name of hormone, organ that produces it, how it helps to control the menstrual cycle.

b Describe the changes that occur in the ovary and the uterus during one cycle.

Some contraceptive pills contain oestrogen and progesterone.

c Explain the meaning of the term contraception.

d Describe how the combined contraceptive pill acts.

e Discuss the concerns that some people have about using hormones to control human fertility.

17 The diagram below was made from an image of the chest (thorax) taken in a whole body scanner.

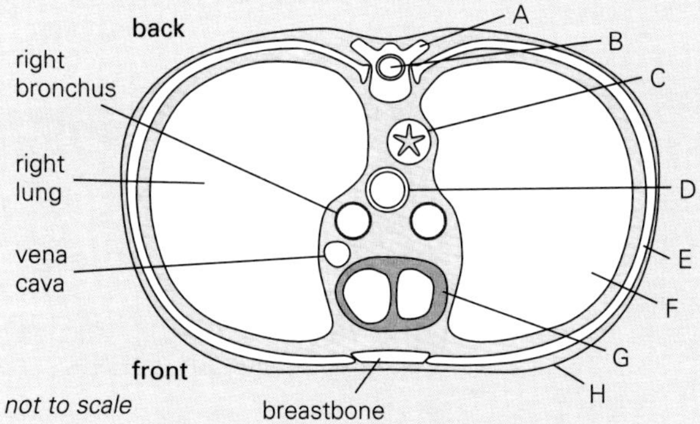

a Identify the parts of the body labelled **A** to **H**.

b Explain how this type of image may be useful in diagnosing lung diseases.

c Describe how the cells lining the trachea and bronchi prevent dust and dirt reaching the lungs.

d Describe the effect of tobacco smoke on these cells.

18 Study the bar chart below and the graphs in 4.5.

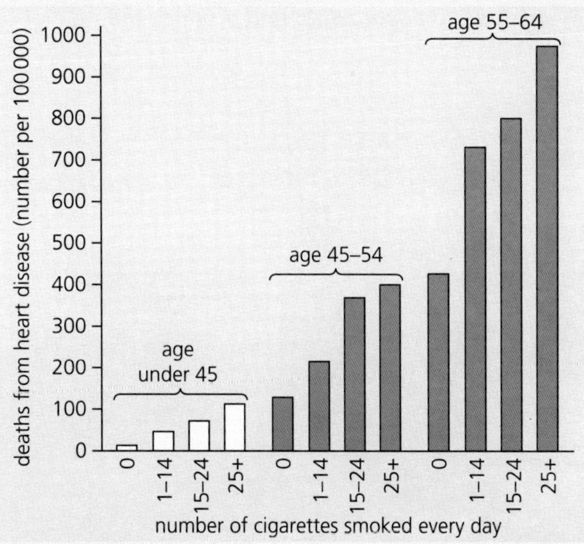

a Many people develop heart disease. Which group of people shown in the bar chart are:

i most at risk

ii least at risk?

b What is the evidence from the bar chart that smoking is not the only risk factor involved in heart disease?

c Summarise the evidence from the bar chart and the two graphs in 4.5 to show the relationship between smoking and

i heart disease

ii lung cancer.

19a Describe, in a fetus, how:

i oxygen is supplied, and

ii how carbon dioxide is removed.

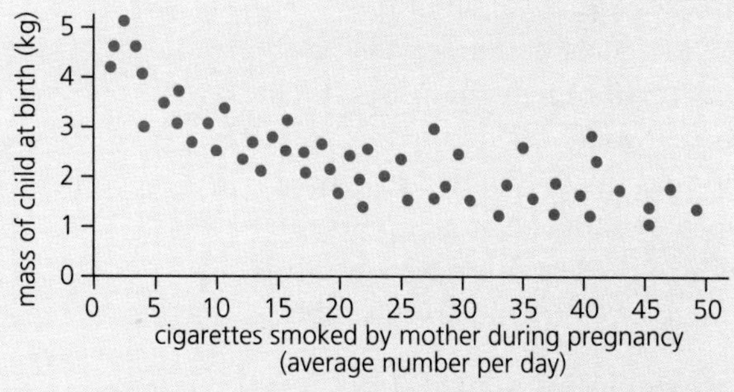

b Use the information in the graph above to describe the relationship between smoking and mass at birth.

c Cigarette packets in the UK carry a health warning. Discuss the reasons for printing this health warning and suggest more effective ways in which people could be encouraged to give up smoking.

20a List the diseases for which you have been vaccinated.

b Explain the advantage of these vaccinations.

c Find out how the following diseases are spread: tuberculosis (TB), tetanus, diphtheria, whooping cough, rubella, measles, influenza, malaria, polio, cholera.

On 9 December 1995, a mass vaccination programme to eradicate polio took place in India. The government attempted to vaccinate all children in the country.

d Why was it necessary to attempt to vaccinate all the children?

e Find out the effects of polio and suggest why the Indian government wants to eradicate the disease.

5.1 *Green leaves*

Plants make their food

We all need energy in some form or other. Animals get their energy by eating plants or other animals. Plants cannot eat food. They can do better than that. They make their own food by taking in (or fixing) carbon from the carbon dioxide in the air. To do this they absorb light energy from the Sun and transfer it for use in the reactions which convert carbon dioxide from the atmosphere into sugars. Synthesis is the building up of large substances from smaller ones. Plants need light to make food and so the process is called **photosynthesis**.

Made for the job

Green leaves can absorb light and produce the substances plants need. Most leaves are flat and thin providing a large surface area for the absorption of light and gases. Light passes through the transparent surface and into small, rounded structures called chloroplasts in the **palisade cells** of the leaf (see diagrams). It is here that photosynthesis takes place.

Carbon dioxide diffuses into the leaf from the atmosphere through the **stomata** (singular, **stoma**). Each stoma consists of a pore (or opening) and two **guard cells** which control the size of the pore. During the day the guard cells open the pores to allow carbon dioxide to diffuse into the leaf and enter the cells that contain chloroplasts. Water, the other raw material needed for photosynthesis, moves into the cells from the veins.

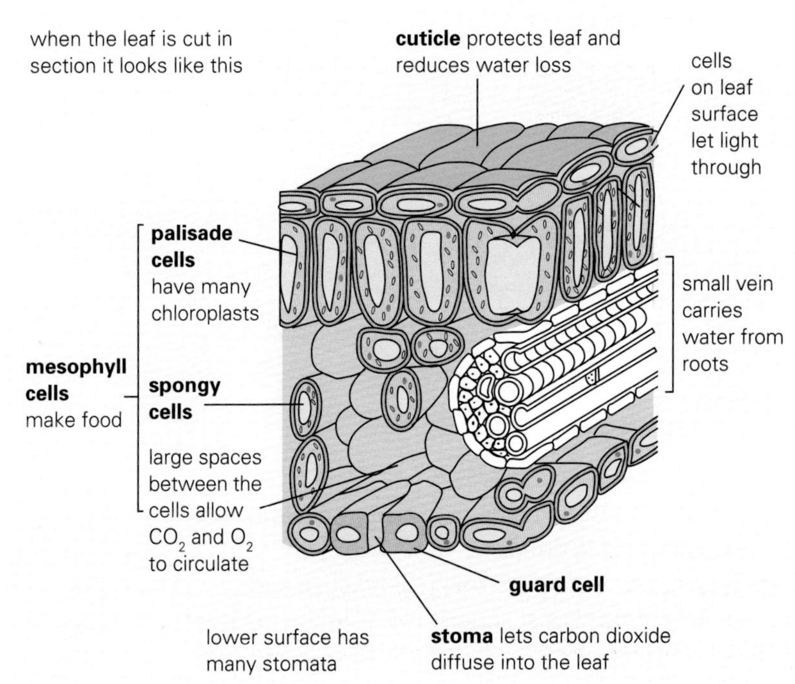

Leaves are specially adapted to absorb light and produce the substances plants need.

Chlorophyll

Most of the plant's food is made in the palisade cells, where there are a large number of chloroplasts. Each chloroplast contains the green pigment chlorophyll which gives the leaf its green colour and captures light energy for use in photosynthesis.

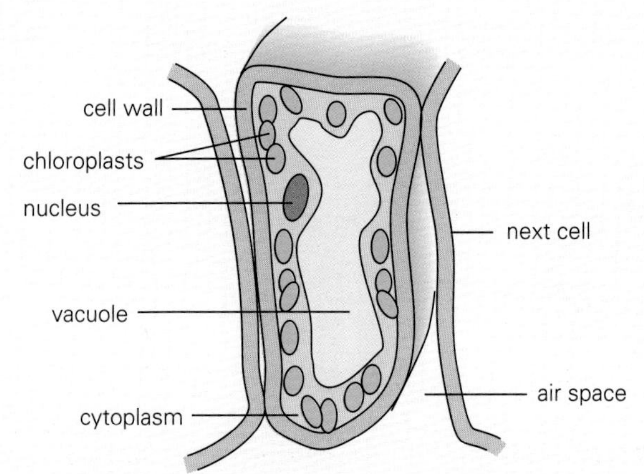

Palisade cells are found near the upper surface of the leaf and contain chloroplasts which absorb light.

The chemistry of photosynthesis

In photosynthesis the light energy absorbed by chlorophyll drives the reactions that convert water and carbon dioxide in the leaves into simple sugars and oxygen. The equation below summarises the process of photosynthesis. Notice that oxygen is produced. This important by-product is used by animals (and plants) in respiration.

Glucose is synthesised using carbon dioxide and water in the presence of energy from the Sun.

$$\text{carbon dioxide} + \text{water} \xrightarrow[\text{chlorophyll}]{\text{light energy}} \text{glucose} + \text{oxygen}$$

This is the balanced equation for photosynthesis.

$$6CO_2 + 6H_2O \xrightarrow[\text{chlorophyll}]{\text{light energy}} C_6H_{12}O_6 + 6O_2$$

1 Chlorophyll is soluble in alcohol and has to be removed from the leaf for the iodine test to be visible. The leaf is decolourised by boiling it in alcohol for about 10 minutes as shown.

2 Washing in water removes the alcohol and softens the leaf.

3 This leaf contains starch because it has stained blue-black with iodine.

Testing for photosynthesis

Some of the sugar produced in photosynthesis is turned into starch and stored in the leaves. A simple way of finding out whether or not a leaf is photosynthesising is to test it for the presence of starch. Plants kept in the dark for some time stop producing starch. Starch reacts with iodine solution turning it from yellow to a distinctive blue-black colour. If the leaf shows this colour change with iodine it contains starch and has carried out photosynthesis. If it remains yellow, the leaf has not photosynthesised.

QUESTIONS

1 Name the raw materials and the source of energy used in photosynthesis.

2 Describe how a leaf is adapted to obtain the energy and raw materials it needs for photosynthesis.

3 Give a use for the oxygen produced during photosynthesis.

4 Explain why photosynthesis is such an important process.

5 Plan a fair test to show that a leaf needs light for photosynthesis.

5.2 *Limits on photosynthesis*

Bigger and better

Arable farmers and growers of glasshouse crops such as tomatoes and cucumbers want to improve the quality of their crops and produce as much food as possible. Whether plants grow quickly or slowly is partly determined by their rate of photosynthesis. Growth of crops can be improved by investigating the environmental factors that influence how fast photosynthesis occurs in leaves.

Investigating photosynthesis

The easiest way to study the rate of photosynthesis in plants is to measure the output of oxygen. Examples of factors that affect the rate of photosynthesis include

- temperature
- light intensity
- carbon dioxide concentration
- wavelength of light (that is different colours e.g. red, green and blue light).

In the experiment shown in the photograph the rate of photosynthesis can be followed by measuring the volume of gas produced. Finding the rate at which gas bubbles are produced is one way of doing this.

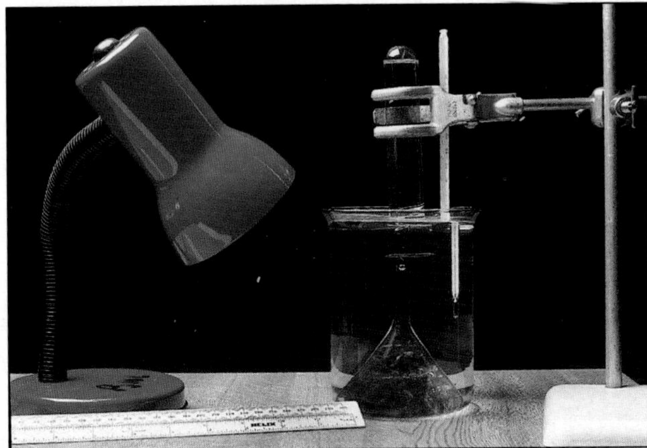

Measuring the rate at which pondweed releases oxygen-rich gas into the atmosphere.

Light intensity, carbon dioxide concentration, and temperature are the environmental factors that determine or **limit** the rate of photosynthesis. If you investigated the effects of these separately, using the pondweed experiment shown, you might get the results shown in the graphs.

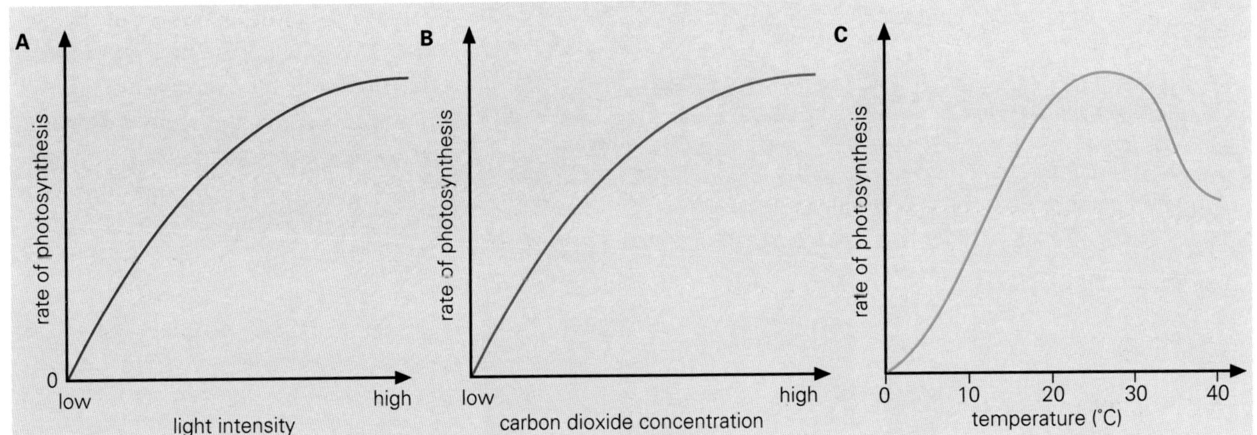

*The effect of three **limiting factors** on the rate of photosynthesis.*

Making sense of the results

Look at graph **A**. If a plant is kept at a low light intensity the rate of photosynthesis is low. The rate of photosynthesis increases with increasing light intensity. This means that light intensity is the limiting factor. As light intensity increases more energy is absorbed by chlorophyll and transferred for use in the conversion of carbon dioxide into sugars. As the light intensity is increased the rate of gas production increases until a maximum rate is achieved.

In making measurements varying the light intensity, it is important to keep temperature and carbon dioxide concentration around the plant constant so that only one factor is changed.

Limiting factors affect each other

If experiment **A** is repeated at a higher carbon dioxide concentration then plants use the high light intensities more efficiently and the rate of photosynthesis increases. Similarly if the temperature is increased the rate of photosynthesis is higher so long as there is sufficient carbon dioxide available.

On warm, bright days carbon dioxide is the major limiting factor for most plants since it is present in the atmosphere at such a low concentration (0.035%).

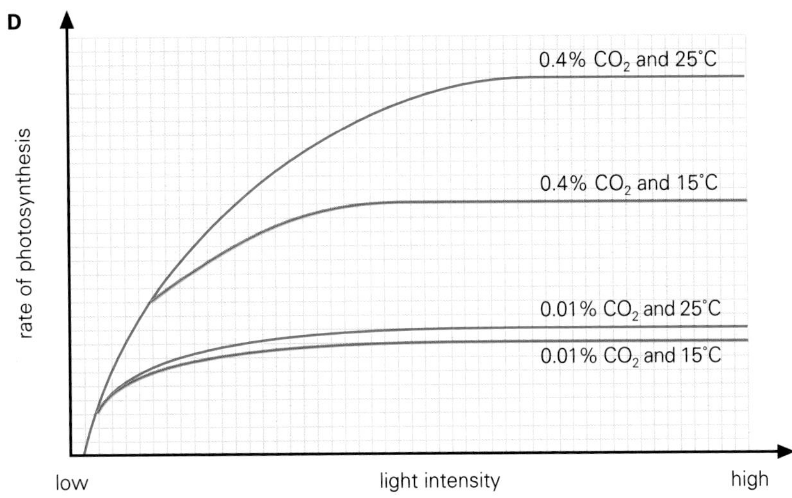

These results show how the rate of photosynthesis in a plant is affected by increasing light intensity at two different concentrations of carbon dioxide and at two different temperatures.

Plenty of sunlight, warmth and water provide good conditions for growing sugar cane.

QUESTIONS

1 List three environmental conditions which can limit the rate of photosynthesis.

2 Explain why the rate of growth of plants is determined by their rate of photosynthesis.

3 Name the limiting factor for photosynthesis on **a** a cold, bright day **b** an overcast, warm day.

4 Describe how you could investigate the effect of light of different wavelengths on photosynthesis in pondweed. Explain how your experiment is a fair test and how you would obtain accurate and reliable results.

Different plants – different needs

The light intensity determines the supply of energy, the carbon dioxide concentration determines the supply of raw material for photosynthesis, and the temperature determines the rate of activity of the enzymes in the chloroplasts. The best (or **optimum**) conditions for photosynthesis vary in different plants – tropical plants reach their highest rates of photosynthesis at higher light intensities and temperatures than temperate plants. In Britain, light and temperature are usually the limiting factors in winter whereas, in a good summer, carbon dioxide is usually the limiting factor.

5.3 *Life under glass*

Growing crops

Farmers who grow arable crops like wheat, barley and potatoes have little control over the three limiting factors discussed in 5.2. Temperature and light intensity depend on the weather. Carbon dioxide concentration is always near 0.035% and it is this which limits the rate of photosynthesis, and hence crop growth, on bright, warm days.

These factors can be controlled in glasshouses. Crops such as cucumbers, tomatoes, peppers, celery and lettuce and many ornamental plants, are grown in glasshouses all the year round. In this protected environment the limiting factors can be controlled and growers can control pests and disease more easily (see 9.4).

Growing crops in glasshouses is an important part of the economy in countries like Holland and Israel. It is also a big business in Britain.

There are several advantages to growing crops in glasshouses:

- temperature can be regulated and kept at an optimum
- extra lighting can be given on overcast days or used to extend the hours of daylight
- the air can be enriched with carbon dioxide
- water and nutrient supply can be regulated and monitored.

Keeping glasshouses warm means that the enzymes involved in photosynthesis and in growth can work quite fast. This all encourages growth. The temperature in a greenhouse can be kept fairly constant by using heaters and providing ventilation.

Keeping glasshouses warm means that crops can be grown for much longer periods of time as they are not exposed to very cold temperatures and do not get damaged by frost. For example, six to ten lettuce crops can be harvested each year.

Changing day length by using lights in winter or shading in summer is used to make plants, for example chrysanthemums, flower all year round.

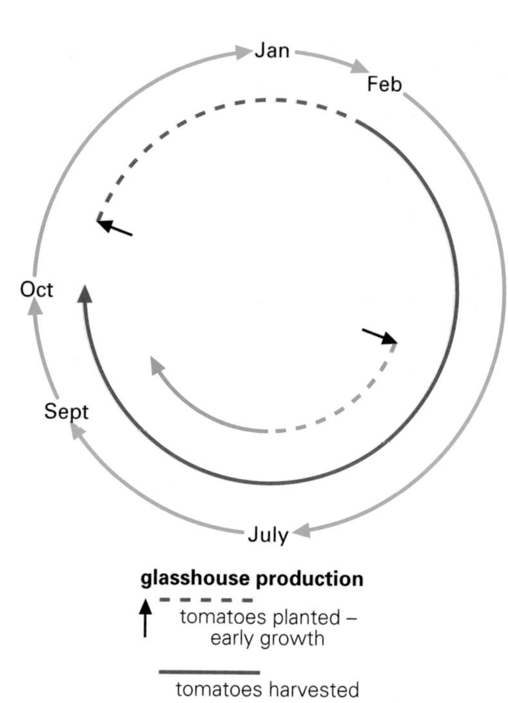

Inside a glasshouse

Much of the Sun's energy that enters a glasshouse is converted to heat energy. Only some wavelengths of visible light are used by plants. The main regions of the spectrum absorbed by plants are the red and blue regions. Many growers use special bulbs which only emit light in the wavelengths absorbed by plants and this saves money.

Carbon dioxide made by burning butane fuel is pumped into glasshouses to raise the concentration to 0.1% or more. This is often the best way of improving crop production, but it is only effective if the plants have sufficient light and are at a warm temperature. To ensure a plentiful supply, water is pumped through channels or supplied by a plastic tube. Another way of ensuring the plants receive enough water is to use fine mist sprays.

Minerals are added to the water and the concentrations of these are adjusted to meet the different demands of the crop as it grows, flowers and produces fruit.

Computer control

Most modern chemical glasshouses are controlled by computer. Sensors in different parts of the glasshouse provide information which the computer monitors continuously. Whenever there is a change in conditions from those set by the operator, the computer makes the necessary adjustments to return the conditions to those needed to maximise crop production. This is an example of negative feedback (see 3.3).

To study the effect on photosynthesis of varying one factor scientists use computer-controlled growth chambers that are like modern glasshouses. This type of control makes it easier to keep all other factors constant.

These seedlings are growing in a growth chamber. Light intensity, temperature, humidity and carbon dioxide concentration are controlled.

QUESTIONS

1 List the advantages of growing crops in glasshouses.

2 Explain how the limiting factors of photosynthesis are controlled in a modern commercial glasshouse to maximise crop production.

3 Describe the adjustments that a computer would make to a glasshouse on a hot sunny day.

4 Plan an investigation using a controlled growth chamber to find the best conditions for growing tomatoes.

5.4 Respiration

Using energy

Some of the glucose produced in photosynthesis moves out from the chloroplasts and is immediately broken down within leaf cells to release energy in **respiration**.

Some of the energy released is used to convert glucose into:

- starch as a store of energy
- sucrose, for transporting around the plant and for storing in fruit
- cellulose for making cell walls
- lipids (oils) for storing in seeds to provide energy when the seeds germinate.

Amino acids are made in the leaves from the sugars produced in photosynthesis and **nitrates** absorbed from the soil (see 5.6).

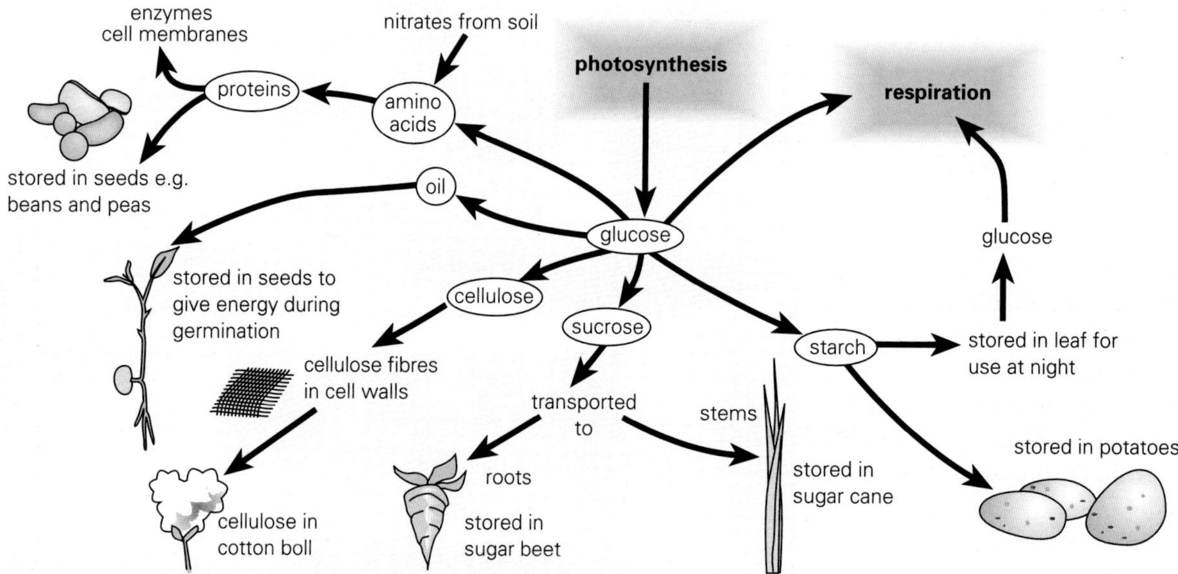

How the plant uses glucose made by photosynthesis.

Respiration and photosynthesis

Respiration is the breakdown of glucose (or fat or protein) using oxygen to release energy. This takes place in the cytoplasm of cells. All the reactions are speeded up by enzymes and by increases in temperature. The most important reactions take place in the mitochondria.

Mitochondria need oxygen to complete respiration. Respiration goes on all the time to release energy from sugars. During the day oxygen is provided by photosynthesis and at night it diffuses in from the air outside. Photosynthesis only occurs during the day.

The two products of photosynthesis (glucose and oxygen) are used in respiration. The waste products of respiration (carbon dioxide and water) are the raw materials for photosynthesis. The energy changes that occur in the two processes are different. Photosynthesis converts light energy into chemical energy in the form of sugars. Respiration releases the chemical energy from sugars for use by the cells.

photosynthesis and respiration occur during the day

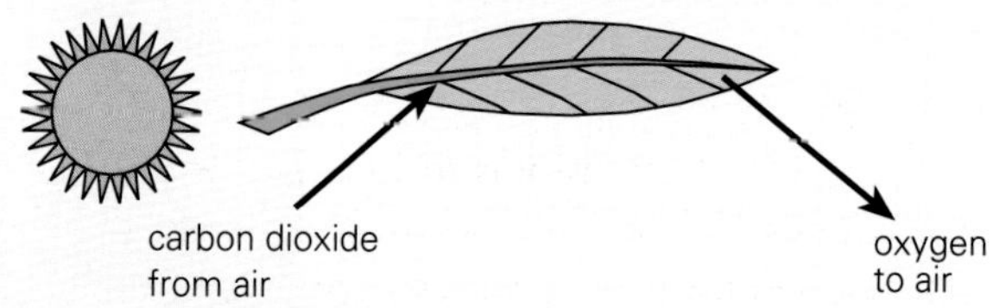

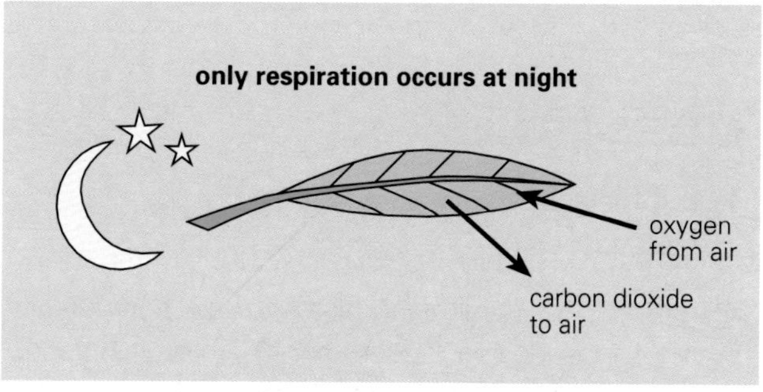

Exchange of gases between leaves and the air is the result of phototsynthesis and respiration.

Why store starch?

During the day, leaf cells store some of the glucose they produce as starch. They will then have a supply of energy at night when there is no photosynthesis. The rest of the glucose is used in the cell or converted to sucrose and transported to other parts of the plant. Roots respire this glucose and also store it as starch.

The build-up of large quantities of sugars, like glucose and sucrose, inside cells causes water molecules to diffuse in by osmosis (see 1.6). This causes the cells to swell and the cytoplasm to be pushed against the cell walls. Only soluble substances like sugars cause this absorption of water by osmosis. As starch is not soluble (insoluble), plant cells can store many molecules of glucose without absorbing large quantities of water.

Day and night

The gases moving in and out of a leaf depend on the relative rates of photosynthesis and respiration taking place. Photosynthesis can only take place during the day when there is enough light. Respiration, however, goes on all the time to release energy from starch providing energy for the activities of the cell.

During the day the rate of photosynthesis is usually much higher than the rate of respiration so plants absorb most of the carbon dioxide they need from the air by diffusion. The amount of oxygen produced is far greater than the amount needed for respiration of the cells, so it builds up inside the leaf and diffuses out in the air through the stomata. At night no photosynthesis takes place so the leaf absorbs the oxygen it requires from the atmosphere.

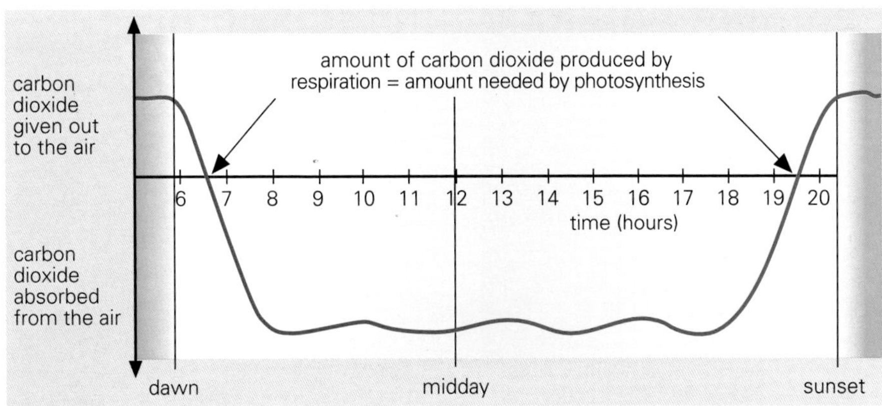

The carbon dioxide exchanged by a plant changes over time as the Sun rises and sets.

A day in the life of a plant

At dawn, the light intensity is so low that very little photosynthesis takes place. The small amount of carbon dioxide needed for photosynthesis comes from that produced during respiration.

Later, as the Sun climbs in the sky and the light intensity increases, the amount of carbon dioxide needed for photosynthesis is exactly equal to that produced by respiration. At this point no exchange of gas occurs with the atmosphere.

As light intensity increases further, carbon dioxide is absorbed from the atmosphere. Variations in light intensity or available water causes the rate of photosynthesis to change during the day. This causes changes in the amounts of oxygen and carbon dioxide exchanged between the leaves and the atmosphere.

QUESTIONS

1 Why do plants need to respire?

2 Explain, with reference to both photosynthesis and respiration, why carbon dioxide is absorbed by leaves during the day, but oxygen is absorbed at night.

3 Name the main environmental factor that influences the rate of respiration in a plant.

4 Describe how a plant uses the simple sugars made by photosynthesis.

5 Describe how you might find the best conditions for growing sunflowers so that they produce a large crop of oil-rich seeds.

5.5 *Transport in plants*

Water can reach the tops of trees 100 m high.

Moving materials

Water and minerals are taken in by the roots and transported to other parts of the plant, even to the tops of tall trees. Sugar is made in the leaves and moved out to be used by the plant or stored. A transport system exists to carry essential materials from one part of the plant to another.

Tissues for transport

Together **xylem** and **phloem** make up the plant's **transport tissues**. They are grouped in bundles near the outside of the stem (see diagram).

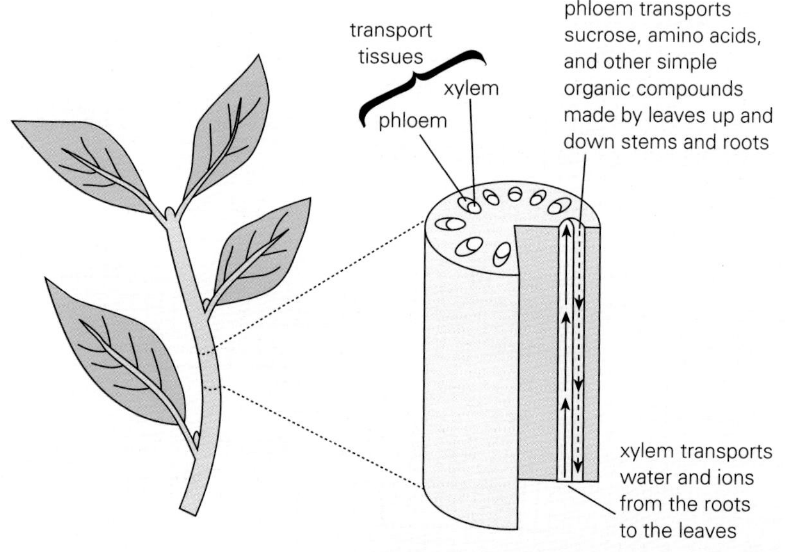

Phloem cells

Soluble compounds, such as sucrose and amino acids, are made in the leaves and transported to sites of growth and storage. In the summer, plants transport these substances through the phloem to the growing tips of shoots and roots and also to flowers, seeds and fruits. Phloem cells are living cells.

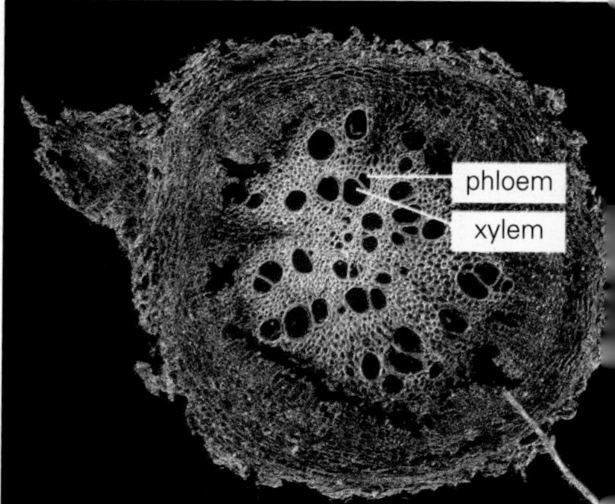

A scanning electron microscope was used to take this photograph of xylem and phloem in a root.

Aphids feeding

Aphids feed on the sugar-rich liquid from the phloem. To protect against aphids which carry plant diseases farmers and growers spray plants with insecticides. The chemicals are absorbed by the leaves and transported throughout the plant in the phloem. This protects the whole of the plant as aphids absorb the insecticide when they feed. Some fungicides are also transported in the phloem.

Each root hair is a single cell. Plants have millions of them to give a large surface area for absorption of water.

The water pathway

Water is absorbed from the soil by osmosis (see 1.6). Water molecules diffuse from the soil into the **root hair cells** and then into the xylem in the centre of the root. Huge numbers of root hair cells are found at the ends of young roots. They are usually a few millimetres long and provide a large surface area for water absorption. Their cell walls are thin so that they can absorb water easily by osmosis.

Movement in the xylem

The cells of the xylem make up a system of pipes – rather like the plumbing in a house. The cells, called vessels, are dead, empty cells which form continuous columns. Xylem vessels have cellulose cell walls strengthened with **lignin**. The lignin in xylem prevents the cells collapsing inwards when there is a great deal of water loss from the leaves and the column of water is under a lot of tension. The xylem also provides some support for the plant.

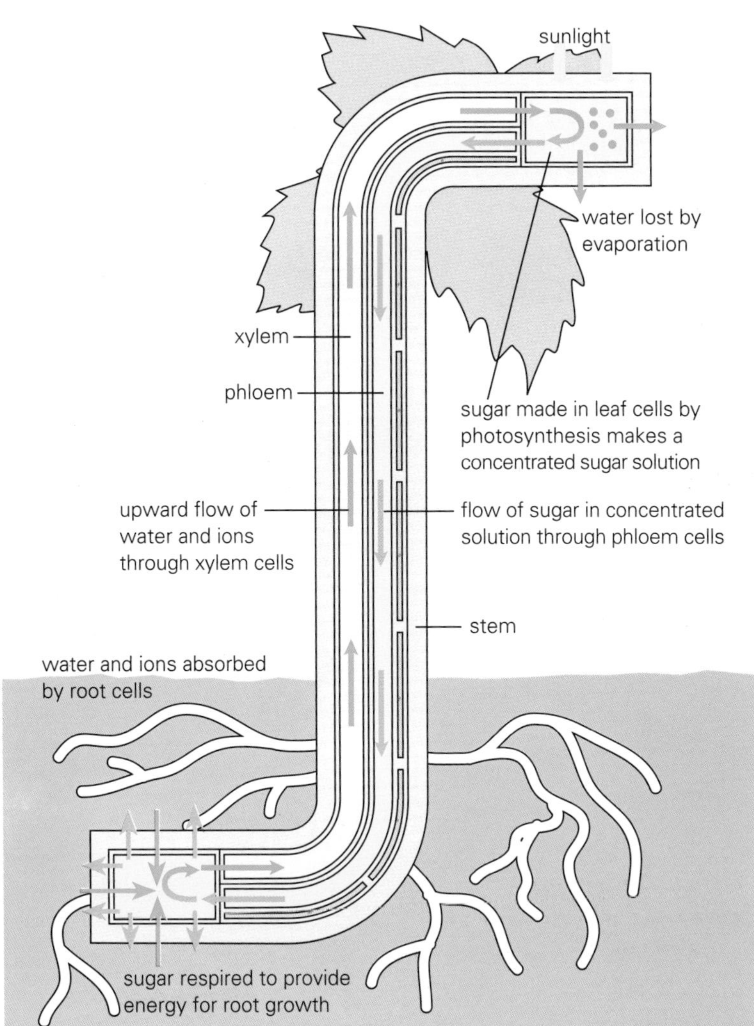

This diagram shows the flow of water and sugar through the plant.

As water evaporates from the leaves, more water moves along through the cell walls to take its place. The pull created by the loss of water in the leaves is enough to support a column of water many metres in length in the xylem. The plant does not provide any energy for this: it is all driven by energy from the Sun.

QUESTIONS

1 Name the substances that are transported in **a** xylem, and **b** phloem.

2 Draw simple diagrams to show where in the root and stem you can find the xylem and phloem.

3 Describe the pathway taken by a water molecule from the soil to the atmosphere as it passes through a plant.

4 Describe how root cells in plants are especially suited to absorbing water.

5 Explain how water moves to the tops of tall trees.

5.6 *Mineral nutrition*

Plant nutrients

For healthy growth plants need water, carbon dioxide, light and small amounts of mineral ions. Plants absorb these mineral ions from the water in the soil. Ions form naturally in the soil from the weathering of rocks and the decay of animal or plant remains (see 8.11). Crops need a good supply of ions to produce a good yield.

Flour is made from wheat. Farmers improve the quality and yield of the crop by using fertilisers.

Element needed	Ion	Use
nitrogen, N	nitrate, NO_3^-	Nitrate ions are used by the plant to make amino acids for proteins.
phosphorus, P	phosphate, PO_4^{3-}	Involved in energy transfer in photosynthesis and respiration. Nucleic acids (DNA) also contain phosphorus.
potassium, K	potassium, K^+	Many enzymes need potassium to work. It is also necessary for the opening and closing of stomata.
magnesium, Mg	magnesium, Mg^{2+}	Part of the chlorophyll molecule.
iron, Fe	iron, Fe^{2+}	Needed for chlorophyll synthesis.

This table shows some of the minerals that are important to plants. The major ones are nitrogen, phosphorus and potassium.

Ions from the soil

The mineral elements are absorbed from the soil as ions. The ions are absorbed by diffusion or active transport. When concentrations of ions are lower in the soil than in the root, plants cannot absorb ions by diffusion. Instead, energy is used to absorb them. This is active transport (see 1.5).

Respiration in the root hair cells provides the energy needed to pump the ions. Once ions are in root hair cells they are taken up in solution in the xylem vessels to the leaves.

Mineral deficiency

If a plant does not get enough of one or more of the ions it needs, then it does not grow very well. After a while it starts to show signs (symptoms) of disease due to lack of one or more mineral ions. These are called deficiency diseases.

We can see the effect of the shortage of one mineral on the growing plant by adjusting growth solutions so that one of the important minerals is missing. The diagrams and photos show the effect of deficiency clearly. The plant in **A** was grown in a growth solution containing all the minerals it requires. Plants often lose their leaves quickly, if nitrogen is deficient (**B**). Plants deficient in phosphorus show stunted growth and have dark leaves with reddening along the veins and spots of dead tissue (**C**). Where potassium is deficient, older leaves become yellow round the edges and the leaf tips start to die (**D**).

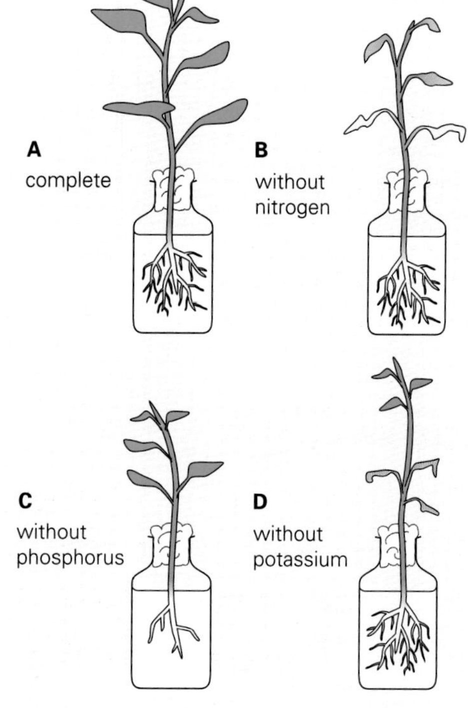

*These bean plants have been grown either with everything necessary for healthy growth (**A**) or deficient in a mineral (**B, C, D**).*

*With all the necessary minerals, leaves show healthy growth (**A**).*

Improving crops

A farmer does not want to wait until crops show deficiency symptoms. The results of soil analysis are used to apply appropriate fertilisers to the soil when the crop is sown and later on as it grows. This ensures that the soil is not exhausted and crops can be grown year after year in the same field.

Nitrate ions are very water soluble. If there is plenty of nitrate available the ions will be drawn towards the roots in the flow of water through the soil. Other ions, especially phosphate are bound tightly to soil particles so the roots must continually grow to reach new sources of phosphate. Some trees have a total of 12–18 km of roots.

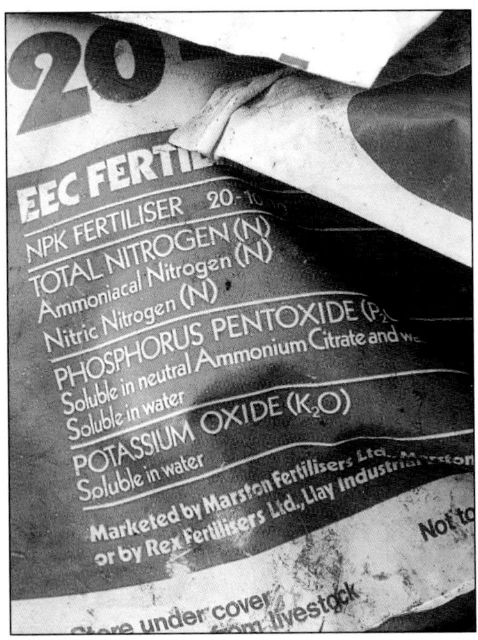

Intensive agriculture deprives the soil of minerals so farmers replace them by applying fertilisers.

QUESTIONS

1 List the functions in plants of the following elements **a** nitrogen, **b** phosphorus, and **c** potassium.

2 Explain why plant roots use energy from respiration to take up ions from the soil.

3 Describe the features of nitrogen, potassium and phosphorus deficiency in plants.

4 Explain the benefits of soil analysis to farmers and growers.

5 Design an experiment to measure the effect of nitrate deficiency on the growth of barley seedlings. Make it clear in your plan how many seedlings you are going to use and how you will take accurate and reliable results.

5.7 Transpiration

The transpiration stream

A leaf can lose its own mass of water on a hot, dry day. Water evaporates from plant cell walls and into the atmosphere. Most of the water vapour diffuses through the stomata in the leaves. This loss of water from a plant by evaporation and diffusion is called **transpiration**.

Water must be replaced as it is needed

- for photosynthesis
- to maintain the pressure inside that keeps the cells rigid (that is maintain cell **turgidity** – see 1.6).

To replace the water lost, plants must absorb large quantities of water from the soil. The flow of water through the plant is called the **transpiration stream**.

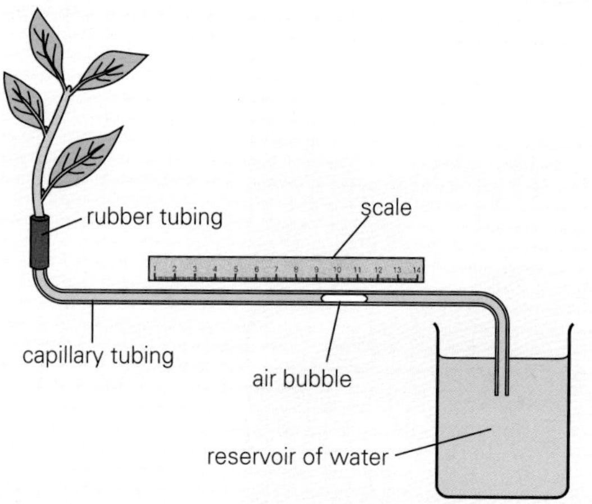

You can use a potometer to measure the rate of water uptake by a leafy plant.

Most plants have a waxy layer on their leaves to stop them losing too much water.

Benefits

Transpiration has an important role to play in keeping a plant healthy.

- Evaporation of water from the surface cools the plant so that on hot days the temperature may be several degrees below that of the air.
- Transpiration acts to pull up a column of water from the stem and roots in the xylem. This ensures a constant supply of water to the cells in the leaves.
- Transpiration also causes a movement of water through the soil bringing ions like nitrates to the roots. After the ions are absorbed into the root they are carried to the leaves in the transpiration stream.

Environmental factors

Any environmental factor which affects evaporation or the diffusion of water vapour will bring about changes in the rate of transpiration. There are several factors:

- *Temperature* If the temperature increases, then the rate of transpiration increases as warm air holds more water vapour than cold air.
- *Humidity* The rate of diffusion of water vapour depends on the difference in concentration between the air inside the leaf and the atmosphere. As the leaf is often surrounded by dry air water is usually lost from the plant.
- *Light intensity* Stomata open fully in bright light and close at night. The rate of transpiration is low at night, but increases in the day as the stomata open.
- *Wind speed* Water vapour is blown away from the surface of the leaf very quickly in windy conditions. This increases the rate of transpiration.

Transpiration poses problems for plants when there is a drought. In some parts of the world crops need constant irrigation if farmers are to grow anything.

Wilting

The water in plant cells gives support, especially for young plants. When water is lost by evaporation at a much faster rate than it can be taken up by the roots leaf cells become soft and limp (lose **turgor**). Leaves droop so that they are out of the direct rays of the Sun. This is called **wilting**.

On guard

Each stoma in the leaf is surrounded by two **guard cells** which control the size of the opening of the stoma (the pore). Guard cells have thick cell walls on the side facing the pore. The other walls are thin. When filled with water the cells become swollen. They expand more at the ends and at the sides facing the surrounding cells so that the pore opens.

When the guard cells lose water, they become less turgid and are pushed closer together by the neighbouring cells. The closed pore reduces water loss. On hot days the stomata close around midday if there is a high rate of transpiration and not enough water is absorbed from the soil.

Guard cells detect changes in the carbon dioxide concentration in the leaf. When it decreases in the early morning as photosynthesis begins, the guard cells absorb water and open the stomata. In the evening when photosynthesis stops, the carbon dioxide concentration inside the leaf increases. The guard cells respond by losing water and closing.

This plant has wilted, but it will soon recover when it absorbs more water.

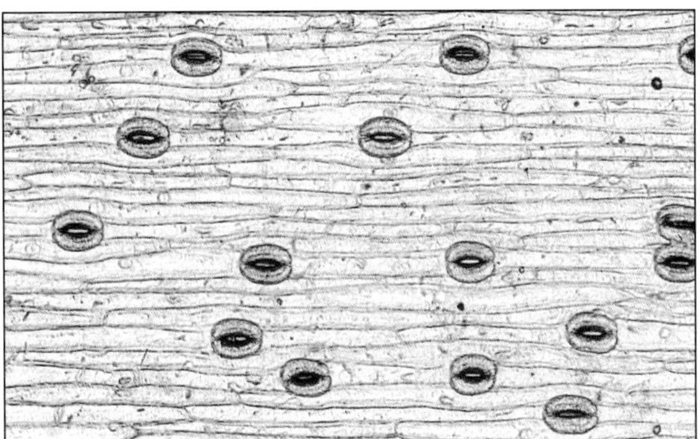

This is how stomata look using a microscope (× 100). They control the exchange of carbon dioxide and oxygen and the rate of transpiration.

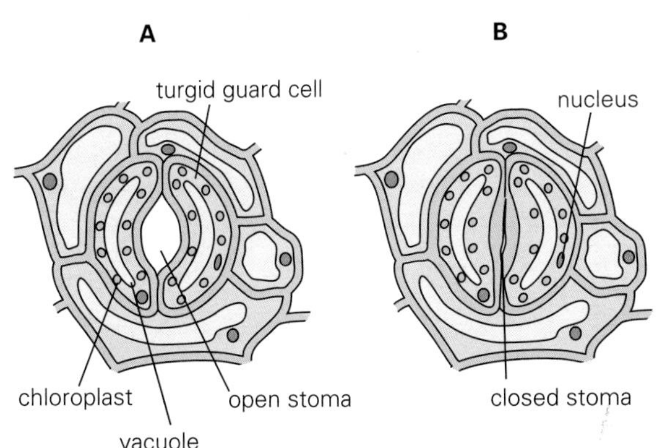

*In **A** the guard cells have taken in water and become turgid. The stoma is open.*
*In **B** the stoma is closed. The cells have lost water and become flaccid.*

QUESTIONS

1 Explain the term transpiration.

2 List three advantages of transpiration to plants.

3 Explain how the following factors influence the rate of transpiration: **a** light intensity, **b** humidity, **c** temperature.

4 Describe how wilting takes place.

5 Draw a diagram of a stoma and explain how the guard cells open and close the stoma.

6 Describe how you would use a potometer to investigate the effect of different environmental conditions on the water absorption of a leafy twig.

5.8 Plant growth and control

Regions of growth

Like other animals, your growth occurs all over your body and stops when you become an adult. In contrast, most plants keep growing until they die. Plant growth takes place only in certain regions as shown in the diagram. Young seedlings grow in length with cell division occurring in the tips of the roots and shoots. Growth also occurs at the tips of side buds and in side roots.

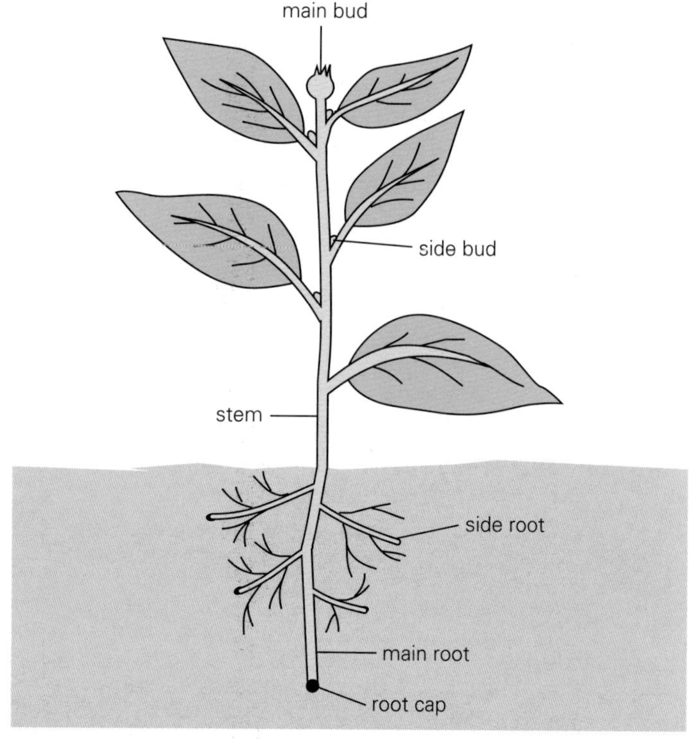

The areas of growth in this young plant are labelled.

Stages of growth

Cells divide to increase the number of cells. Each time a cell divides in two, one of the new cells divides again, while the other absorbs water and enlarges.

As the cells in the root enlarge lengthways they cause the root tip to be pushed further down into the soil; the cells in the stem push the shoot tip into the air.

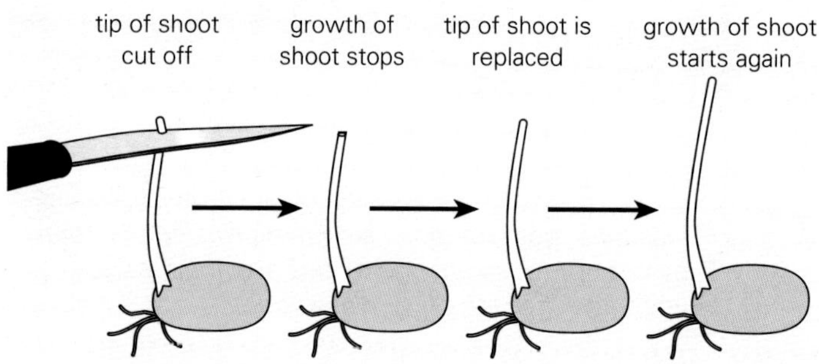

Cutting the tip off a shoot will stop it growing. Putting the cut tip back on again will restart growth.

Gardeners sometimes remove the top of a stem to stop the flow of auxin. This encourages the formation of side shoots and the production of bushier plants.

Controlling plant growth

Plant growth regulators (also known as **plant hormones**) control and coordinate the activities of plant cells. Just a few of these chemicals control all aspects of plant growth and development.

The **auxins** are a group of plant growth regulators. They are made in shoot tips, young leaves and developing fruits. As auxin passes through the plant it coordinates the growth and development of cells in various ways. Sometimes it stimulates the lengthways growth of cells (growth by elongation). It can also prevent growth by stopping side branches growing out from the stem, which encourages the plant to grow tall and straight.

Commercial applications

When a gardener or grower takes cuttings from a plant, the base of each cutting is first dipped into a **rooting compound** to stimulate the growth of roots. Many rooting compounds contain an auxin called NAA.

Another auxin is used by farmers to kill the broad-leaved weeds of cereal crops. Chemicals which function like this are called **herbicides**. The weeds rather than the cereal plants are killed partly because their leaves are held out horizontally to the main stem thus exposing a greater surface area over which to absorb the herbicide.

Cuttings 'take' faster if the cut end is dipped into rooting compound before planting.

*Auxin-based herbicides upset the normal growth pattern of weeds like dock (**A**) so that they grow into twisted shapes and die (**B**).*

Auxins cause the ovaries to develop into a fruit. Auxins can be sprayed on to flowers so that fruits develop without pollination or fertilisation. These fruits are seedless. Auxins are also used to delay the ripening of fruits so that a whole crop can be harvested at the same time and not ripen before it gets to the customer.

Some people prefer to eat fruit without seeds. Auxins are used to produce seedless fruits.

QUESTIONS

1 Where, in a young plant, does growth occur?

2 How does the growth of flowering plants differ from the growth of mammals?

3 Explain how auxins control plant growth.

4 Describe three ways in which auxins are used in agriculture and horticulture.

5 Plan an investigation to compare the efficiency of different brands of rooting compounds.

5.9 *Plant responses*

Sensitivity in plants

Animals respond to changes in their environment by movement of their whole body; plants cannot do this since they are anchored to the ground and must respond slowly to changes in their environment by growing.

During the early growth of a seedling it is important that it responds to gravity and to light. Roots and shoots can emerge from the seed pointing in any direction. The root must immediately grow downwards to find sources of water and minerals, and also form a firm anchorage in the soil.

The shoot must grow upwards to reach a source of light for photosynthesis. When the shoot comes out into the light, the seedling must adjust the position of its leaves so that they receive the maximum amount of light. Depending on where the light is coming from, the plant responds by growing more on one side than the other. These responses, essential for the survival of the plant, are called **tropisms**.

How this happens is not entirely understood. Here are some of the current theories.

Plants respond to gravity

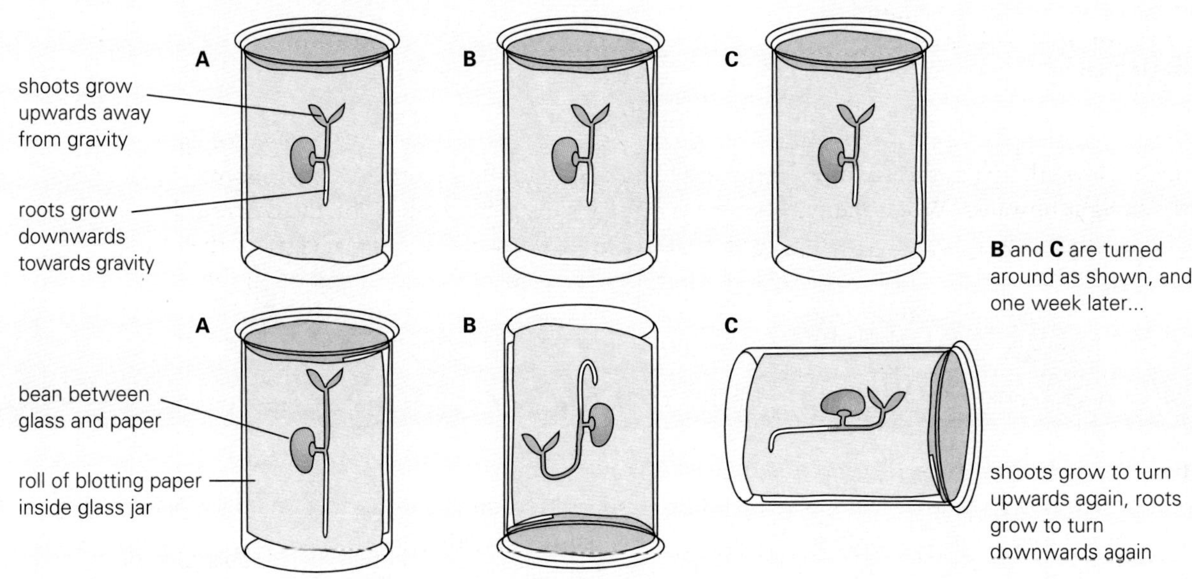

*Plants respond to the direction of gravity. This is called **geotropism**.*

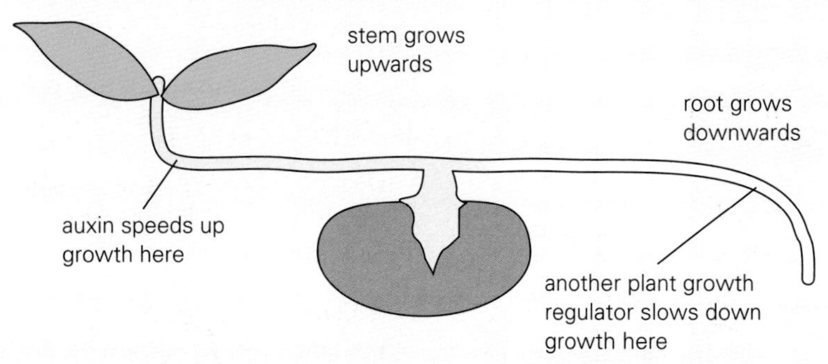

This diagram provides one explanation of how plants respond to gravity.

In horizontally placed roots a plant growth regulator collects in the lower part of the root and *slows down* growth. This brings about the difference in growth rates which causes the root to grow downwards. In the shoot another plant growth regulator may bring about an *increase* in growth rate, which again produces unequal growth causing the shoot to grow away from gravity.

Plants respond to light

*These tomato seedlings have been grown in light coming from one side. The stems and leaves have turned towards the light. This is called **phototropism**.*

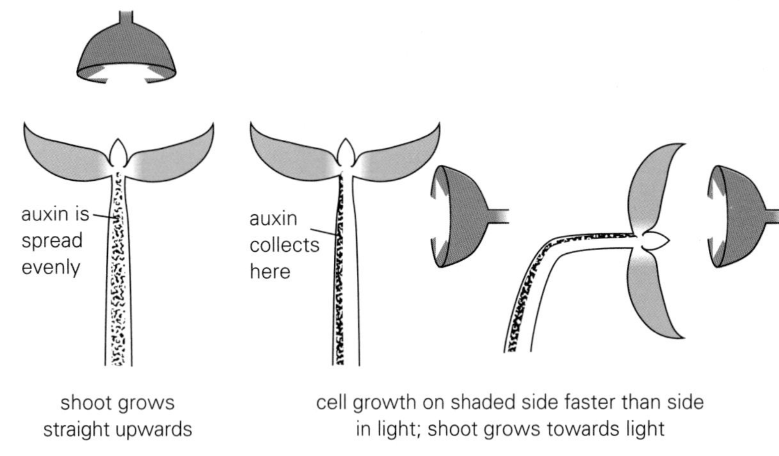

This diagram provides one possible explanation of phototropism in plants.

Auxins can make plant cells grow faster. One theory about phototropism is that when the light source is above the plant the auxin is evenly distributed around the shoot and so the shoot grows straight upwards. When the light source is on one side, auxin collects on the darker side of the shoot making the cells on that side grow faster. As a result of this unequal growth the shoot bends over towards the light. Another theory is that growth does not increase on the shaded side but decreases on the side facing the light, making the shoot bend.

QUESTIONS

1 Write a sentence or two to explain the term **tropism** in plants.

2 Describe **a** how roots and shoots respond to gravity, **b** how shoots respond to light.

3 Describe the advantages of the following responses during the early growth of a seedling, **a** geotropism of the root, **b** geotropism of the shoot, **c** phototropism of the shoot.

4 The drawings below show the results obtained by a student investigating plant growth. Write a conclusion for these results. What would you do next to find out more about shoot growth?

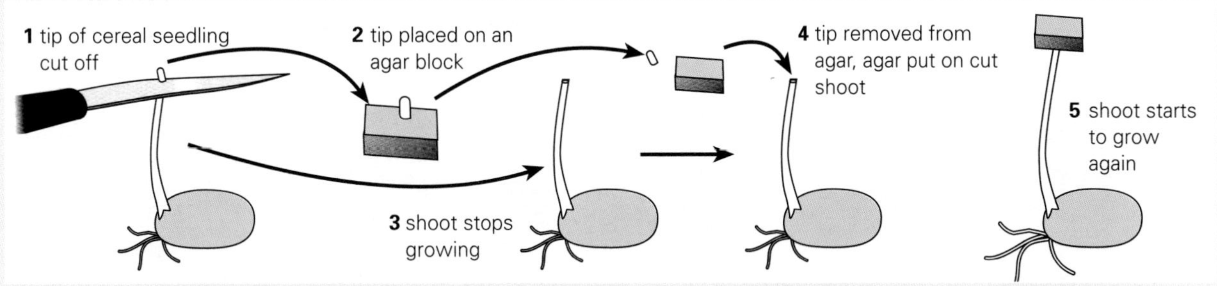

Plant growth regulators can diffuse into agar blocks.

SECTION C: QUESTIONS

1a Complete the word equation below for photosynthesis:

water + ___________ → glucose + ___________

Some plants grow shoots which have white leaves. The drawing shows one of these plants.

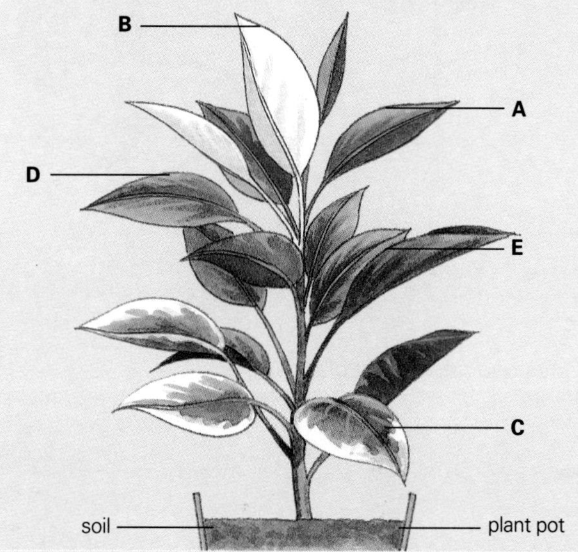

b Explain why some leaves are green (**A**) and others are white (**B**).

Leaves **A** and **B** were tested for starch with iodine in potassium iodide solution. Leaf **A** went blue-black, leaf **B** was orange.

c Explain these results.

d What result would you expect if you tested leaf **C** for starch?

e Explain, in terms of osmosis, why plants store the sugar they produce in photosynthesis as starch.

Two of the green leaves (**D** and **E**) were enclosed in clear plastic bags as follows. **D** was put into a bag containing a small container of sodium hydrogencarbonate which decomposes to release carbon dioxide. **E** was put into a bag containing potassium hydroxide which absorbs carbon dioxide from the air. The plant was kept in the light and **D** and **E** were tested for starch after four days.

f Predict the results you would expect and give reasons for your predictions.

g Would you expect to find starch in a green leaf after keeping it in a black plastic bag for four days? Explain your answer.

Cuttings were taken from the green and the white shoots.

h Describe how the cuttings would be taken.

i Suggest how the white cuttings could be kept alive.

2a Explain how leaves are adapted to:

i absorb light

ii obtain carbon dioxide from the atmosphere

iii reduce water loss.

b Describe how xylem is adapted for the transport of water in plants.

3 A piece of pondweed was put in some water and illuminated by a bright lamp to investigate the exhange of gases in the light and in the dark. Sensors for oxygen concentration, pH and temperature were put into the water and the changes monitored by a data logger for 36 hours. The results were printed out as shown below.

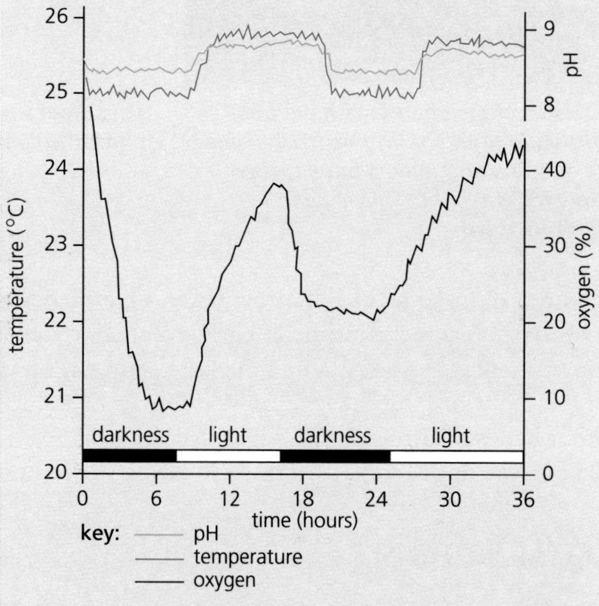

a Describe fully the changes recorded by the data logger.

b Explain why the oxygen concentration

i decreased when the plant was in the dark

ii increased when the plant was in the light.

c Explain why the pH of the water

i increased when the plant was in the dark

ii decreased when the plant was in the light.

d Explain why the temperature changed during the experiment.

e Describe how you could use this method to investigate the effects on the rate of photosynthesis of:

i light intensity

ii temperature.

4a List the factors that influence the yields of crop plants.

In the UK the yield of tomatoes in glasshouses is up to 500 tonnes per hectare.

b Describe how tomatoes are grown in glasshouses to achieve these high yields.

c In Israel some crops are grown in glasshouses. Although the daytime temperature may be 40°C, at night it can be as low as 0°C or lower. Plants only absorb light of certain wavelengths. Some new glasshouses are fitted with lights which only emit these wavelengths and they have glass which filters out other wavelengths from the Sun. Discuss the advantages of these new developments.

5 Radishes were grown in small pots containing washed sand which did not contain any mineral nutrients. The radishes were divided into four groups and watered with different nutrient solutions. The results are shown in the table.

Mineral nutrient solution	Number of plants	Dry mass (mg)		
		leaves	roots	total
complete solution with all nutrients	8	1880	1110	2990
all nutrients except potassium	10	1880	1390	3270
all nutrients except nitrogen	10	1410	750	2160
all nutrients except phosphorus	9	1670	140	1810

a Calculate the average dry mass of the plants in each treatment.

b Calculate the average dry mass of the leaves and the roots for the plants in each treatment.

c Draw a bar chart to show the data you have calculated from **a** and **b**.

d Explain why the complete solution was included in this experiment.

e Explain why dry mass measurements were taken instead of just weighing the plants.

f Describe and explain the effects of the three mineral deficiencies on the growth of radish plants.

g Why should farmers analyse the soil for mineral nutrients before sowing crops?

6 Leaves lose water to the atmosphere by transpiration.

a Explain how water is lost by transpiration.

b Suggest two ways in which transpiration benefits plants.

A leafy shoot was kept in a potometer and exposed to a variety of conditions. The time taken for a bubble of air to move 50 mm along the capillary tubing was recorded for each set of conditions. The results are shown below.

Humidity of the air	Air movement	Temperature (°C)	Time taken to move 50 mm (min)
dry	still	20	113
dry	moving	20	80
dry	still	30	51
damp	still	20	180
damp	moving	20	88
damp	still	30	64

The diameter of the capillary tubing in the potometer is 2.0 mm.

c Calculate the volume of water absorbed per minute by the leafy shoot under each condition. (Volume of cylinder = $\pi r^2 h$.) Draw a bar chart to show the volume of water absorbed for each set of conditions.

d Under which conditions was the rate of water uptake:

i fastest

ii slowest?

e Use the results to explain the effects on water uptake of:

i humidity

ii air movement

iii temperature.

f Suggest two ways in which you could check that these results are valid.

The lower surfaces of all the leaves of the shoot were covered in petroleum jelly which is impermeable to water vapour. The shoot was then exposed to dry, moving air.

g Predict what would happen to the rate of water uptake and explain your answer.

7 A maize seedling was placed horizontally and photographed at intervals for four hours. Drawings of the photographs are shown here.

a Make a drawing of the seedling after 3 hours and use it to explain how this growth response is coordinated.

b State the name of this response and explain its advantage to the seedling.

6.1 *Biodiversity*

Species

A **species** is a group of organisms with many features in common: their bodies have the same structure, they behave in a similar way, and feed on the same food. The males and females of a species have the ability to reproduce with one another, but do not usually reproduce with individuals of other species. Tigers and lions are examples of different species which are quite similar.

No one knows for certain how many species there are but over 1.7 million have been described. About 15 000 new ones (mostly insects) are added to the list every year. This vast range of living organisms is known as **biodiversity**.

Species are divided into six main groups as shown in the pie chart. The pie chart shows that most known species are animals and most of those are arthropods.

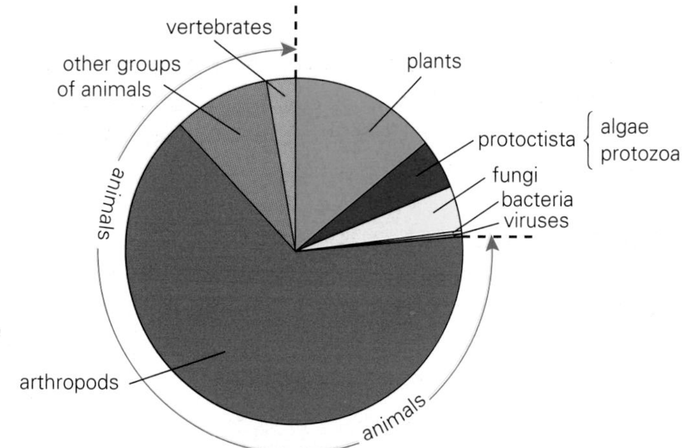

Major groups of organisms.

Animals with backbones

All animals with a backbone are grouped together in the **vertebrate** group. Within this group there is a great variety of different animals, and so they are subdivided into five classes, fish, amphibians, reptiles, birds and mammals.

Fish

Fish have bodies covered by scales and they use gills for gas exchange. They have a tail and fins for swimming. In most species, the eggs are fertilised in the water and develop outside the body.

Square spot fish

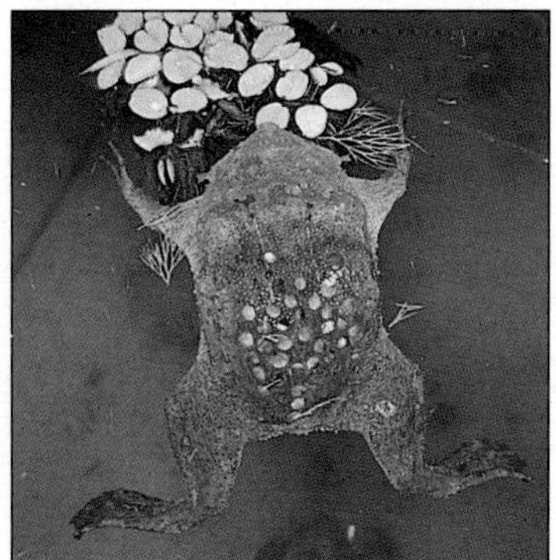

Female Surinam toad. Eggs develop inside little pockets in the skin. After 3–4 months tadpoles change into adults.

Amphibians

Animals like frogs, toads, newts and salamanders develop from eggs which are laid in water. The young hatch as tadpoles which breathe by using gills and have a tail for swimming. When a tadpole changes into an adult, it grows lungs for breathing and loses its gills. Amphibians have moist skin which they can use for gas exchange.

Reptiles

Reptiles like iguanas, crocodiles and tortoises have a body covered in scales which protect them and cut down water loss through their skin. They have lungs for breathing. They develop in eggs with leathery shells and hatch as miniature adults.

Iguana

Birds

Birds are very like reptiles. They too hatch from eggs as miniature adults. Their skin is like that of reptiles but is covered with feathers. They have wings and most can fly. Unlike reptiles, amphibians and fish, they maintain a constant body temperature.

Purple-crested lourie

Mammals

Mammals have hair, and the females have mammary glands which produce milk to feed their young. The young develop in a womb inside the female's body. Like birds, mammals keep a constant body temperature.

Okapi

Animals without backbones

There are several groups of animals that do not have backbones. These include jellyfish, starfish, molluscs, worms and arthropods. The biggest group is the arthropods which have external skeletons and jointed legs.

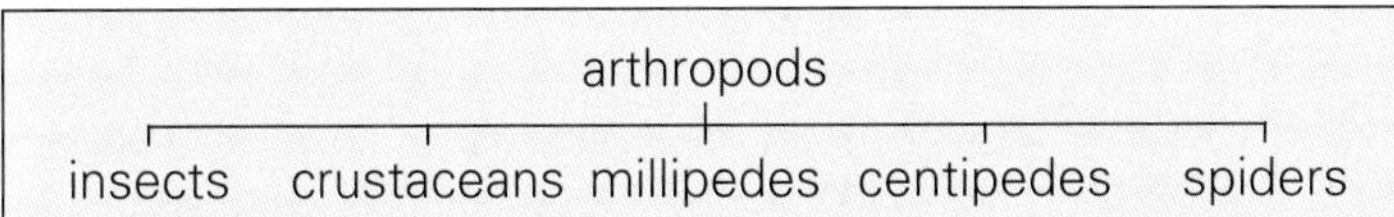

This chart shows that the arthropod group is subdivided into five.

Each of these arthropod groups has easily recognisable features. This table compares two of them.

	Spiders	Insects
Number of legs **Wings**	8 0	6 4
Antennae	0	2
Body sections	2	3

Chilean rose tarantula (spider)

Great green bush cricket (insect)

QUESTIONS

1 What is biodiversity?

2 Explain what biologists mean by the term species.

3 Draw up a table to compare the five vertebrate groups using the following headings:
 a method of gas exchange
 b type of skin
 c type of reproduction.

6.2 *Variation*

Variation within a species

Slight differences in the instructions we inherit make us all different from each other.

We are all different. Within the same species there is a great deal of **variation**. Variation within a species depends on the instructions that all organisms inherit from their parents. These instructions are called **genes**.

Types of variation

Some differences between people are of clear, distinct types. For example, the two sexes, male and female are a good example of **discontinuous variation**. Human blood groups are another example. There are four blood groups, A, B, AB and O. You can only have blood of one type. There are no intermediate types of blood groups.

When data about human height or body mass is collected there is a range between two extremes. There is a range between the shortest and the tallest and the lightest to the heaviest. This is **continuous variation**. Data of this type is plotted as a bar chart.

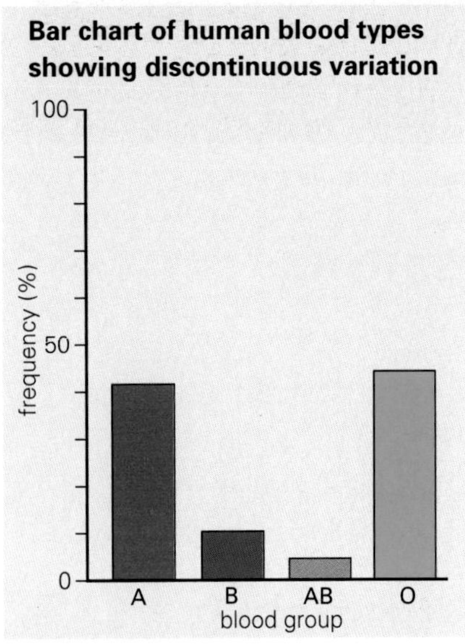

This bar chart shows the frequencies of the four blood groups, A, B, AB and O in the population of the UK.

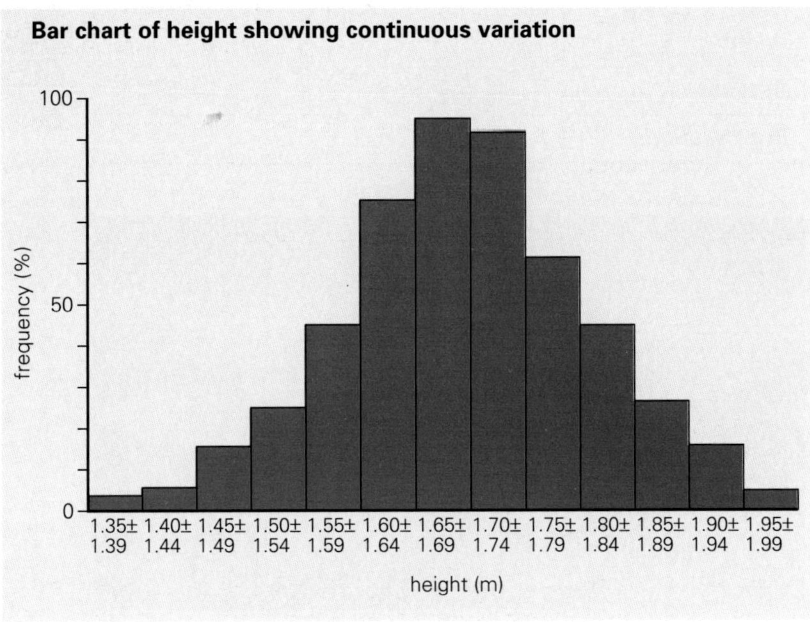

This shows the continuous range of heights in humans.

Nature versus nurture

Your blood group is determined by the genes that you inherited from your parents and it will remain the same throughout your life. The same is true if you have inherited a genetic disease, such as cystic fibrosis, haemophilia or sickle cell anaemia. These are also examples of discontinuous variation as people either have these diseases or they do not. The way you have been brought up (**nurtured**) has no effect on blood group or inherited diseases. They are determined by genes. The environment has no effect.

Early in the 20th century there was a significant difference in growth and health between children from rich and poor families.

This is not true for features which show continuous variation. Some features are influenced both by the environment in which you have grown up and by the genes you inherited. Genes may well determine the maximum height you may reach, but this is also influenced by the quantity and quality of food which you eat, maybe by how much exercise you take and by the amount of sunlight your skin receives.

Genes control bone growth, but bones will not grow well without a good supply of energy, protein and calcium in the diet. Sunlight stimulates the skin to make vitamin D, which promotes the growth of bones. Without enough energy or nutrients no one can reach their potential height. People who are often ill during their childhood grow slowly. This is because their bodies are using energy to fight disease rather than using it for growth.

QUESTIONS

1 Explain the difference between continuous and discontinuous variation.

2 Give a list of examples of human features that show **a** continuous and **b** discontinuous variation.

3 Describe how you would carry out a survey to investigate the variation in height in your class.

4 List the factors that might influence your final height (that is, when you stop growing).

6.3 *Inheritance*

Families

You often hear that people resemble their parents or grandparents. This is because people who are closely related share many genes in common.

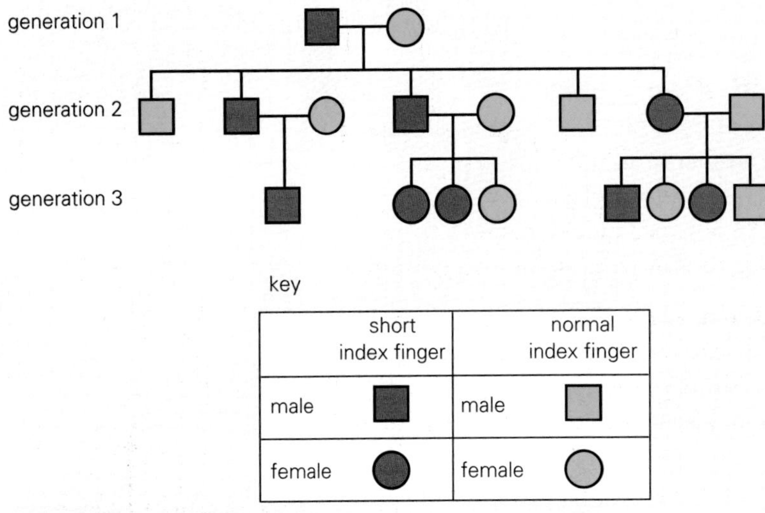

This pedigree diagram shows how some people in this family have inherited brachydactyly and others have not.

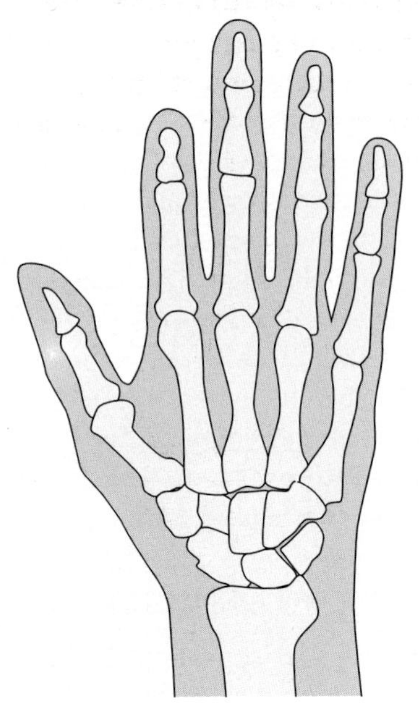

In brachydactyly the index finger is short because one of the finger bones is missing.

Many of the people in the family tree shown above have a very rare inherited condition: they have a short index finger. Only one person in a million has this condition, but it is common in this family. This is clearly a feature which 'runs' in this family and is controlled by one gene that many in this family possess.

Musical talent and scientific ability, susceptibility to diseases such as cancer and heart disease, also 'run' in families but not in such a regular pattern.

Studies of identical twins can tell us much about the effect on us of inheritance and the environment.

Identical twins

Identical twins develop from the same sperm and the same egg. After fertilisation the embryo divides into two. Since identical twins have inherited exactly the same genes any differences between them must be due to the effect of their environment – how they have been brought up.

Occasionally such twins are brought up in different homes. The development of twins separated from birth can tell us how important inheritance is in determining such things as intelligence and susceptibility to disease. Some of the similarities between twins who were separated at birth are uncanny – even down to trivial things such as food likes and dislikes. This suggests that inheritance has a very big part to play in determining our personality.

Studying inheritance

To carry out experiments on inheritance, it helps to have an organism that is easy to keep, has a short life cycle, produces large numbers of offspring and has few genes. For these reasons, scientists use small animals or plants to find out about inheritance.

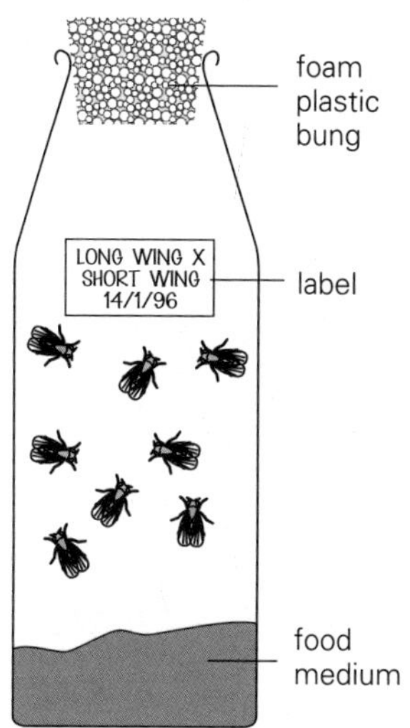

A culture bottle with fruit flies.

Fruit flies

It is possible to produce a new generation of fruit flies in about 3–4 weeks. This means that the results of an experiment can be obtained quite quickly without having to wait years as with larger animals.

Male and female flies are kept together for several days until the females have laid eggs. Shortly afterwards the parents are removed from the culture bottle and the eggs hatch into tiny larvae (maggots). These eat and pupate. When the adult flies emerge from pupae, they can be counted and their features observed.

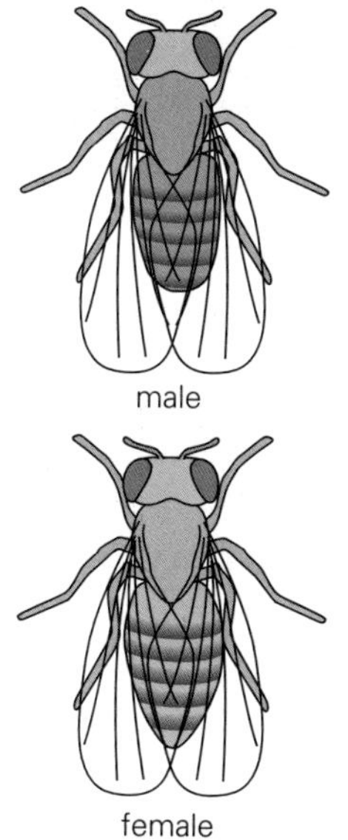

Male fruit flies have more rounded and darker abdomens than females.

Fruit flies have many features which show continuous or discontinuous variation. The features that show discontinuous variation are especially clear cut and easy to see. For example, almost all fruit flies in the wild have one pair of wings, with a second small pair shaped like drum sticks, which help them keep their balance. Occasionally, some fruit flies appear that have very small wings and are unable to fly. These do not survive in the wild, but they can be kept in the laboratory and used in breeding experiments (see 6.8).

Thale cress

Thale cress plants are so small that they can be grown in large numbers in the laboratory. They complete their life cycle in 6–8 weeks, so eight generations are produced in a year. This is not possible with most of our crop plants which only produce one or perhaps two generations every year.

When the plants flower, pollen is transferred from the anthers of one flower to the stigma of another. The pollen contains the male gametes, so fertilisation soon follows. To stop unwanted pollen transferring to the stigmas the flowers are kept in plastic bags. Seeds develop and are then collected and stored or sown. When the seeds germinate the plants can be scored for the features being studied.

Thale cress is a tiny weed commonly found in Britain on waste ground, hedgerows, and walls.

QUESTIONS

1. Explain the advantages of using fruit flies and thale cress in studying inheritance.
2. Explain why identical twins are useful in studies of inheritance.
3. Describe how breeding experiments are carried out with fruit flies and with small flowering plants like thale cress.
4. Why do doctors studying some human diseases collect information about people's families?
5. Plan an investigation to find out if wing size in fruit flies is determined by genes or by the environment.

6.4 *Mitosis*

Growth

When an organism grows its cells divide in two. You can see this through a microscope if you look at the growing points of plants or the embryos of animals. Most cells have a nucleus. When a cell divides the nucleus goes through a series of changes so that each new cell receives its own nucleus. Without it a cell will not survive for long and it certainly will not be able to grow and divide. The nucleus contains the genetic programme for the cell.

Chromosomes

The dark circles within some of the cells in the photograph of the root cells are the nuclei. Thread-like structures become visible inside the nucleus of a cell that is about to divide.
These are the **chromosomes**.

Chromosomes carry the cell's genetic instructions. Every time new cells are formed the same number of chromosomes are contained in each cell. This means that all the cells in the body have exactly the same genetic information. The chromosomes in most cells are always in pairs.

Species	Number of chromosomes
Humans	46
Fruit flies	8
Thale cress	10
Yeast	34
Mouse	40

Different species have different numbers of chromosomes.

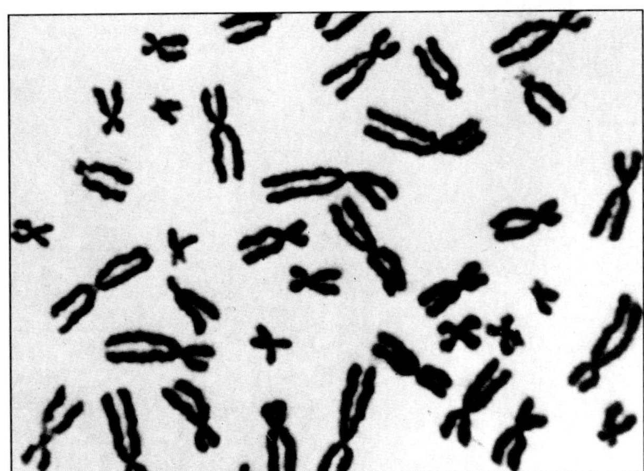

These chomosomes were photographed in a dividing human (female) cell.

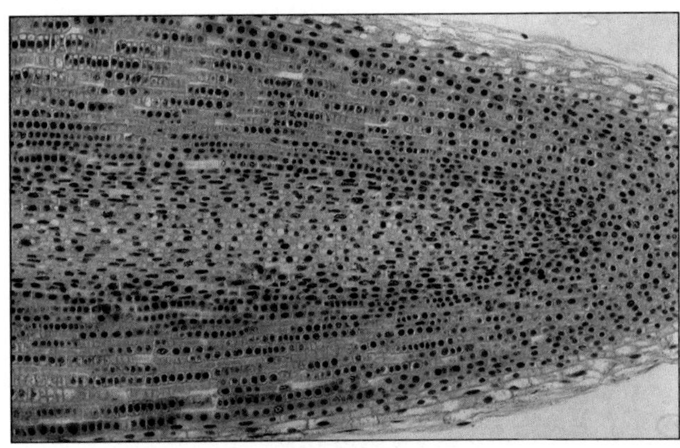

Some of these root cells are dividing to form new cells.

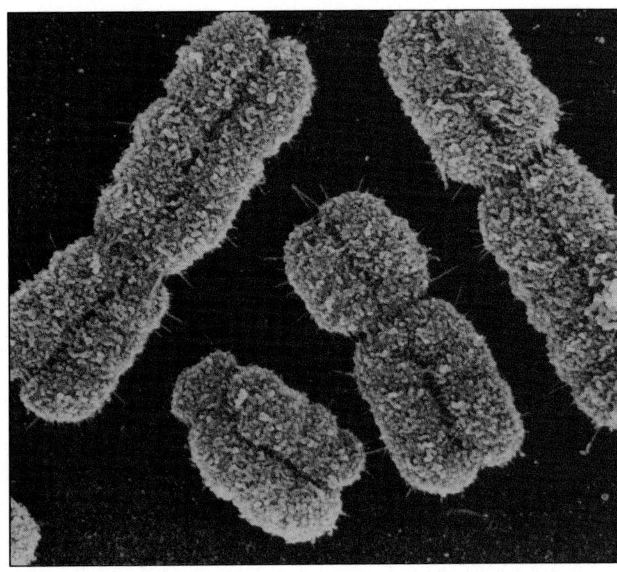

Four different human chromosomes photographed during mitosis (× 14 000).

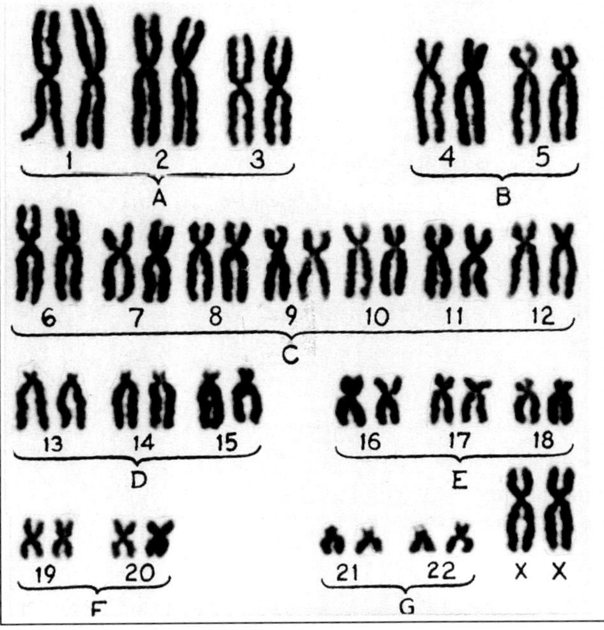

This shows the 23 pairs of chromosomes obtained from a dividing human cell (female).

The genetic blueprint

Chromosomes are made of **DNA** and protein (see 6.11). Our genes are made from short sections of DNA and each gene contains instructions for some characteristic like, for example, eye colour. Each chromosome carries a number of genes. Some human chromosomes carry large numbers of genes, the smaller ones carry a much smaller number.

Dividing up

A cell copies its chromosomes so that when it divides the two new cells each receive a copy of each chromosome and a full set of genes (see the diagram, right). When a chromosome is photographed during cell division it has two strands of identical DNA attached together at a point which is often near the centre. The two copies of DNA remain attached to each other until they are pulled apart when the cell divides. This is why they appear to get thicker and become visible under a microscope.

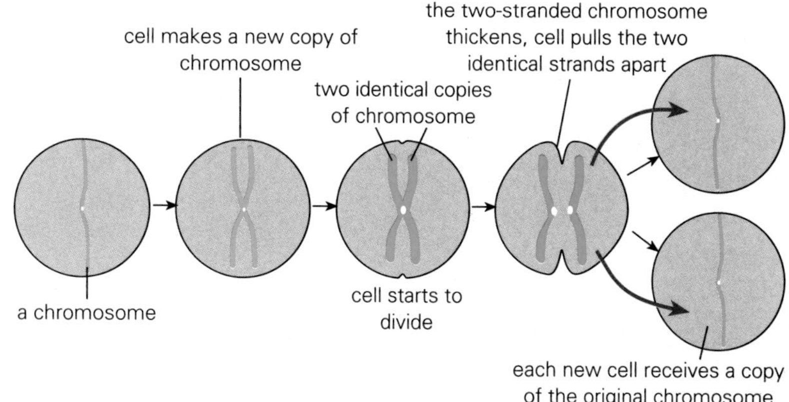

Cells must copy the DNA of their chromosomes before they divide so that the two new cells receive a copy of each chromosome and a full set of genes.

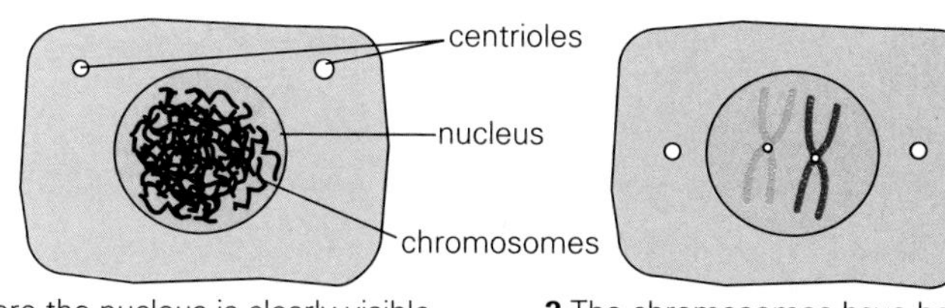

1 Here the nucleus is clearly visible as a separate structure within the cell.

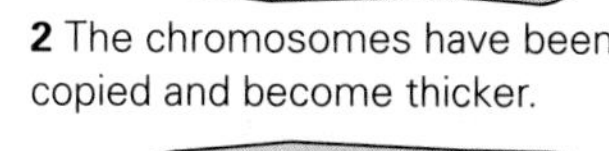

2 The chromosomes have been copied and become thicker.

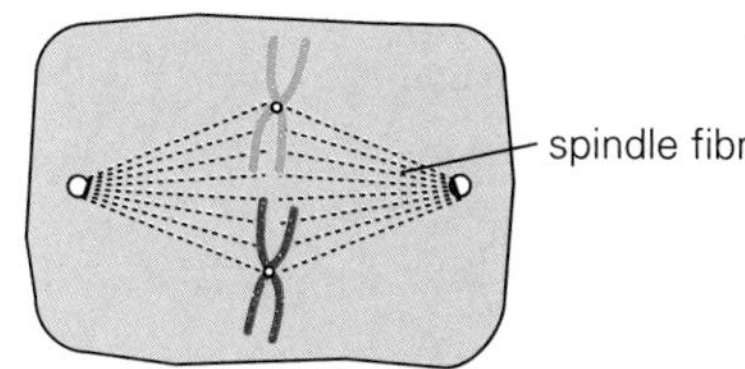

3 The chromosomes are arranged in the middle of the cell. The nucleus is now no longer a separate structure. Centrioles make spindle fibres to pull the chromosomes apart.

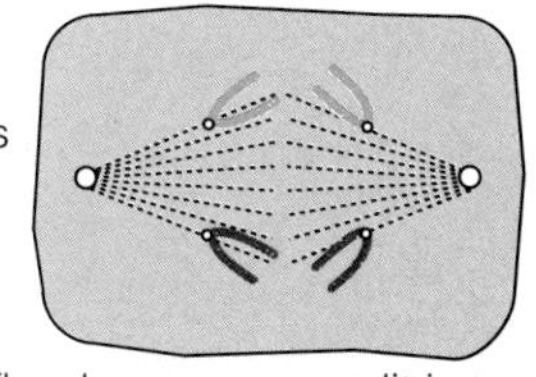

4 The chromosomes split in two and move to opposite ends of the cell.

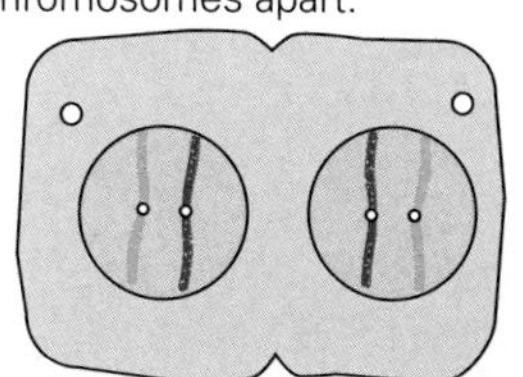

5 Two nuclei reform at either end of the cell.

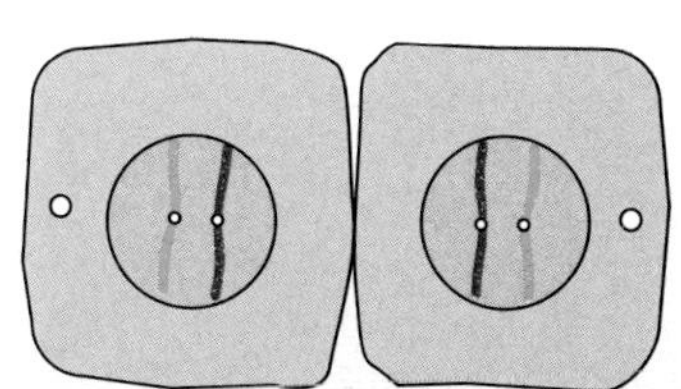

6 The cell divides into two. The two new cells have a nucleus with the same number of chromosomes as the original cell.

In mitosis, the cell divides into two new cells each with the same number of chromosomes as the original cell.

Mitosis

When a cell divides, the nucleus divides first. Each new nucleus that forms has the same number of chromosomes as the original nucleus so the new cells have exactly the same genetic information as the original cell. This type of division is **mitosis**. The diagram on the left shows what happens to two of the chomosomes in a cell.

QUESTIONS

1 Explain why it is important for a cell to have a nucleus.

2 Name the two substances that make up a chromosome.

3 Describe what happens to chromosomes before and during mitosis.

4 Explain why mitosis is important during growth.

6.5 *Life cycles*

Organisms, including humans, age and die. If species are to continue they must reproduce.

Asexual reproduction

The simplest form of reproduction is when a parent cell or organism divides into two or many parts. All the new individuals are formed from one parent. This is called asexual reproduction.

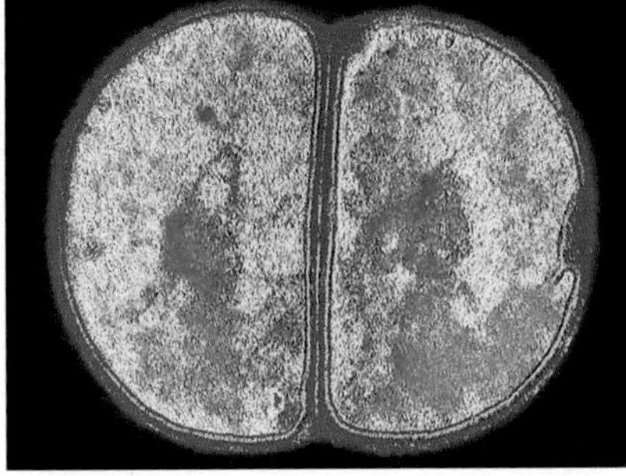

Under ideal conditions some bacteria can divide into two every 20 minutes.

New potato tubers formed by asexual reproduction

Farmers make use of asexual reproduction when they grow potatoes. From a single potato plant stems grow out into the soil and swell with stored food, forming tubers. If they are left in the ground the tubers will grow into new potato plants. Since the potatoes have all grown from one parent they are identical – they have all inherited the same genes. This is because the cells that grew to make the new tubers divided by mitosis.

Plants which are **genetically identical** form a **clone**. All the members of a clone are resistant to the same diseases and they give a uniform crop of the same quality. This is of great benefit to farmers who grow crops for canning, freezing or for sale in supermarkets.

Sexual reproduction

In sexual reproduction sex cells, or **gametes**, fuse (join) together. These sex cells come from a male and a female of the same species. In animals the gametes are eggs (**ova**) and sperm.

In humans sperm develop in the testes and eggs develop in the ovaries. At fertilisation an egg and a sperm fuse together. The two parents both contribute genetic information to the next generation. This means that their children will not be identical to either parent – they will have a mixture of features from both parents. This gives rise to variation within our species and explains why we do not all look alike.

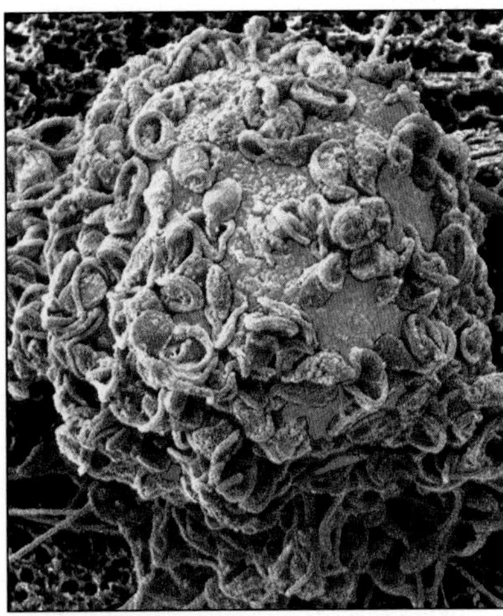

The human egg surrounded by sperm before fertilisation (× 500).

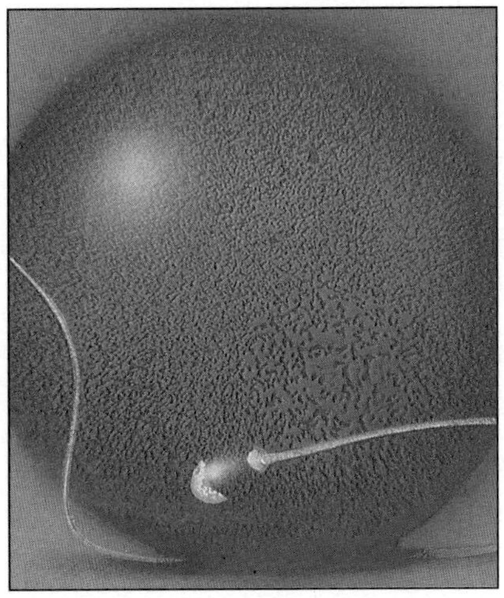

The moment of fertilisation. The sperm, about 0.02 mm, pierces the surface of the egg. The fertilised egg is called a ***zygote****.*

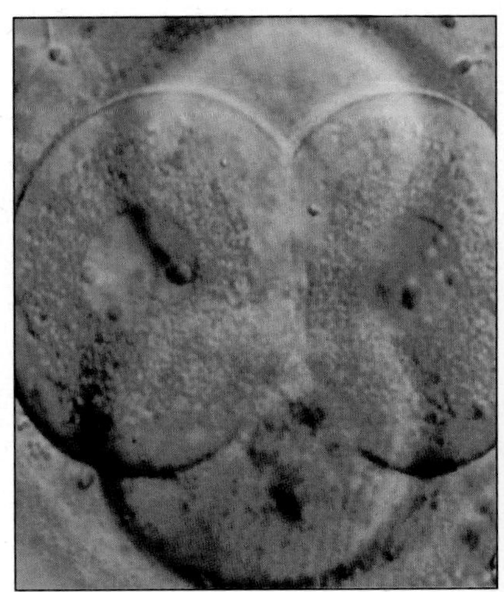

After fertilisation the zygote divides to form an embryo. Here it has reached the 4-cell stage.

Sex in plants

Flowering plants reproduce by making flowers. Most flowers contain both male parts and female parts. The male parts (anthers) produce pollen grains which contain male gametes. The female part contains the stigma and the ovary where eggs are formed.

When flowering plants reproduce sexually, pollen grains are transferred from the anthers to the stigma. The male gamete is transferred in the pollen grain so that fertilisation can occur. This is **pollination**. The gametes fuse at fertilisation inside the ovary to produce a zygote. The zygote develops into an embryo inside a seed.

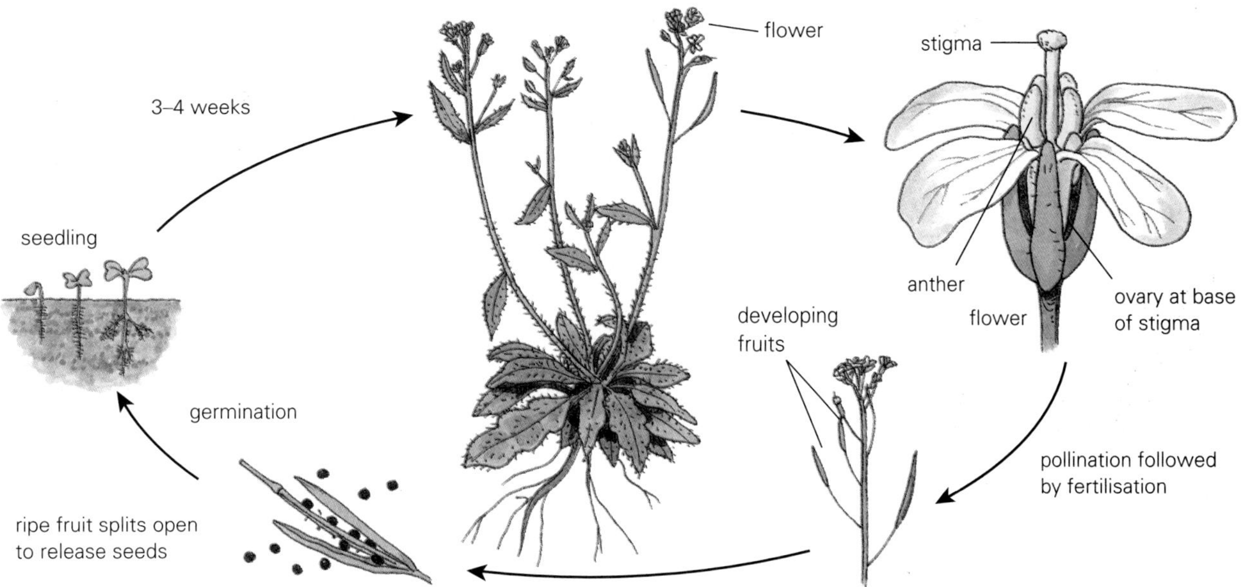

This shows the life cycle of the flowering plant thale cress.

Pollination

If pollination occurs within the same flower it is termed **self-pollination**. At fertilisation when the gametes fuse the resulting zygote has two sets of chromosomes that have come from the same parent. This means the next generation will look very similar to the parent plant.

More common is **cross-pollination** where the pollen grains are transferred to another plant of the same species. Plant breeders use both types of pollination. Self-pollination is used when they want to produce many plants of the same type but cannot use asexual reproduction to make a clone. Cross-pollination is used when they want to combine features from two different varieties of plants of the same species.

QUESTIONS

1. State the differences between sexual and asexual reproduction.
2. Describe the advantages of asexual reproduction of crops to farmers and growers.
3. Draw a diagram to show the stages in a life cycle of humans.
4. Explain the difference between pollination and fertilisation in plants.
5. What is the difference between self-pollination and cross-pollination? Why are these two types of pollination useful to plant breeders?

6.6 *Meiosis*

Passing on the programme

In sexual reproduction gametes contain a nucleus with chromosomes. The nucleus in the zygote (the fertilised egg) is formed by fusion of two nuclei – one from the male gamete and one from the female gamete. But the zygote's cells have the same number of chromosomes as the parent cells. This means that the gametes themselves cannot contain the full number of chromosomes otherwise the number would double with every generation.

Look carefully at the human chromosomes shown in the photographs in 6.4. As you can see in a cell there are two copies of each chromosome. Gametes (eggs and sperms) are different in that they contain a single copy of each chromosome, making 23 in all. The chromosome number is halved from 46 to 23 in a process called **meiosis**. At fertilisation the gametes fuse to form a zygote with 46 chromosomes in the nucleus.

Sexual reproduction results in offspring with characteristics from both parents.

Meiosis

As a cell divides to form gametes in the ovary or in the testis, the nucleus divides to halve the number of chromosomes. This involves two separate divisions of the cell.

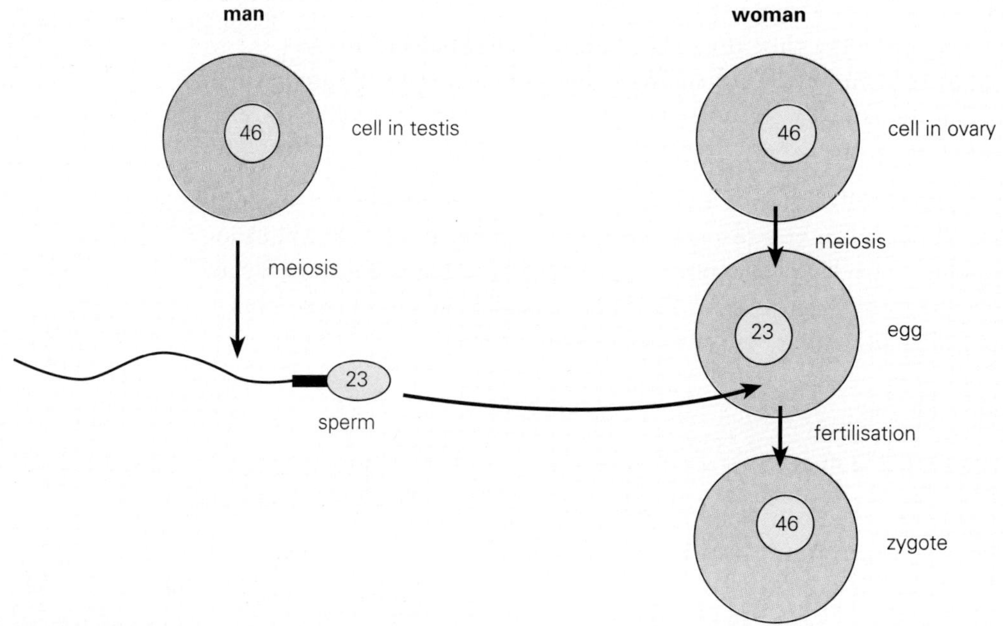

Meiosis results in gametes with half *the number of chromosomes. The full number is restored at fertilisation.*

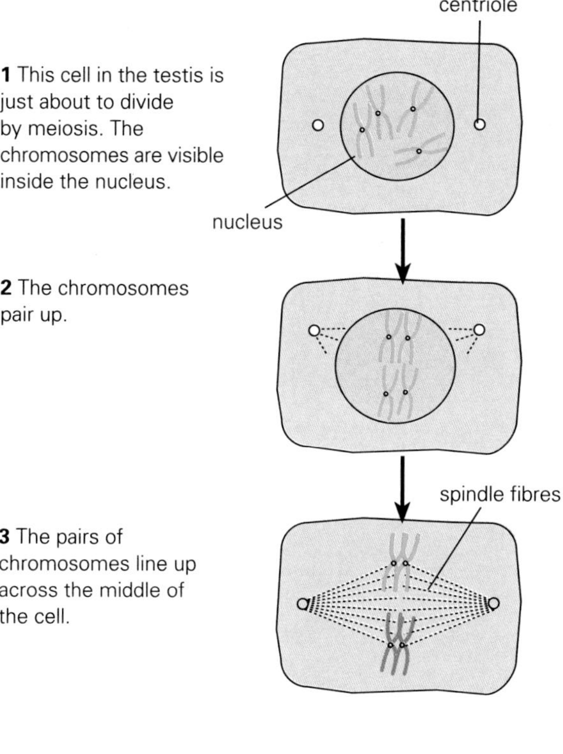

4 The pairs of chromosomes separate. Half of the chromosomes go to each end of the cell.

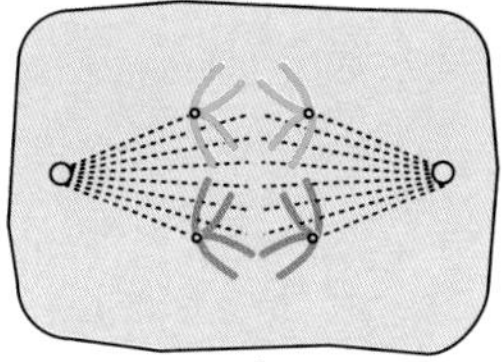

5 The cell divides into two cells.

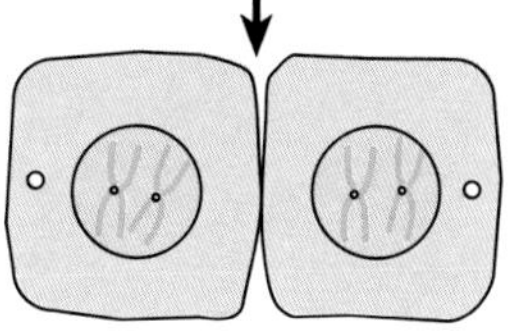

6 The two cells divide again to form four cells which then develop into sperm.

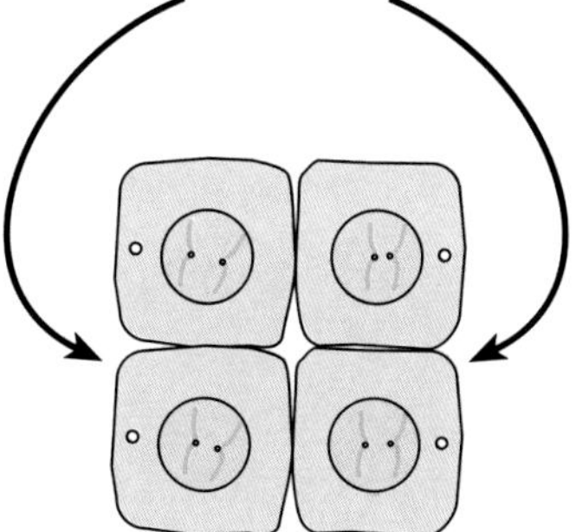

This shows what happens to four chromosomes in meiosis.

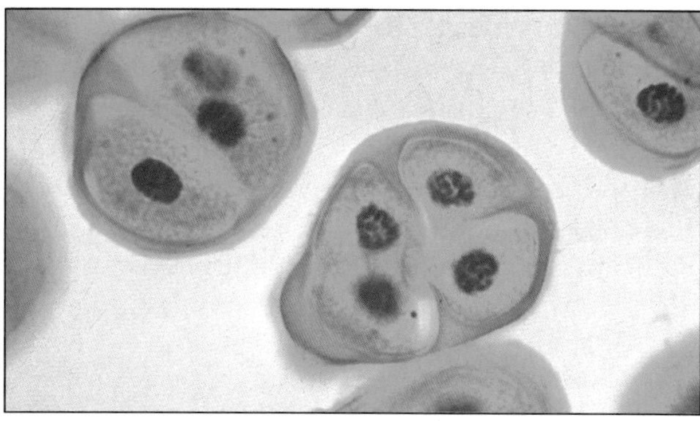

In flowering plants some cells divide by meiosis to produce pollen grains (which contain the male gametes). Others divide by meiosis to produce eggs.

Diploid and haploid numbers

The number of chromosomes in the zygote, and the number in all the cells that form from it during growth, is called the **diploid** number. In humans the diploid number is 46. The number of chromosomes in gametes is the **haploid** number, which is half the diploid number. During meiosis the diploid number changes to the haploid and at fertilisation the diploid number is restored.

Species	Number of chromosomes in the zygote and body cells (diploid number)	Number of chromosomes in gametes (haploid number)
Humans	46	23
Fruit flies	8	4
Thale cress	10	5
Mouse	40	20

QUESTIONS

1 Explain the terms **a** gamete, **b** zygote, **c** embryo, **d** meiosis.

2 Where are human gametes produced?

3 State the chromosome number in human body cells and in human gametes.

4 What happens to the number of chromosomes during meiosis and at fertilisation? Explain why this is important.

5 Describe briefly what happens during meiosis.

6.7 *Chromosome inheritance*

Sex determination

Most animals have two sexes, male and female. The sex of an animal is determined in a number of different ways. In some cases it is inherited, in others it is determined by the environment. Young crocodiles and alligators become male if the eggs are incubated at 33°C or above, but female if incubated at 30°C or below. Some animals change sex during their lifetime.

Sex in mammals is determined genetically at fertilisation by the two **sex chromosomes** known as **X** and **Y**. The Y chromosome carries a gene which determines maleness, the X chromosome carries a large number of important genes including those that control blood clotting, colour vision and muscle contraction.

The sex of young alligators depends on the temperature at which the eggs have been incubated.

These X and Y chromosomes determine our sex (× 16 000).

Sex chromosomes

Of the 23 pairs of chromosomes in human cells, one pair determines which sex you are. In females, both chromosomes in this pair are X chromosomes, in males one is X and the other is Y.

Since females have two X chromosomes, all the gametes (eggs) they produce have one X chromosome together with the other 22 chromosomes. Males, being XY, produce two different types of sperm. During meiosis the XY chromosome pair separates so that some sperm carry an X chromosome and the others carry a Y chromosome.

There is an equal chance of a sperm receiving either chromosome: X or Y. In other words 50% of sperm are X-bearing and 50% are Y-bearing. Since all eggs carry an X chromosome this should mean that 50% of the population will be female and 50% male. In practice this is not so, because there are slightly more females born than males.

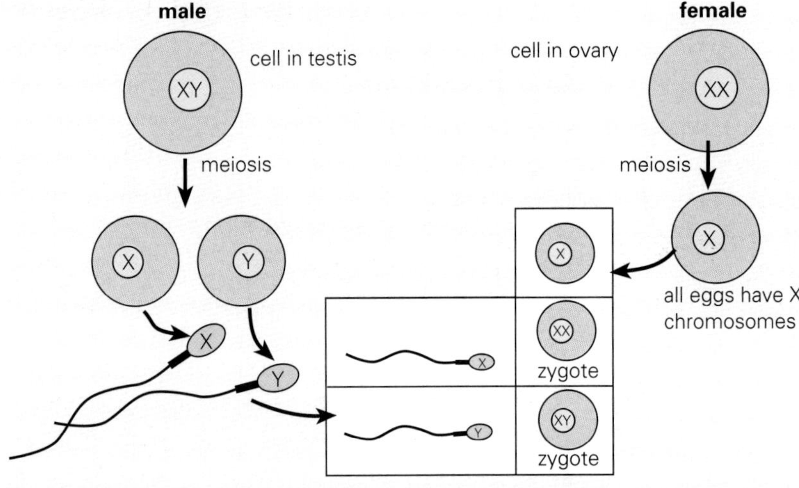

This shows that it is the male who determines the sex of his children.

Genetic reassortment

People inherit some features from their mother and others from their father. We are all a mixture of the features of both our parents, and yet in some ways we may be totally unlike them. Each person is a unique combination of factors.

The reason for this is that there are differences between the chromosomes in every pair of chromosomes not just the sex chromosomes.

Each chromosome carries genes which control the same characteristics (e.g. eye colour) but the genes themselves may be different. So on one chromosome in the pair the gene for eye colour might be for brown and on the other for blue.

The diagram below shows two pairs of non-sex chromosomes. During meiosis these pairs can be arranged as in the first part of **A** or as in **B**. Some cells will divide as in **A**, others as in **B**.

Gametes are haploid and contain one chromosome of each pair. When meiosis is completed, the gametes will contain different combinations of chromosomes. Therefore gametes will contain different combinations of genes. Imagine the number of different combinations possible with 23 pairs of chromosomes. The genetic reassortment that occurs during meiosis gives rise to variation in inherited features and explains why we inherit a mixture of features from our parents, e.g. eye colour from one and hair colour from the other.

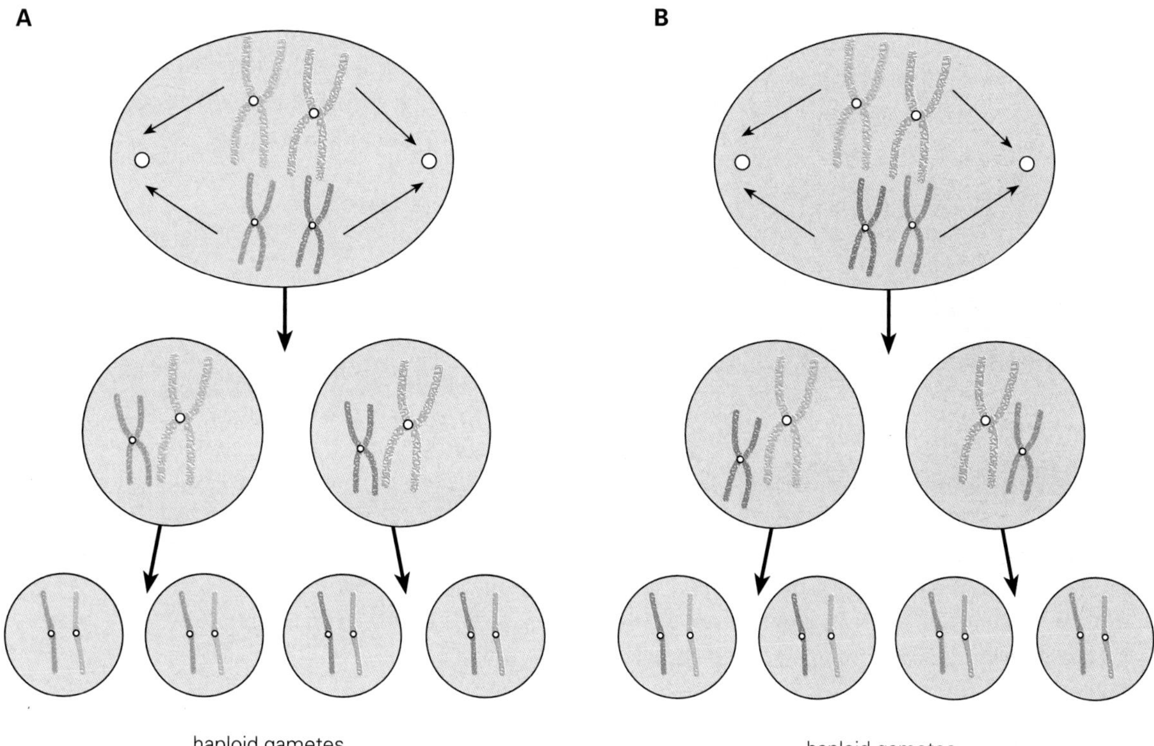

*Two cells are dividing by meiosis. In **A** two pairs of chromosomes are arranged in one way. In **B** they are arranged differently. Notice how this leads to different combinations of chromosomes in the gametes.*

QUESTIONS

1 Explain how the sex of children is determined in humans.

2 Use a diagram to explain how a man determines the sex of his children.

3 We are all different. Use what you know about meiosis to explain why this should be so.

6.8 Genes and inheritance

Cat breeders know that if they breed together two cats which both have long hair, all the kittens will have long hair. If two short-haired cats are bred together then there may be some long-haired kittens in the litter. Alternatively, there may not be any at all.

Sometimes fruit flies appear with very small wings. If the small-winged flies are mated with flies with normal wings, then all the offspring have normal wings (see photograph below).

Some breeds of cats are short-haired like this Siamese, left, others long-haired like this Persian, right.

Genes

These features of cats and fruit flies are all controlled by genes. A gene is a small length of the DNA in a chromosome. It is the genetic instruction for one particular feature in an organism.

Pure bred lines

When long-haired cats are bred together they always **breed true**, meaning that they always produce long-haired cats. The same feature continues over many generations. These cats are all long-haired and said to be **pure bred**. An animal breeder has to make sure that a short-haired cat does not mate with a long-haired breed if the next generation is to be long-haired and breed true for fur length.

Dominance

In sexual reproduction each organism receives a set of genetic instructions from each of its parents. Two copies of every instruction are inherited therefore a cat which has a pure bred short-haired mother and a pure bred long-haired father must inherit genes for both short and long hair. But it has short hair.

This means that the gene for short hair is **dominant**. It overrides the gene for long hair. A feature like this which appears in the first generation when two pure bred lines are crossed is called a dominant feature. Short hair in cats is a dominant feature and appears (is **expressed**) even if only one gene for short hair is inherited. Long hair is not expressed if there is only one gene for long hair – it is called a **recessive** feature. Long hair is controlled by a recessive version of the gene for hair length.

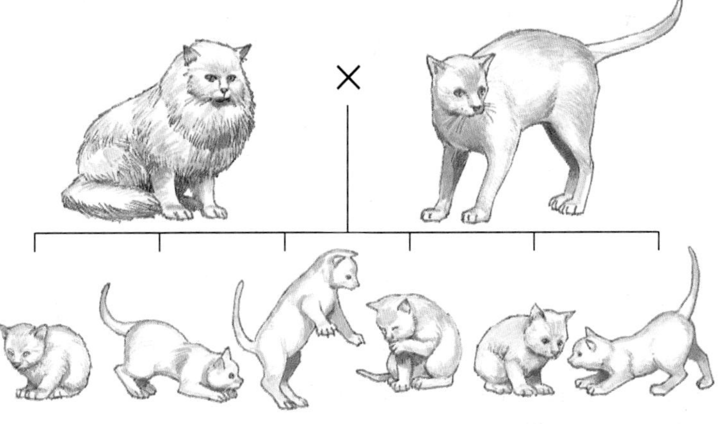

Plants or animals produced when two different pure lines are bred (crossed) are called **hybrids**.

In the pea plant example shown here all the hybrid pea plants have red flowers. To show that they are not pure breeding they can be bred by self-pollination. The result of this is that the next generation of plants are not all alike. Some have red flowers and others have white flowers. This shows that the hybrid plants had both the dominant and the recessive versions of the gene for flower colour. It also shows that the dominant gene is for red flowers and the recessive is for white.

Inheritance in fruit flies

Exactly the same thing is seen in fruit flies. When normal, long-winged pure bred flies are mated with the short-winged pure bred flies all the offspring in the next generation have long wings. When these are allowed to mate among themselves, the second generation contains many normal looking flies with long wings and some with short wings. Here the short wing condition is recessive; long wing is the dominant condition.

When red and white pea flowers are cross-pollinated all the next generation have red flowers.

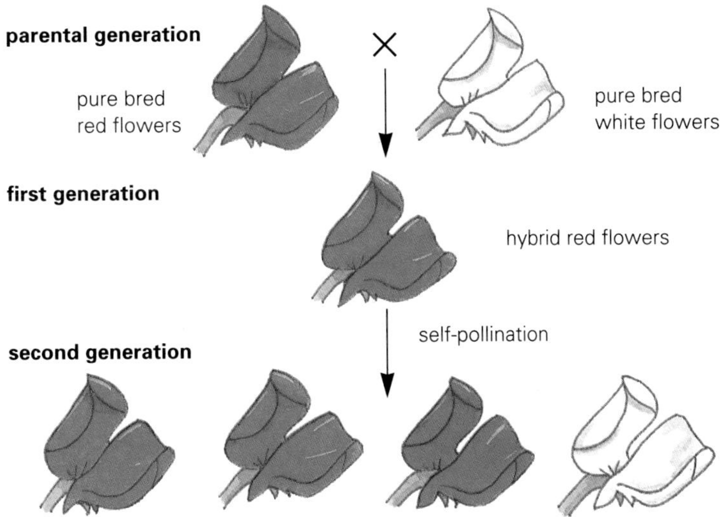

In the second generation some plants have red flowers and some have white flowers.

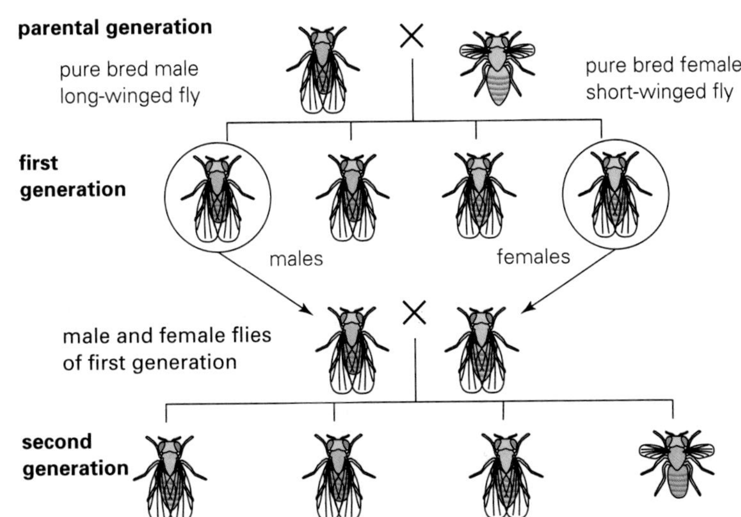

What is the ratio of long- to short-winged flies in the second generation?

QUESTIONS

1. Explain the terms **a** gene, **b** pure bred line, **c** hybrid.
2. Describe how the following are inherited: hair length in cats, flower colour in peas and wing size in fruit flies.
3. Explain the patterns of inheritance you describe by using the terms dominant and recessive.
4. Mice can have brown coloured fur or white. Explain how you would find out which colour is the dominant one.

6.9 Genetic diagrams

First generation

Patterns of inheritance can be simplified as genetic diagrams. This diagram follows the inheritance of the gene which controls development of wings in fruit flies.

- The letter W represents the gene for wing size. The capital letter always represents the dominant gene and the small letter the recessive (always use the same letter for both). So a capital **W** represents long wings and a small **w** represents small wings.
- *The parental generation* Pure bred parent flies are used for the first cross. The genetic make-up of the long-winged flies is **WW**, that of the short-winged flies is **ww**. Each has two letters because there are two copies of the gene in each cell.
- *Gametes* All the eggs will have the **w** gene since the females were all short-winged. All the sperm will have **W** as the males were long-winged. There will only be one letter in each gamete because there is only one copy of each chromosome in each gamete as a result of meiosis (see 6.7).
- *Zygotes and the first generation* The gametes are then combined as happens at fertilisation. This means that all the offspring have both versions of the gene: **W** and **w**. We can write this as **Ww**.
- The offspring are all long-winged flies because **W** is the dominant version of the gene, **w** is recessive. These offspring are known as the **first generation** (written as the F_1 generation).

parental generation

male WW

female ww

gametes

W

w

all sperm are (W)

all eggs are (w)

zygotes Ww

first generation (F_1)

Ww

To summarise, a genetic diagram can be used. The gametes produced by each parent are written at the top and side of a grid as shown. This shows that 100% of the offspring, male or female, will be long-winged flies.

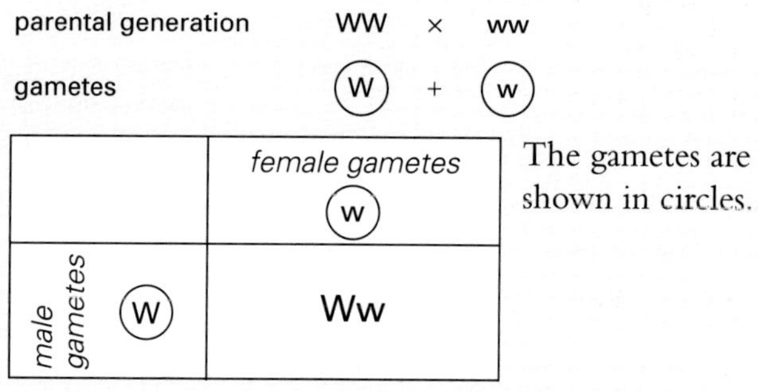

The gametes are shown in circles.

Phenotype and genotype

All the features of an organism, both internal and external are called its **phenotype**. An organism's genetic make-up is known as its **genotype**. If an organism has two different versions of a gene (e.g. **Ww**) then it is **heterozygous**. When it has identical versions of a gene (e.g. **WW** or **ww**) then it is described as **homozygous**.

Genes and alleles

The different versions of genes are called **alleles**. Dominant alleles are those that are expressed when two different alleles are present together in the genotype. For example, in fruit flies the allele for long wings (**W**) is dominant and the allele (**w**) for short wings is recessive. Recessive alleles are those which are only expressed if they are present together, e.g. **ww** in fruit flies.

Second generation

The genetic make-up of the F_1 generation flies is **Ww**. They are now mated among themselves.

In the male, 50% of the sperm produced by the male will carry **W**, 50% will carry **w**. In the female, 50% of the eggs will carry **W** and 50% will carry **w**.

As the genes are different there are two types of sperm and two types of egg. The zygotes produced from these gametes are of three types shown below.

zygotes: **WW** **Ww** **Ww** **ww**

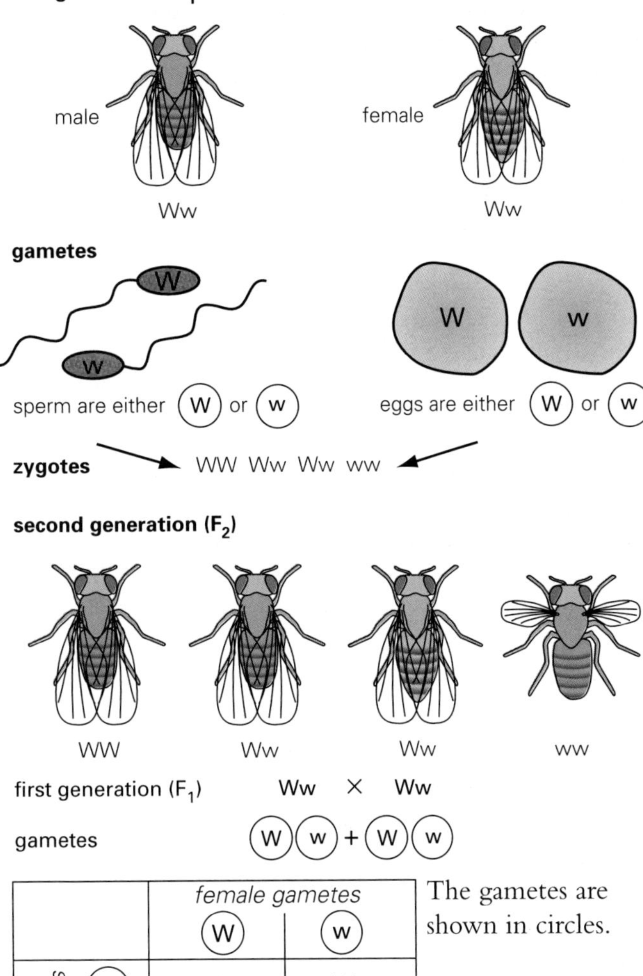

Again this can be summarised in a genetic diagram. Here you can see that for the second generation (F_2) of these flies, male or female:

25% are **WW** and have long wings
50% are **Ww** and have long wings
25% are **ww** and have short wings.

So 75% of the F_2 generation will have long wings and 25% will have short wings.

first generation (F_1) Ww × Ww

gametes (W)(w) + (W)(w)

		female gametes (W)	*female gametes* (w)
male gametes	(W)	WW	Ww
male gametes	(w)	Ww	ww

The gametes are shown in circles.

QUESTIONS

1 Explain the terms **a** phenotype, **b** genotype, **c** allele, **d** homozygous and **e** heterozygous.

2 Peas have a gene for controlling flower colour. **R** is the dominant allele for red flowers and **r** is the recessive allele for white flowers.

a What will be the phenotype of a flower with the genotype **Rr**?

b Complete the genetic diagram below to predict the genotype and the phenotype of the F_1 generation of flowers when flowers of the genotype **RR** are pollinated with flowers of the genotype **rr**.

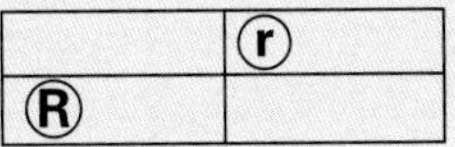

	(r)
(R)	

c Use a genetic diagram to predict the outcome if the F_1 generation of these flowers is self-pollinated.

3 Use genetic diagrams to

a explain how hair length is inherited in cats

b predict the phenotype of the offspring when fruit flies with the genotype **Ww** are crossed with flies with the genotype **ww**.

4 The allele for brown coat colour in rabbits is dominant to that for white. Explain how you would show that a brown rabbit was homozygous dominant.

6.10 *Inherited diseases*

Genetic diseases

Some diseases, like cystic fibrosis and Huntington's chorea (often called Huntington's disease) are inherited. Two more, sickle cell anaemia and haemophilia, are described in 6.13. Cystic fibrosis affects young children and, until recently, they did not live very long. Huntington's chorea only begins to show itself at a much later stage in life, often after a person has had children. Both males and females can inherit these diseases.

Cystic fibrosis

Children with cystic fibrosis find it very hard to breathe and digest their food so they grow slowly. They are very prone to infection and need special treatment from a very early age. Cell membranes in cells lining the lungs and elsewhere do not function properly and this causes mucus to build up.

Cystic fibrosis is controlled by the recessive allele, **f**. The dominant version, **F**, works properly. Almost all children with cystic fibrosis are born to parents who do not have the disease, because until recently sufferers of cystic fibrosis have not lived long enough to have children. People who have the disease are homozygous – they have two copies of the abnormal allele (**f**).

This girl is being treated by a physiotherapist to remove mucus from the lungs.

The genetic diagram on the page opposite shows how cystic fibrosis is inherited. To suffer from cystic fibrosis a child must have two copies of the abnormal allele (**ff**), the parents must be heterozygous (**Ff**) since they do not have the disease. Of the other two genotypes in the genetic diagram, one is homozygous (**FF**) and does not have the abnormal allele at all. The other is heterozygous (**Ff**), like the parents, and is a carrier of the disease.

Huntington's chorea

Huntington's chorea is a genetic disease named after the first person to describe it. The gene involved is concerned with the functioning of the nervous system. The abnormal allele is dominant and so can be passed on if only one parent has the disease.

In Huntington's chorea nerve cells fail to work properly. At first people suffer from rapid, jerky movements. Then they go into a mental decline and suffer from dementia. The disease is fatal.

Men and women with Huntington's inherit it from one parent who has one abnormal version of the gene. They do not start to suffer from the disease until later in life. The symptoms can start to appear at any age between 20 and about 50.

The genetic diagram on the page opposite shows how Huntington's is inherited. The dominant allele, **H**, causes the disease, while **h** is used for its normal recessive alternative. People with Huntington's chorea have the genotype **Hh**; those without it are **hh**. One parent is heterozygous and the other homozygous recessive. It is very unlikely that anyone who is homozygous dominant (**HH**) will be found since an embryo with the genotype **HH** is unlikely to develop.

Genetic counselling

Genetic counselling can now be given to people who have genetic diseases or who have children with genetic diseases.

A counsellor will explain to parents who have already had a child with cystic fibrosis that there is a 3 in 4 chance that their next child may be free of the disease. The fact that they already have one child with the disease does not change that probability. People who know of relatives with cystic fibrosis may also consult a genetic counsellor before having any children. They can be offered a genetic test to see if they have the abnormal allele.

If someone has a parent with Huntington's chorea then they have a 50% chance of inheriting the abnormal allele. As with cystic fibrosis there is a test for the gene to see if it is present or not. Some people want to know if they are carriers to avoid passing the disease on to another generation.

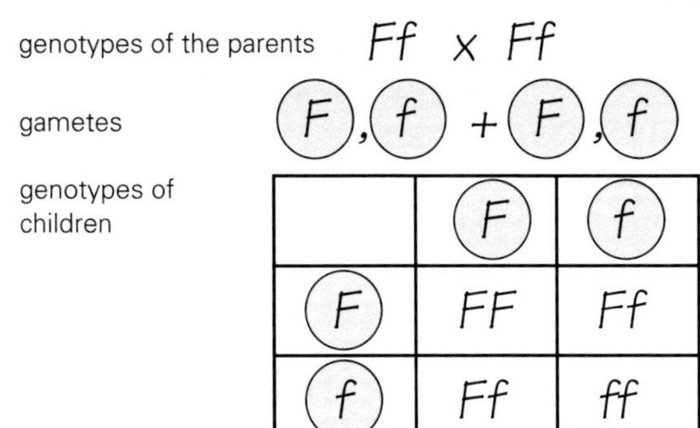

This genetic diagram shows how the counsellor can say that there is a 3 in 4 (75%) chance of having a normal child who will be free of cystic fibrosis.

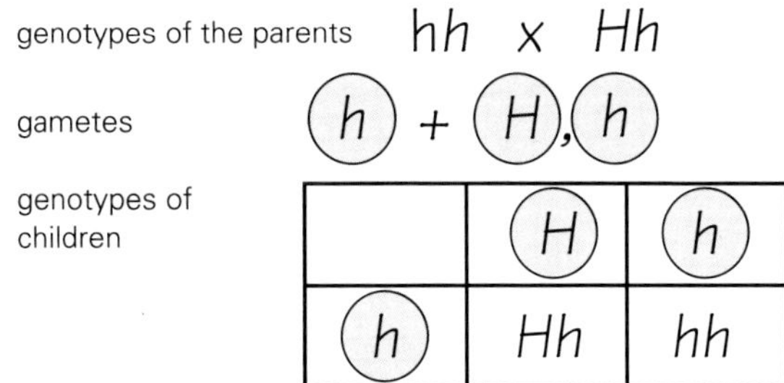

This genetic diagram shows that there is a 50% chance of inheriting Huntington's chorea from a parent with the dominant allele for the disease.

QUESTIONS

1 Explain the term genetic disease.

2 Explain how genetic counselling can reduce the incidence of genetic diseases like cystic fibrosis and Huntington's chorea.

3 Should everyone in the country be screened for cystic fibrosis and Huntington's chorea? Write out your arguments in two columns, *for* and *against* screening the entire population. Try to include the views of as many people as possible.

4 The pedigree shows a family with one child with cystic fibrosis.

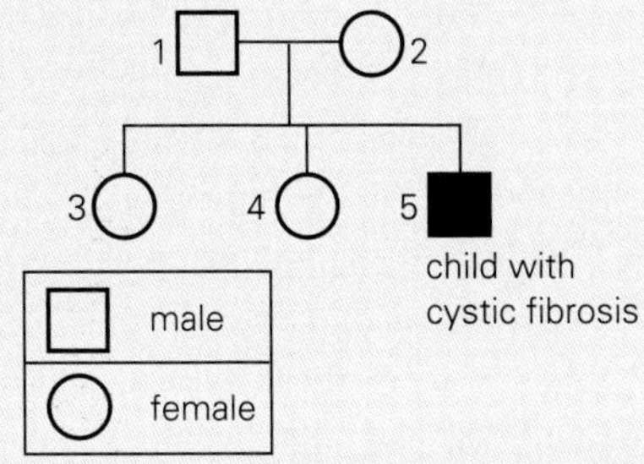

a State the genotypes of the people numbered 1, 2 and 5.

b State the possible genotypes of 3 and 4.

c What is the probability that the next child of these parents will have cystic fibrosis?

5 This pedigree shows a family in which a mother and her son have Huntington's chorea.

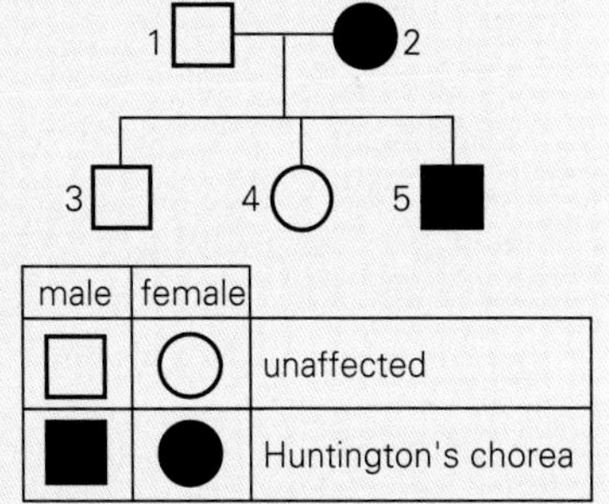

a State the genotypes of the people in this family.

b Use a genetic diagram to explain how the son has inherited the disease.

6.11 *DNA*

Discovering DNA

Our present understanding of many aspects of biology began with a knowledge of the structure of the molecule deoxyribonucleic acid (DNA). It is the genetic material, the substance of inheritance. DNA determines our physical features and controls how our cells work. We inherit our genes in the form of DNA and we make new life by passing on our genes to future generations.

DNA in chromosomes

Human chromosomes are made of DNA and protein. Each chromosome is one very large molecule of DNA wound up very tightly around protein molecules like many balls of string.

This is a computer-generated model of DNA. If all the DNA in your body was stretched out it would reach to the moon and back 8000 times.

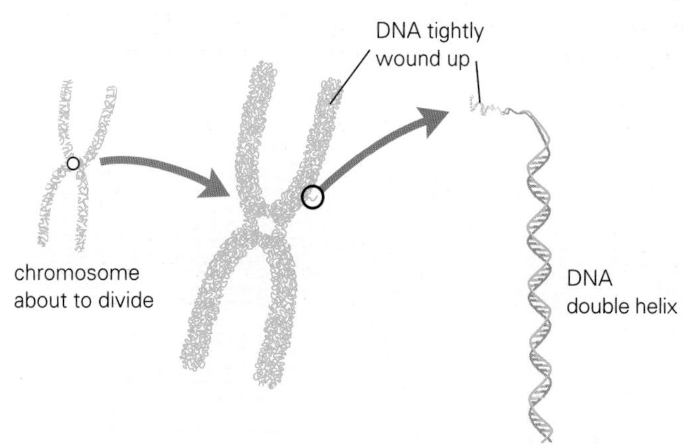

A DNA molecule in the longest human chromosome is 160 mm long. It is packed tightly into a chromosome 0.01 mm long.

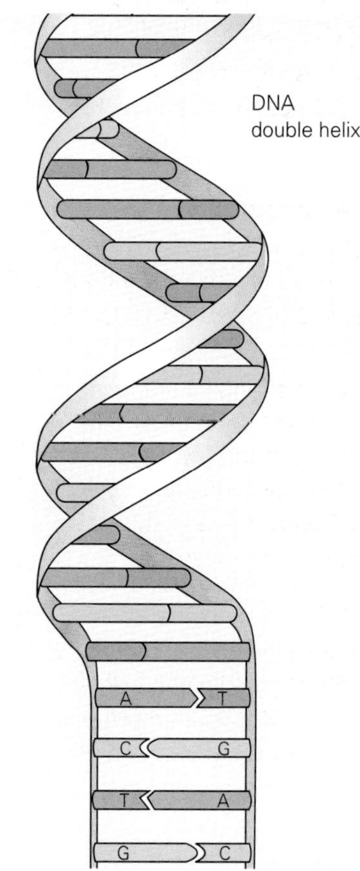

In a DNA molecule two twisted strands are held together by the base-pairs AT and GC.

The structure of DNA

The diagram shows DNA to be a bit like a ladder that has been twisted round. This type of spiral structure is called a helix and DNA is a **double helix** as it has two strands.

DNA is a long chain molecule made of four smaller, different molecules called bases. These are called adenine, thymine, guanine and cytosine (usually represented by the letters A, T, G and C). The base adenine (A) always pairs with thymine (T) to form one of the rungs of the ladder of the double helix. Guanine (G) always pairs with cytosine (C).

Exact copies

Before cells divide they copy their chromosomes. When this happens, DNA splits down the middle or 'unzips'. The two sides of the 'ladder' open out to expose the bases on each strand. The cell makes two new strands, one to match each side of the opened DNA 'ladder'. The order of bases on the two old strands determines the sequence of bases in the newly formed strands and the resulting identical DNA molecule. You can see this in the diagram opposite.

The rules of base pairing (A:T and C:G) means that the two sides of DNA are complementary. When they are 'unzipped' each acts as a **template** to build another strand. When the old and new strands combine a new molecule of DNA forms that keeps the same sequence of bases. This copying process is **replication**. It ensures that the genetic code is passed on unchanged.

The genetic code

A gene is a section of DNA. It may only be about a hundred base pairs long or it may have many thousands of base pairs. The order of the base pairs on the gene is a code to inform the cell how to assemble amino acids in the correct order into proteins. This is called protein synthesis and it occurs in the cytoplasm.

One strand of DNA codes for the sequence of amino acids in a protein. A group of three bases codes for one amino acid.

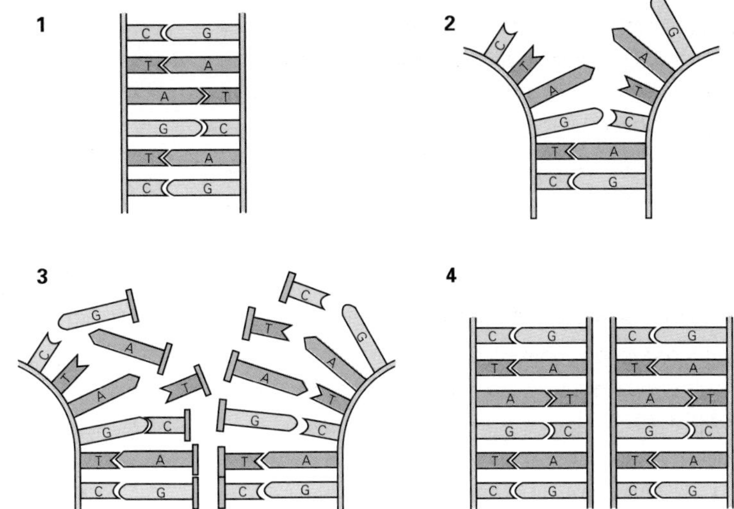

Notice how the rules of base pairing are followed during copying: A always pairs with T, C always pairs with G.

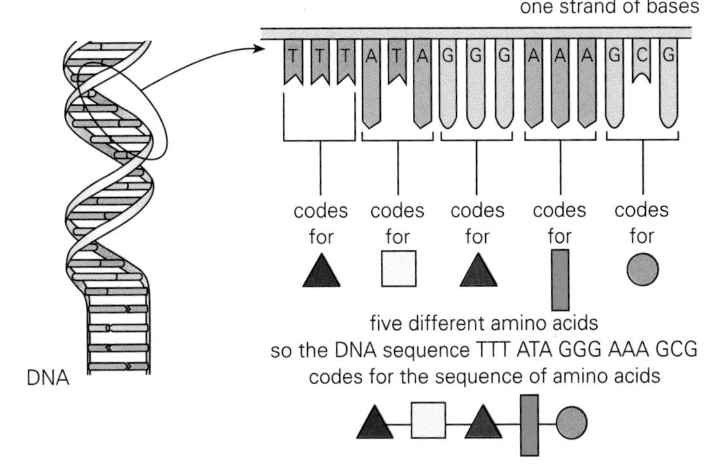

Here 15 bases code for 5 amino acids.

QUESTIONS

1 Make a diagram to show a model of DNA. Show and label at least four base pairs.

2 Draw a labelled diagram to explain how a short length of DNA is copied.

3 Explain the importance of base pairing in DNA.

4 Explain why an understanding of DNA is so important in biology.

6.12 *Mutation*

Gene mutation

DNA can change. During copying it is possible that a base can be inserted in the wrong place. If the change is not corrected, then the base pair will be different and a new sequence of bases will be produced. This change in DNA is called a **gene mutation**. Some mutations like this do not change the amino acid sequence in the protein coded by the gene so nothing happens.

However, very often a new sequence of bases codes for a protein that does not function properly or fails to work at all. If this happens a new allele (a **mutant allele**) of the gene is formed and can be inherited. Human genetic diseases such as cystic fibrosis and Huntington's chorea (see 6.10), sickle cell anaemia and haemophilia (see 6.13) are caused by gene mutations.

Mutagens

Mutations occur naturally but the chances of such a change taking place are increased in a number of ways.

- Various forms of electromagnetic radiation such as X-rays, gamma rays and ultra violet light can damage DNA. The radiation causes ionisation of the atoms in DNA and if the dose is high enough can cause severe damage to chromosome structure.
- Some chemicals, such as the tar in tobacco smoke, cause mutations. They cause base pairs to change.

Any chemical or physical agent that causes a mutation to occur is called a **mutagen**.

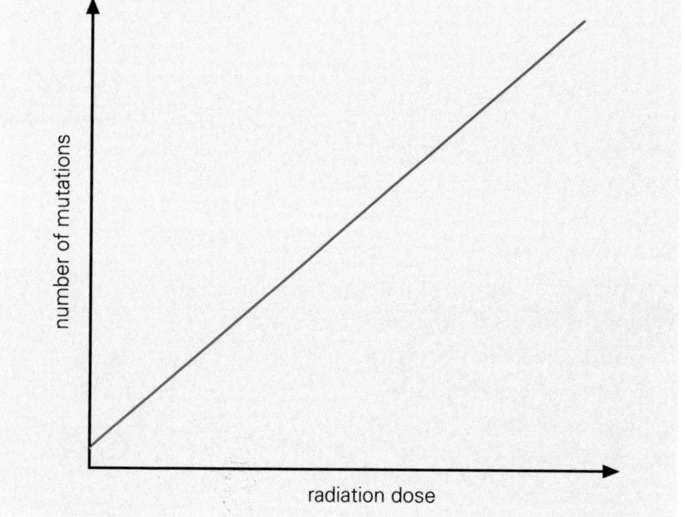

The higher the dose of radiation, the greater the chance of mutation.

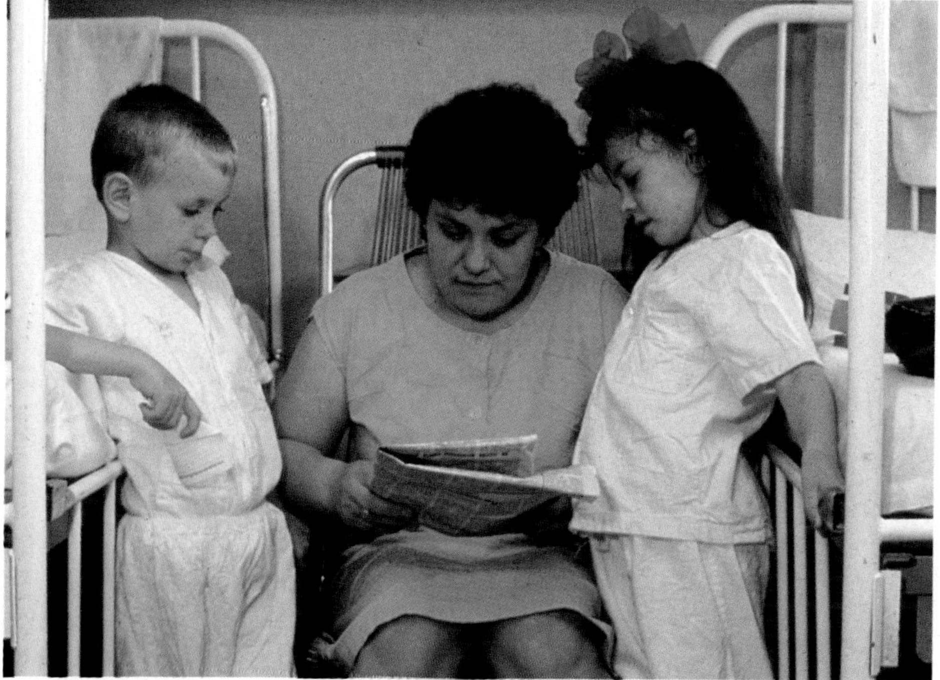

These Russian children were born shortly before the nuclear power station at Chernobyl exploded releasing radioactivity. They suffer from thyroid cancer. Their thyroid glands have been removed so they will need injections of thyroid hormone made by the gland for the rest of their lives.

Cancer

When a gene that helps to control cell growth and division mutates cells can divide uncontrollably. A group of such cells is called a **tumour**. The usual control mechanisms in the body that stop cells growing and dividing do not work properly and so a cell gets out of control. Mutations resulting in cancer occur more frequently when cells are exposed to certain chemical or physical agents known as **carcinogens**.

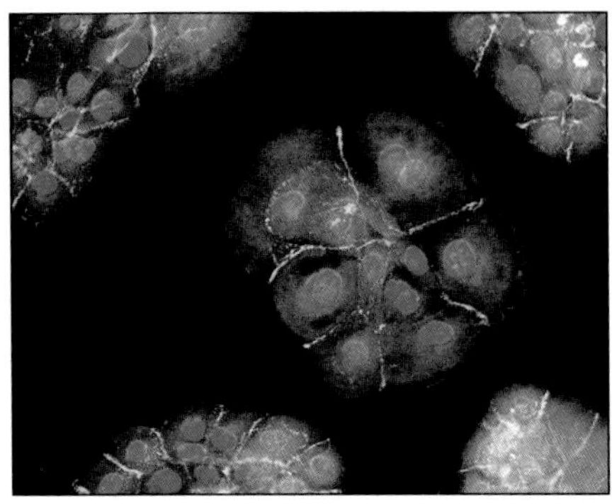

These skin cancer cells have started to divide uncontrollably as a result of a mutation.

Inherited mutations

A newly mutated gene is only inherited if the mutation occurs in the gametes in reproductive organs such as the ovaries and testes. Mutations that occur elsewhere in the body are not inherited.

Crops like barley have been improved by mutation breeding.

Not always harmful

Most mutations are harmful. Sometimes mutations are useful, but the chances of this are rare because of the great length of time species have existed. It is likely that any beneficial mutations in the past will have become the norm.

However, mutation is the only way in which completely new genetic material is produced. Some mutations that have been harmful in the past may be useful now or in the future (see 7.4).

Deliberate mutations

Plant and animal breeders are always looking out for organisms where a favourable mutation has occurred to use in genetic improvement of crops or domesticated animals. Sometimes they find these by accident, but it is also possible to make them appear by exposing living tissues in a controlled way to mutagens.

Chromosome mutations

Mutations also affect the number of chromosomes. During meiosis chromosomes can fail to separate properly so that gametes have either too few or too many chromosomes. An extra chromosome in humans is the cause of Down's syndrome (47 chromosomes).

One of the boys in this class has Down's syndrome.

QUESTIONS

1 Explain the terms **a** mutation, **b** mutagen and **c** carcinogen.

2 Make a list of different mutagens.

3 Describe what happens to DNA when it mutates.

4 Explain why mutations can be harmful.

5 State the cause of Down's syndrome.

6.13 More inherited disease

Inherited disease

Sickle cell anaemia and haemophilia are genetic diseases. Both affect the blood, but they are inherited in different ways.

Sickle cell anaemia

The red pigment, haemoglobin, inside red blood cells transports oxygen around the body. One gene controls the protein part of the haemoglobin molecule. There are two alleles of this gene:

- **S** is responsible for producing normal haemoglobin
- **s** leads to the production of a form of haemoglobin that is less efficient.

People who have the genotype **ss** have sickle cell anaemia. The body tissues do not receive much oxygen and sufferers are constantly tired. People who are heterozygous (**Ss**) make both types of haemoglobin and have a mild form of anaemia. They are said to show the sickle cell trait.

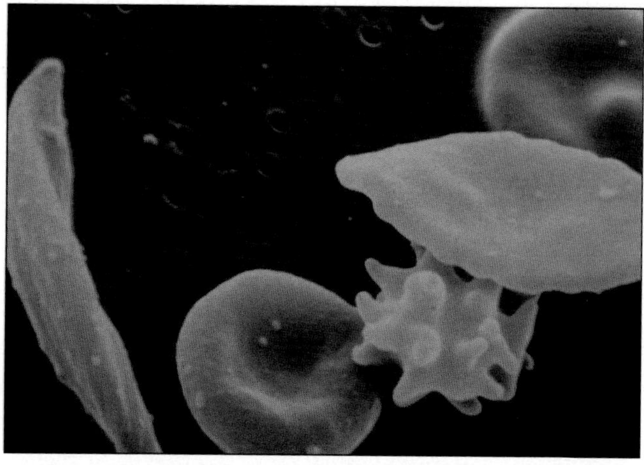

In this photograph you can see normal, round red blood cells and elongated sickle cells (× 4800).

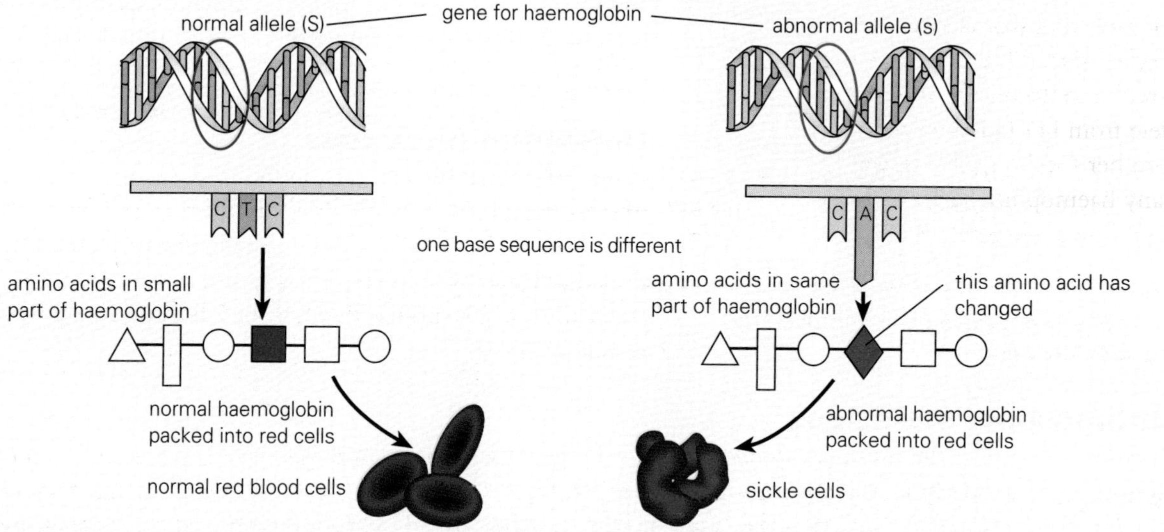

Sickle cell anaemia is the result of a small mutation in the gene for haemoglobin.

Unexpected benefits

Sickle cell anaemia is particularly common in West and East Africa, in parts of Asia and in the Americas. People who are homozygous (**ss**) suffer greatly. Most of them die very young.

The disease is common because people who are heterozygous (**Ss**) are resistant to one of the world's worst diseases – malaria. The microscopic parasite that causes malaria cannot enter the red cells of people who are heterozygous. This protection from a deadly disease gives people who are heterozygous an advantage in places where malaria is common. Here possessing the recessive allele can be an advantage.

However, people who are heterozygous are likely to have children who are homozygous recessive and so the disease continues to appear.

Haemophilia

When genes for a certain feature are carried on the sex chromosome the feature is inherited along with being male or female. Haemophilia is a disease in which the blood clots very slowly. It is caused by a mutation to a gene which is only on the X chromosome. The Y chromosome does not have this gene. The mutant allele is recessive.

A **carrier** of haemophilia is a woman who has the recessive allele (**h**) of the gene that controls blood clotting. Her blood clots normally because she also has the dominant allele (**H**) which produces the blood-clotting protein. She has both alleles because women have two X chromosomes. Men have only one. They can only have one copy of the gene and if this is the recessive allele (**h**) they will have haemophilia. The inheritance of haemophilia is therefore **sex-linked**.

It is rare for a woman to have haemophilia. This is because she would have to inherit the mutant allele from her father as well as from her mother. Historically many haemophiliac men did not live to have children.

Both parents have normal blood, but the mother is a carrier

father's genotype $X^H\ Y$ × $X^H\ X^h$ mother's genotype

gametes (X^H), (Y) + (X^H), (X^h)

	female gametes (X^H)	female gametes (X^h)
male gametes (X^H)	X^HX^H	X^HX^h
male gametes (Y)	X^HY	X^hY

children's genotypes	X^HX^H	X^HX^h	X^HY	X^hY
children's phenotypes	girl with normal blood –she is not a carrier	a girl who is a carrier like her mother	a boy who has normal blood	a boy who has haemophilia

This genetic diagram shows how haemophilia can be inherited from a mother who is a carrier for the disease.

The Tsarevitch Aleksei – great grandson of Queen Victoria, from whom he inherited the mutant allele for haemophilia. Notice his left hand is bandaged.

QUESTIONS

1 How does sickle cell anaemia affect its sufferers?

2 Use genetic diagrams to describe how the following can be inherited from a mother who is a carrier for the disease
 a sickle call anaemia
 b haemophilia.

3 Explain why haemophilia is a sex-linked disease.

4 Explain with a genetic diagram how a woman could inherit haemophilia.

5 What is the probability of a woman who is a carrier of haemophilia having a haemophiliac child if her husband does not have the disease?

7.1 *Fossils*

Scientists estimate that there has been life on Earth for about 4000 million years. The only organisms which existed for nearly 3000 million years were bacteria. The diversity of species that we see today has only developed during the last 1000 million years.

Prehistoric life

To form any idea of what life was like before humans appeared on Earth we rely on **fossils**. Fossils are the remains of organisms that lived in the past. They are found in **sedimentary rocks**, like limestone and chalk, which are formed by the accumulation of muds, sands or clays in rivers, lakes or seas.

We can tell from the age of the rocks which contain fossils how old the fossils are. Studying fossils in different ages of rock allows us to construct a history of the development of a species over time. We can see how much or how little living things have changed. We can also study species, like dinosaurs, which used to live on Earth, but died out.

These humps are stromatolites which are found off the Australian coast. They contain bacteria. Fossilised stromatolites have been found in rocks 3500 million years old (see inset).

*These fossilised footprints (**A**) were made by an iguanadon which lived 135 million years ago. Photograph (**B**) shows a reconstruction of an iguanadon.*

How fossils form

When animals and plants die they decay. Bacteria, fungi and other decomposers feed on their bodies and eventually nothing is left. So the chances of an organism being fossilised are very small.

These chances are improved when dead organisms fall into silt or mud or into a swamp. Here they are covered quickly by sediment where there is little oxygen for decomposition to occur. Their bodies or parts of them remain intact. This is why fossils are usually found in sedimentary rocks. Hard parts such as skeletons and teeth are the most likely to survive because they are the most difficult to break down.

Good fossils have also formed where there are no decomposers because there is no water as it is too dry or too cold. Others form when animals are trapped in tar, plant sap or ice.

Parts of living things can be preserved in other ways. For example when water percolates through a shell it dissolves away the minerals leaving it light and spongy. Sometimes the chemicals that are dissolved are replaced by minerals such as iron and silica compounds. This replacement may preserve the original structure completely.

Many fossils are moulds or casts of the original organism. All the original remains dissolve away leaving a cavity in the surrounding rock. The walls of the cavity are a mould of the organism.

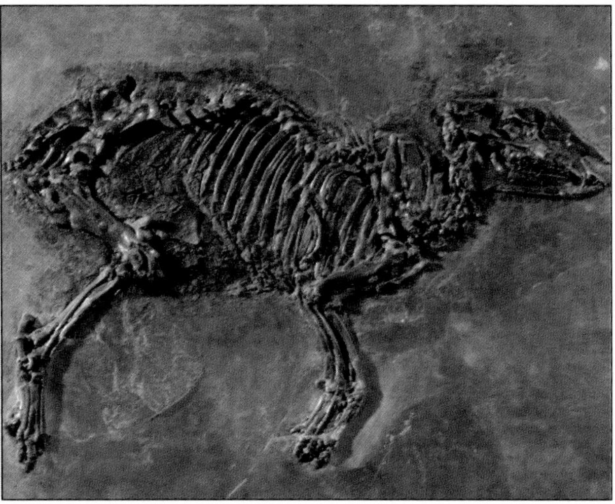

This horse lived 45 million years ago. The fossilised remains of its last meal were found in its stomach, showing that it was a forest-dwelling, soft-fruit eater.

This fossil is a cast of seashells.

Frozen remains of mammoths have enabled us to make models like this.

QUESTIONS

1. How long has life existed on the Earth?
2. Describe the conditions which favour the formation of fossils in rocks.
3. Describe three different ways in which fossils are formed.
4. What can a study of fossils tell us about life in the past?
5. Suggest what scientists can learn about mammoths from a frozen specimen?

7.2 *Evolution*

The fossil record

Fossils are a record of the history of life. They show that organisms have changed from simple bacteria to far more complex animals and plants.

Evolution

The gradual development of organisms over long periods of time is called **evolution**. Some organisms change into many different forms over millions of years. Some remain relatively unchanged. Others appear in the fossil record for millions of years and then disappear.

There are enough fossils surviving from various periods to reconstruct a very clear history of the evolution of the horse from the earliest record to the present day. The earliest horse-like animal was very small, about the size of a small dog. It lived 55 million years ago in forests and probably fed by browsing on trees.

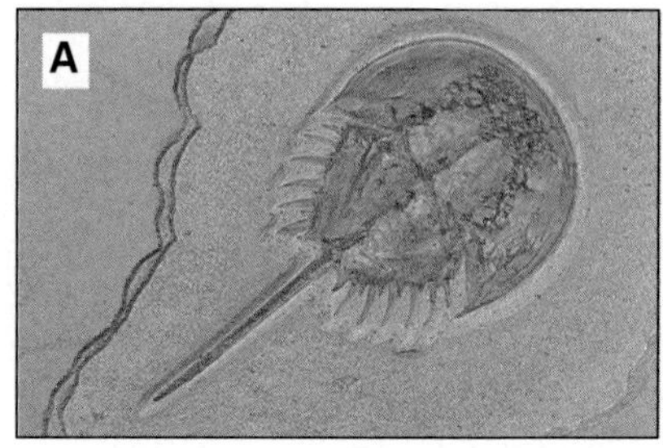

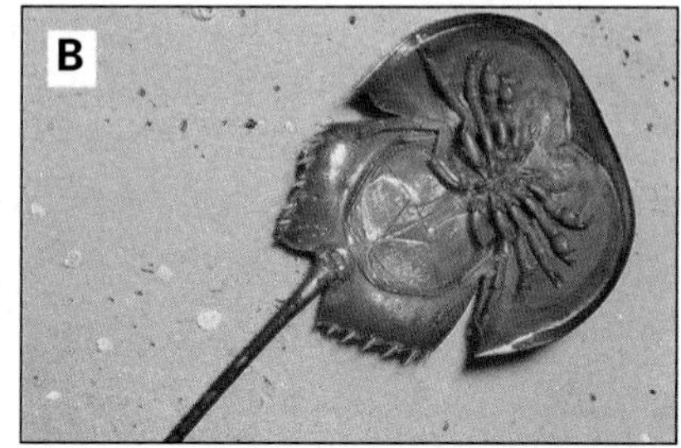

*This fossil horseshoe crab is 150 million years old (**A**). Compare it with one living today (**B**) and you will see very few differences.*

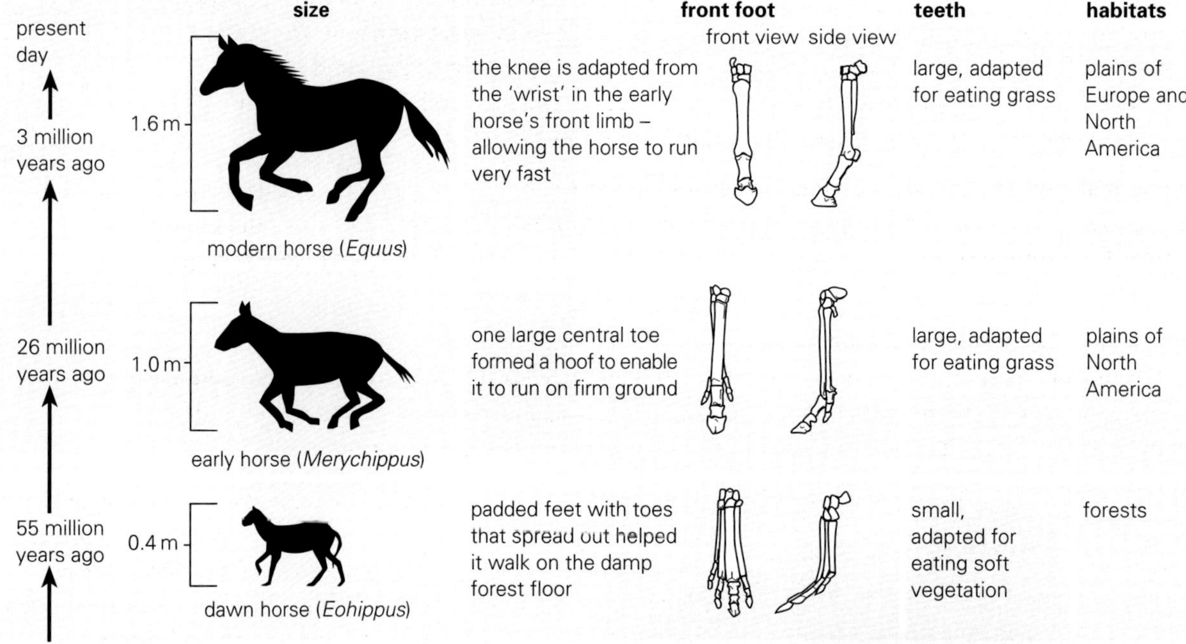

The table shows the changes that occurred in the legs, feet and teeth of these animals as they changed from small browsing animals with padded feet living in dense forest, to large grazing animals that live on open grassland like the prairies or the steppe.

The changes in the legs and feet gave them longer limbs so that they could run much faster. The teeth became large with a rough grinding surface to help them digest grass which is very tough.

The hoof of the modern horse has developed from the nail of the middle toe on each leg. Notice how the side bones have become reduced to thin splint bones.

This painting shows a reconstruction of the dawn horse, which was the size of a dog. Notice the padded feet.

The end of the line

Most of the organisms that we know from fossils are extinct. During the history of the Earth there have been periods when many species ceased to exist. No one knows for sure why this happened but evidence suggests it was because of changes in the climate. For example, as the Earth's climate cooled, sea levels fell as water was locked up as ice. Most life in the sea is found in shallow water. As water levels fell many species were left high and dry and could not survive on the land or in deeper water.

Climate change probably contributed to the decline of the dinosaurs which finally became extinct about 65 million years ago. Another explanation is that a giant meteorite hit the Earth and caused a great cloud of dust. This blocked out the Sun so that plant life grew very poorly and so there was little food available.

New diseases or predators or new species competing for the same food can also lead to a species dying out. Over the past 10 000 years one species by itself has made many others extinct. That species is us.

There were many ammonite species 80 million years ago but now they are all extinct.

Humans

Humans have hunted many species to extinction for food or pleasure. When humans started to colonise the Earth there were many large mammals such as mammoths. Mammoths possibly became extinct because they could not cope with the change in vegetation after the climate warmed suddenly 13 000 years ago, but hunting by humans possibly contributed to their extinction. The dodo, the great auk and the passenger pigeon are three other well known examples of species that humans have hunted to extinction.

We also make other organisms extinct by destroying their habitat. For example, this happens when people cut down trees to make land suitable for farming. The organisms that relied upon the trees for a source of food, or for shelter, or building nests cannot find anywhere else to go. Changing the climate in an area can also make other organisms extinct.

Animals and plants have been introduced into new environments both on purpose and unintentionally; these introduced species often compete successfully with native species, which then become extinct. Rats, rabbits, dogs, cats and goats have done considerable damage in this way on islands in the Indian Ocean and the Pacific where they have been introduced.

Many large mammals like mammoths may have been hunted to extinction by humans.

Equally as serious as the complete extinction is the loss or decline of local populations of animals and plants. When the numbers are so small there is little genetic variation and the species may deteriorate as a result of **inbreeding**. This can result in a much faster rate of extinction of groups of animals and plants.

QUESTIONS

1 Explain, using examples to illustrate your answer, why organisms may have become extinct in the distant past.

2 Describe three stages in the evolution of the horse.

3 How can human activities lead to the extinction of species of animal and plant.

4 Suggest why we should prevent extinctions occurring.

7.3 *Darwin's theory*

Explaining change

The theory of **natural selection** was proposed by Darwin in 1859. He stated that species had changed gradually through time in response to changes in their environment. The idea that living things had evolved was not new, but Darwin was one of the first to suggest a way in which evolution could have occurred. He was able to support his theory with evidence collected over 30 years.

Darwin's theory

The isolated location of the Galapagos Islands has resulted in the evolution of many species not found anywhere else.

Darwin's finches – these closely related species provide evidence for natural selection.

Species 1 and 2 feed on seeds; species 3 and 4 feed on insects.

A young Charles Darwin at the time of his voyage on HMS Beagle.

Darwin spent five weeks in the Galapagos Islands in the Pacific in 1835. The islands are quite different each with its own environment and vegetation. He found that the animals on each island were clearly related to each other but had important variations which were associated with the conditions on each island.

This helped Darwin develop a theory about why species change and die out. His theory consists of the ideas described on these pages and the next two. He did not know anything about the inheritance of genes. We are now able to outline his theory of natural selection using our present understanding of genetics.

Overproduction

Many organisms can produce far more offspring than are needed to maintain a constant population. But huge increases in populations do not usually occur because they are limited by various factors.

Competition

Animals compete for food and water, territories, and nesting sites. Herbivores eat plants and prevent them growing too much; predators prevent large increases in the numbers of herbivores. Diseases kill both plants and animals. All these act to keep the numbers of organisms in check and prevent population explosions (see 8.7).

Struggle for existence

As a result of competition there is a struggle for survival. Many individuals die young because they starve or they are eaten by predators or killed by disease. Mortality among young individuals (seedlings, young adults) is often very high. Many of these die before they have a chance to reproduce therefore they do not pass on their genes.

A pair of elephants could produce 19 million descendants after 700 years.

There is fierce competition for space and resources, such as light, among these plants growing on the branches of a tree in the tropics.

Variation and adaptation

There is often a large amount of variation within species that reproduce sexually. Genetic information in individuals is 'shuffled' every time meiosis occurs to form gametes. New combinations of alleles are formed when gametes fuse at fertilisation. Some individuals may have mutations inherited from their parents. New genotypes are expressed to give the **variation** that occurs in each generation.

In the struggle for existence, it will be those organisms in a species which are better suited than others to their environment which will survive and reproduce to pass on their genes to the next generation. They are said to be better **adapted**.

Animals which are better adapted are most successful at finding food and water, at escaping from predators, surviving disease and finding mates. Successful plants are those with adaptations which give them the competitive edge in the struggle for resources.

Organisms which are better adapted than others reproduce and leave offspring, so the alleles which they pass on to their descendants become common. These alleles are the ones that give organisms the ability to compete successfully and survive. Less useful alleles, or harmful ones, become rare.

QUESTIONS

1. Explain why populations of organisms never grow to their full potential size.
2. Explain what you understand by the term 'struggle for existence'.
3. What causes the variation which appears in each generation?
4. Explain why some alleles are common, but some are rare.

7.4 *Natural selection*

A changing environment

If the environment changes, a species may have to change to suit the new conditions. If it does not it will die out (become extinct).

Some species do evolve to survive in new conditions. Our understanding of genetics combined with Darwin's theory of natural selection allows us to explain how this happens. Two examples demonstrate it very well.

Peppered moths

In Britain there is a species of moth that has two very distinct forms. One has fairly light coloured wings speckled with black dots. The other form is black. The difference is controlled by a gene. One allele gives speckled wings, another makes them black.

Until the Industrial Revolution took place in Britain, the speckled form was the common form all over the country. Its colour camouflages it very well against lichens that grow on trees. The black form only appeared as a rare mutation of the gene for wing colour. Every time one of these black moths appeared it was soon eaten by birds because it was easy for them to see when it rested on trees. The allele for black wings remained rare.

The two types of moth on a lichen covered tree and on bark covered in soot.

This painting of 1801 shows Coalbookdale, Shropshire where the Industrial Revolution began.

With the Industrial Revolution of the 18th and 19th centuries came air pollution from the burning of coal. In woodlands around the large industrial cities such as Manchester, sulphur dioxide in the smoke killed lichens and soot was deposited on trees. Now the background on which the moths settled was very different. The black forms were well camouflaged, and the speckled ones were easily spotted by birds.

The black moths were at an advantage because they were camouflaged and not eaten by predators. They survived to reproduce leaving more black-winged offspring than speckled-winged moths. Soon the population of peppered moths around the industrial cities changed. The black moths were now very common. By the beginning of the 20th century the black type made up over 90% of the peppered moth population in woodlands around industrial cities.

What was once a rare mutant allele had become common. The proportions of the two types changed as a result of natural selection.

Elsewhere in Britain where there was little air pollution the speckled type was still common. Now the air around industrial cities is much cleaner, the numbers of speckled peppered moths is beginning to increase.

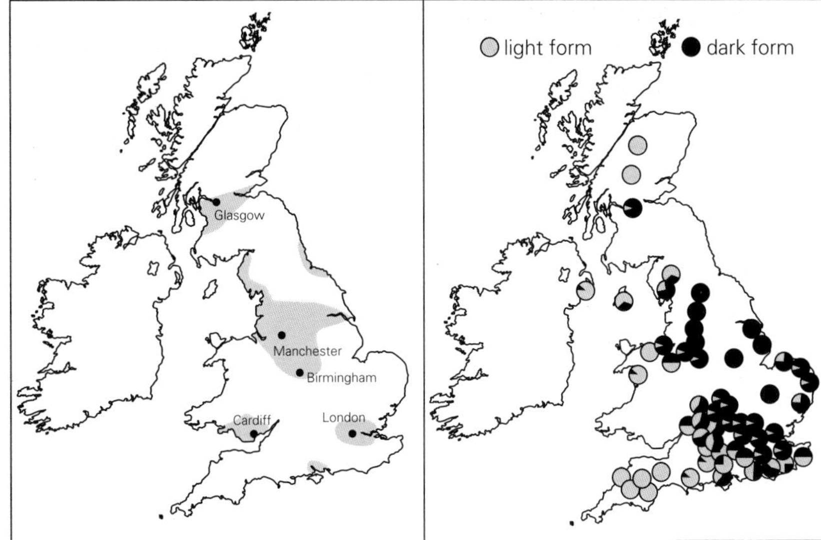

This shows the location of industrial areas and the distribution of the two types of peppered moth in the 1960s.

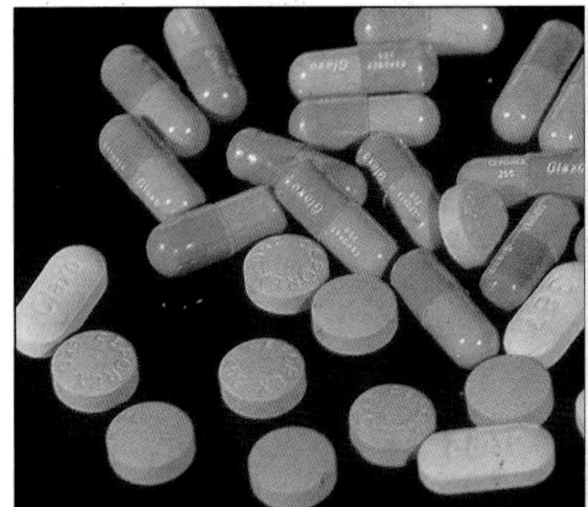

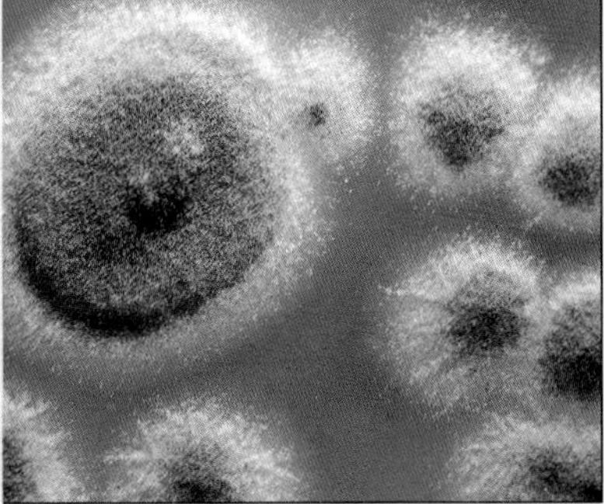

Antibiotics like penicillin are made by fungi and other microbes. They play a very important part in medical treatment of illnesses.

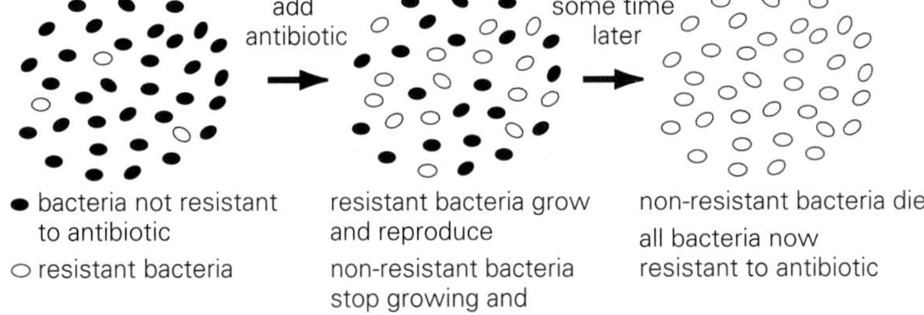

Among these bacteria are some that are resistant to the antibiotic. These spread at the expense of the non-resistant ones.

Antibiotic resistance in bacteria

Antibiotics have been used since the 1940s to treat people with bacterial diseases. By using them, we have changed the environment for bacteria. Any bacterium that has a mutation allowing it to overcome the effect of an antibiotic has an advantage. It will survive and reproduce well compared to other bacteria that are sensitive to the antibiotic.

Over the years the number of resistant types of bacteria has grown. Some of the antibiotics developed years ago are useless in the treatment of people with certain ailments because there are so many antibiotic-resistant bacteria. Some have multiple resistance to several antibiotics. It is therefore important that antibiotics are used only when necessary and that the search for new antibiotics continues.

QUESTIONS

1 Describe how selection occurred in the peppered moth in industrial areas of Britain.

2 Explain why the numbers of speckled peppered moths are increasing now.

3 Why is it dangerous to prescribe antibiotics very widely for all types of minor complaints?

4 Suggest why you are always told to finish a course of antibiotics even when you feel better after taking a few tablets.

7.5 Selective breeding

The origin of farming

About 10 000 years ago cereals such as wheat and barley were cultivated for the first time. Seed from wild grasses was sown and later gathered as a harvest of grain to make flour. Cereals chosen as crops by early farmers were derived from plants which had large grains and did not shed their seed easily. This made them easier to harvest. Some of this seed was saved for the next crop.

In this way people began to choose the best plants for cultivation. This type of selection, which is done by humans, is called **artificial selection**.

Breeding for success

Artificial selection involves breeding together those plants and animals with good qualities and preventing those with unwanted qualities from breeding. **Selective breeding** has changed many features of animals and plants: racehorses run faster; the growth rates and carcass weights of beef cattle and pigs have increased; the yields of crops such as wheat, barley and potatoes have improved. All this began long before the principles of genetics were understood.

This soay sheep is an ancient breed, similar to the sheep originally domesticated by early farmers.

Merino sheep is a modern breed. It has a very thick fleece.

Farmers want to grow varieties of cereals like rice that produce a good yield.

Potatoes were first grown in South America. In Peru and Bolivia there are still many local varieties of potato with many useful genes for future crop improvement.

Animal breeding

A breeder chooses animals which have the desired features, such as long wool length in sheep. These animals are then bred. Among the offspring will be some showing the desired feature. These are used to breed again, the rest are rejected.

Plant breeding

The same principles of selective breeding apply to improving plants. Varieties of plants grown for gardens often have certain colours or petal shapes which are controlled by a few genes. Many plants self-pollinate (see 6.5) so this makes keeping a variety constant easier than it is with animals.

Improving yields

Farmers are interested in features such as yield and need to improve this to cover their costs and show a profit. Livestock farmers need animals that grow fast and are efficient converters of food into meat or wool. They also want them to be free of disease.

Money paid to a dairy farmer is decided by the volume of milk delivered to a creamery and by the milk's butterfat content. Both can be improved by having the best milking cows fertilised by sperm from a bull that has genes for good milk production. By continually selecting the best milkers from the herd, a farmer can improve milk production significantly.

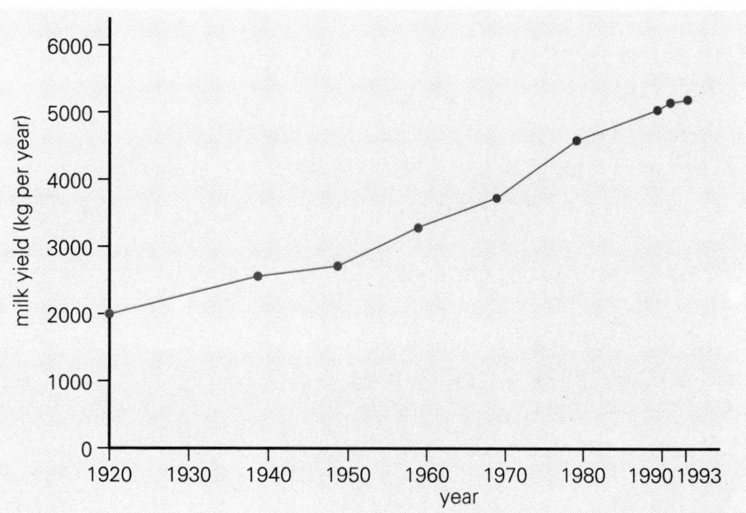

Selective breeding has more than doubled milk yield in cows in the UK.

The disadvantages

Breeding with individuals that are closely related brings problems. This is called **inbreeding**. As well as passing on promising genes, harmful ones may also be passed on and after many generations all sorts of defects may emerge.

You can see this in animal breeding. Some breeds of dog are prone to having weak hips. Inbred dogs are sometimes highly strung and have unreliable temperaments.

Plant breeders have produced many varieties over the years that may differ from each other by only a few genes. This can mean that they are all very susceptible to disease which can spread rapidly when large areas of land are devoted to the cultivation of one variety or several closely related varieties. In 1970, a fungal disease of maize spread throughout the corn belt of the USA.

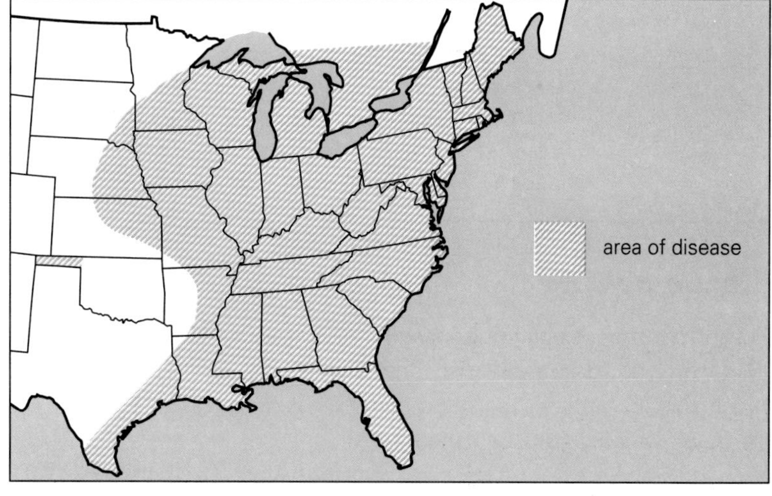

An epidemic of corn leaf blight affected nearly 90% of the maize-growing areas in the USA.

QUESTIONS

1 Outline the differences between natural selection and artificial selection.

2 Describe how an animal breeder might increase the milk production of a herd of dairy cattle.

3 Discuss the advantages and disadvantages of selective breeding.

7.6 Cloning

Often breeders only have a small number of plants or animals with desirable features. They need to increase the numbers quickly and if they relied on the plant's or animal's own method of reproduction they would have to wait a long time.

This problem can be solved by **cloning**. A clone is a group of organisms that are all genetically identical.

Cloning plants

It is possible to propagate many plants by taking cuttings from leaves, roots or stems. These methods have been used for many years for propagating horticultural crops such as ornamental plants. The diagram shows propagation by a stem cutting.

Tissue culture

A modern way of obtaining many identical plants is to use **tissue culture**. This is useful for plants that are difficult to propagate by seeds or cuttings. Whole plants are grown from individual cells or from small parts of plant tissue.

Cells are cultured in a nutrient medium which contains plant growth regulators (see 5.8) to stimulate growth of stems and roots. A small group of cells called a **callus** forms. Commercially, calluses are cut up into thousands of small pieces to produce many small plantlets. Once they have grown roots and leaves they are 'weaned' by planting them in sterile compost and keeping them in a glasshouse with a warm temperature, high humidity and high light intensity.

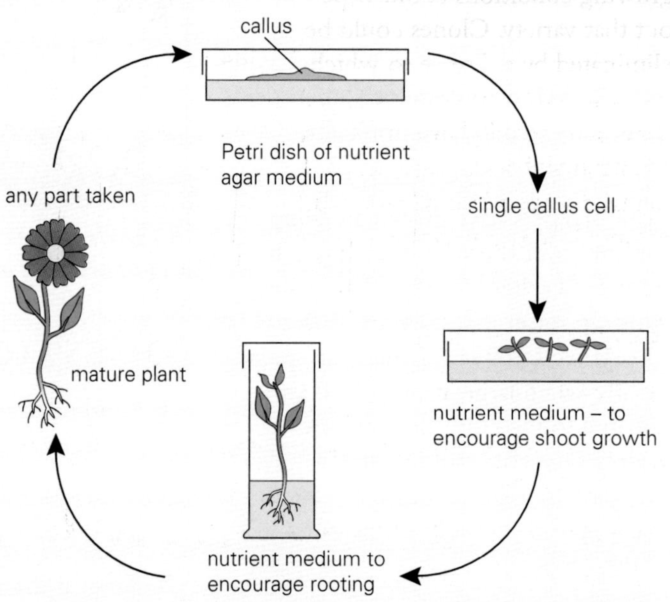

Cloning animals

Animals can also be cloned. If an early embryo is separated into cells then each of them will restart development. The animals that grow from these cells will all have the same genotype and will be clones.

A similar technique is used in cattle breeding. A good milking cow can only produce one or two calves every year. This means that she can only pass on her genes to about ten offspring at best in her lifetime and of these there is a chance that 50% of them will be male.

If she is treated with hormones to make her produce many eggs at one time, the eggs can be removed and fertilised with sperm from a prize bull. The female embryos which form are cloned. The clones are then implanted into several cows. Using this method of embryo transfer, genes from the prize milker are passed on to many more female offspring than would normally be possible.

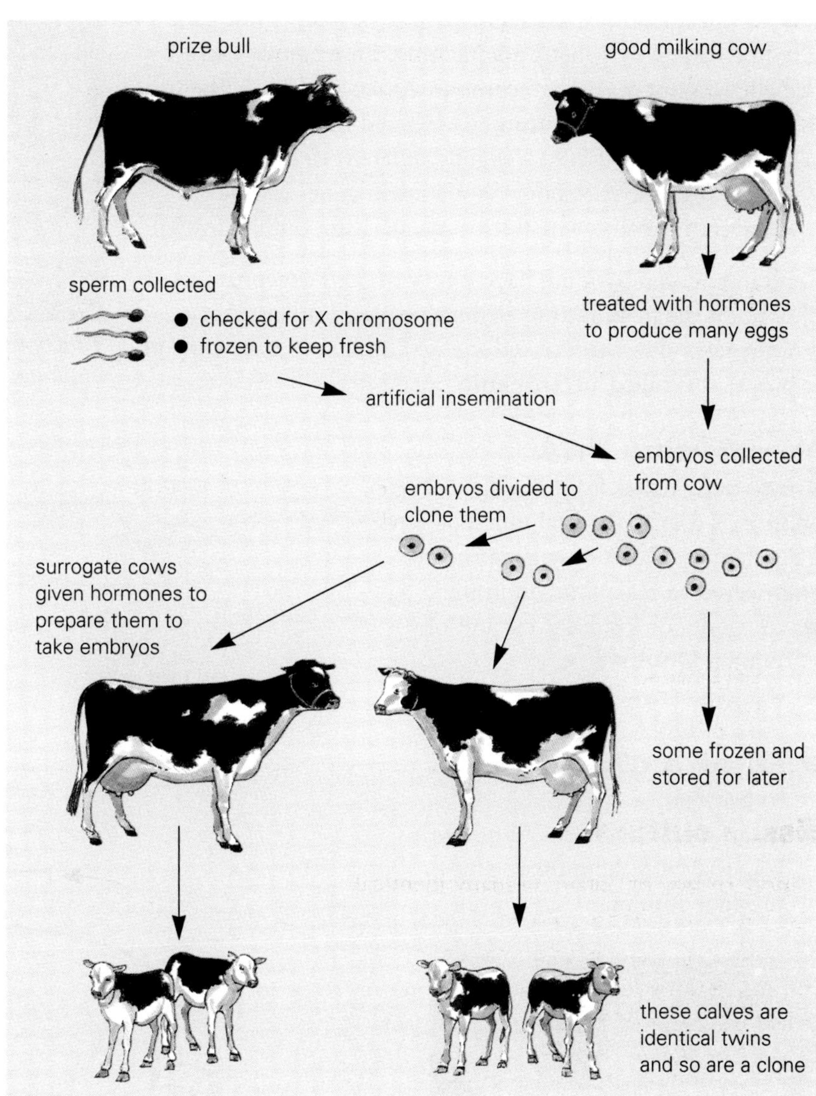

Disadvantages of cloning

There is very little – if any – genetic variation among the members of a clone, particularly in plants. If farmers and growers grow just a few clones of a particular variety or species, then there is a high probability that a disease or a change in climate or growing conditions could wipe out that variety. Clones could be eliminated by a disease to which the crop has no resistance. This is happening to oil palms in Thailand and Malaysia where a fungal disease is killing palms that belong to the same clone.

QUESTIONS

1 Explain the term clone.

2 Describe how plants are propagated by tissue culture.

3 Explain the dangers of cloning crop plants on a large scale.

4 Describe how animals are cloned.

5 In the future we might be able to produce clones of people who are resistant to certain diseases or very good at playing tennis. Discuss the ethical reasons surrounding cloning humans by using artificial methods.

7.7 Genetic engineering

Cut and paste

All species contain DNA and so the same code is used to specify the sequence of amino acids in proteins. Since all organisms use the same code, genes (short lengths of DNA) from one species can be placed into the DNA of another. This is **genetic engineering**.

This cotton crop has been genetically engineered to produce red cotton.

Why change?

People with genetic disorders may suffer terribly. They can often be helped by genetic engineering, for example many diabetics cannot make the hormone insulin (see 3.4). The insulin used to treat them can be extracted from pigs. Unfortunately, pig insulin is slightly different to human insulin and this can cause problems. Now human genes can be inserted into bacteria which then manufacture human insulin.

Several species, including bacteria, yeasts and sheep, are used like this in the manufacture of hormones and other substances. An organism that has received a gene from another species and expresses it is called a **transgenic** organism.

Transferring DNA

Transferring genes from one species to another is done in several different ways. The diagram shows how bacteria are engineered to make human insulin:

- the gene for insulin is cut out of human DNA
- the gene is inserted into a small loop of DNA
- the loop of DNA is transferred to bacteria
- given ideal conditions for growth, bacteria with the human gene produce insulin.

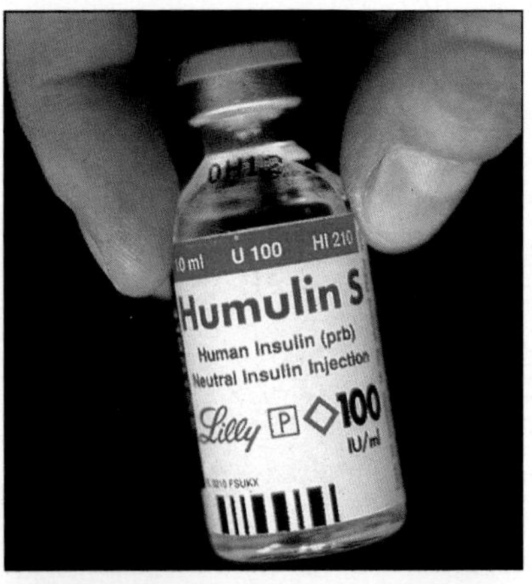

This is human insulin – produced by genetically engineered bacteria.

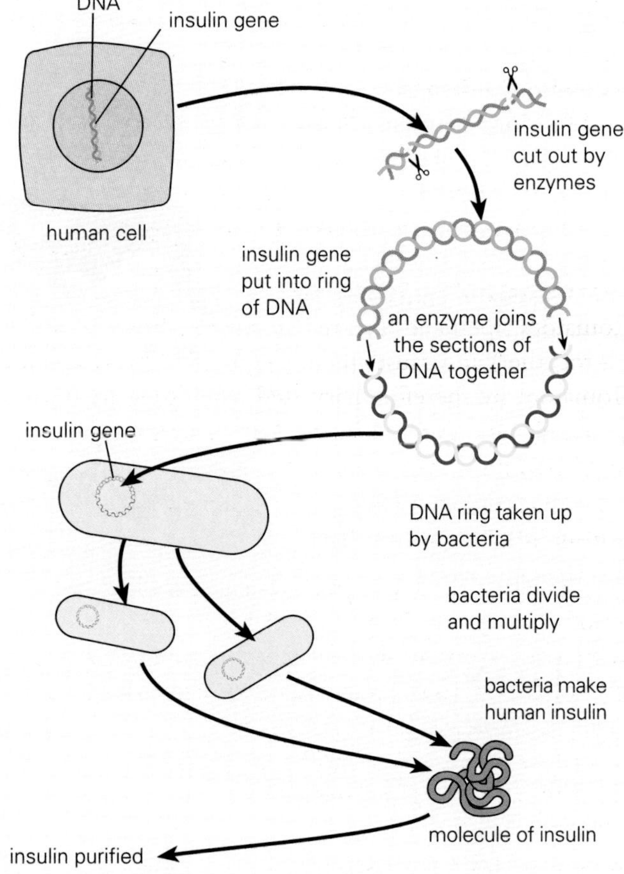

When genetically engineered bacteria multiply they clone the gene inserted into their DNA.

Transgenic sheep are used to produce several human proteins such as a blood-clotting factor. It is not possible to put the gene into an adult sheep. The gene is first cloned in bacteria and then the DNA is inserted into early sheep embryos so that all the cells of the body have the human gene. It is then possible to make sure that the gene is only expressed in the mammary glands so that the human protein is in the sheep's milk.

These are transgenic sheep. Their milk contains a human protein which could be used to treat people with the lung disease emphysema.

A cure for genetic diseases?

Genetic diseases can only be cured when the gene is inserted into human embryos so that all the cells of the body receive a copy of the normal allele. This has not been done yet as a British Government committee recommended that it was unethical to insert genes into human embryos because the gene could then be inherited. However, if the genes are inserted into human embryos, the number of people suffering from genetic diseases could be significantly reduced.

Transgenic plants

Another use for genetic engineering is to alter crops to meet customers' demand for certain characteristics. Genetically modified organisms that have been released for commercial purposes include a modified yeast for bread making, a variety of oil-seed rape resistant to a herbicide and a tomato which does not go squashy.

The non-squashy tomato

When tomatoes ripen and turn red an enzyme breaks down pectin (a substance which holds cell walls together) and causes them to go soft. This makes it difficult for farmers to pick them. Tomatoes are therefore harvested when they are unripe and before they have developed their full flavour. Chemicals such as ethene are used to ripen the tomatoes artificially. Food processing uses heat to reduce the activity of the enzyme when making tomato sauces and purees. Heating tomatoes changes their taste so that food additives have to be used to restore the taste.

Genetic engineers have developed a tomato that does not become soft as it ripens. Tomato DNA has been modified so that less enzyme is produced. The tomatoes are not harvested so early: they are left to ripen and develop their full flavour without going squashy. The advantages are

- the tomatoes have a better taste
- the tomatoes have a longer shelf life
- less energy is used in processing
- fewer food additives are used.

Puree made from these tomatoes will be widely available in British supermarkets in 1997.

QUESTIONS

1 Explain the following terms: **a** gene cloning, **b** a transgenic organism.

2 Describe the steps involved in the production of human insulin by bacteria indicating where enzymes are used.

3 Make two lists of arguments, one *for* and one *against* genetic engineering.

SECTION D: QUESTIONS

1 Make a table to show the differences between arthropods and vertebrates.

2 *Bryophyllum*, shown in the diagram, develops tiny plantlets on the edges of its leaves. These drop off and grow roots. The tiny plants form a clone as they are all genetically identical.

a State the name of this type of reproduction and explain its advantages.
b Explain why the plants are genetically identical.
c Select one of the following and describe how you could investigate its effect on the growth of *Bryophyllum*: light intensity, the wavelength of light, hours of light, temperature, mineral nutrition. Remember to include all practical precautions and state what measurements you are going to make.
d Explain the advantage of using clones in investigations like this.

3 Some broad bean plants were grown in a garden. When they produced pods (fruits), 40 seeds were collected from six different plants and weighed. The results are shown below.

Mass of each seed (g)									
1.0	1.2	2.3	1.6	1.4	2.4	1.3	2.5	2.2	2.3
1.2	1.0	2.4	1.5	2.6	2.3	1.7	2.4	1.5	1.9
1.2	2.1	2.4	2.1	2.0	2.3	1.7	1.5	1.3	2.0
1.7	2.8	1.2	2.3	1.7	1.8	2.2	2.0	2.6	1.7

a Draw a tally table to find out how many seeds there were in each group. The groups can be 1.0–1.1 g; 1.2–1.3g, etc., to 2.8–2.9g.
b Plot the data from your tally table as a histogram.
c State the name of this type of variation.
d What is the evidence to support the idea that there are two types of bean plant – one with heavier seeds than the other?
e Suggest four environmental factors that may be responsible for the differences noted in **d**.

4a Name the two substances that are found in chromosomes and describe briefly how they are organised.
b Explain the relationship between genes and chromosomes.
This diagram shows the chromosomes from a human cell. They have been arranged into pairs.

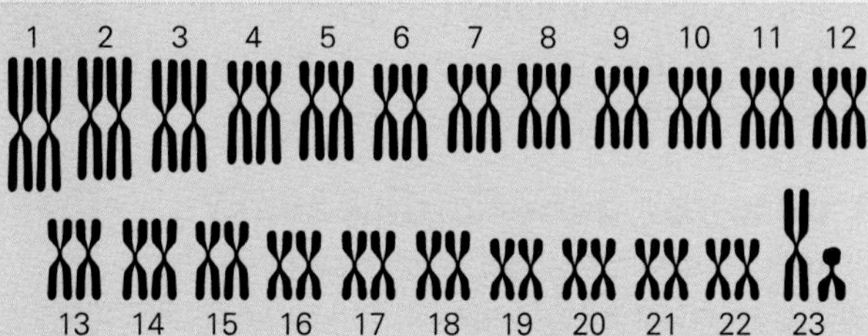

c State the total number of chromosomes in this cell.
d Could this cell be:
  i a sperm cell
  ii a red blood cell
  iii from a female
  iv from a child with Down's syndrome?
Give a reason for each answer.
e Describe what happens to chromosomes during mitosis.

5a Name the organs in which meiosis occurs in humans.
b Copy the table below and complete it by indicating whether each feature applies to mitosis, meiosis or both. Put a tick where you think the answer is yes, and a cross where you think the answer is no.

Feature	Mitosis	Meiosis
occurs in growth and repair		
movement of chromosomes occurs		
daughter cells are identical to the parent cell		
chromosome number is halved		
produces haploid cells from diploid cells		
daughter cells can be different from each other		

c Explain what happens during meiosis to bring about variation in the daughter cells.

6a Name the parts of a flower where the male and female gametes are produced.
A gene in thale cress controls the colour of the leaves. Green leaf colour is dominant to yellow. (Follow the steps in 6.9 when doing **b** and **d**.)

b A plant that is homozygous for green is crossed with one that is homozygous for yellow. Use a genetic diagram to predict the colour of the leaves of the next generation.

c In order to carry out the cross in **b** the two plants were cross-pollinated. Explain what this means. When the seeds were ripe they were collected and sown to give the F_1 generation. When these plants flowered they were left to self-pollinate.

d Use a genetic diagram to show the possible genotypes and phenotypes in the F_2 generation. Include a diagram to show all the possible combinations.

e What is the expected ratio of green and yellow plants in the F_2 generation?

7 In tabby cats the pattern of stripes is controlled by a gene. The allele for parallel stripes (T) is dominant to the allele for blotched stripes (t).

a Use genetic diagrams to show the types of cats expected in the following crosses: TT × Tt; Tt × Tt; TT × tt, tt × tt, TT × TT; Tt × tt.

b Explain why it is possible to state the genotype of a tabby with blotched stripes, but not one with parallel stripes.

c Explain why two tabbies with blotched stripes cannot produce a kitten with parallel stripes.

8 The pedigree shows a family some of whom have Huntington's chorea. The symptoms usually appear between the ages of 35 and 40.

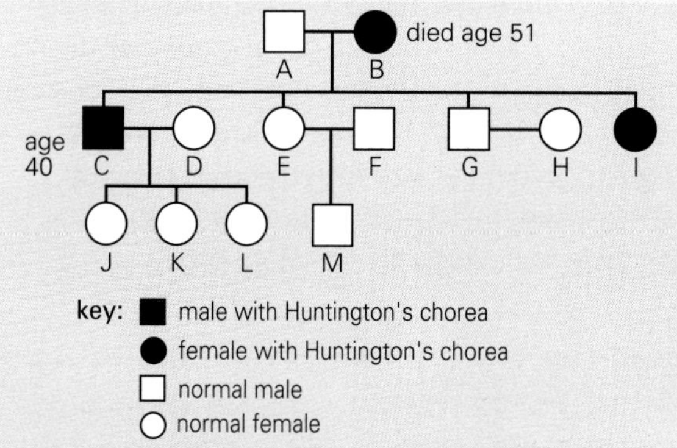

a What is the probability of **K** developing the disease? Draw a genetic diagram to explain your answer.

b A genetic test shows that **E** does not have the allele for the disease. How does this affect the probability of **M** inheriting it?

c Discuss the way in which a genetic counsellor might explain the inheritance of Huntington's chorea to a family like the one in the pedigree above.

9 Aleksei, the Tsarevitch of Russia, suffered from the sex-linked disease haemophilia (see 6.13). He inherited the allele for haemophilia from his great grandmother, Queen Victoria. The pedigree shows part of his family tree.

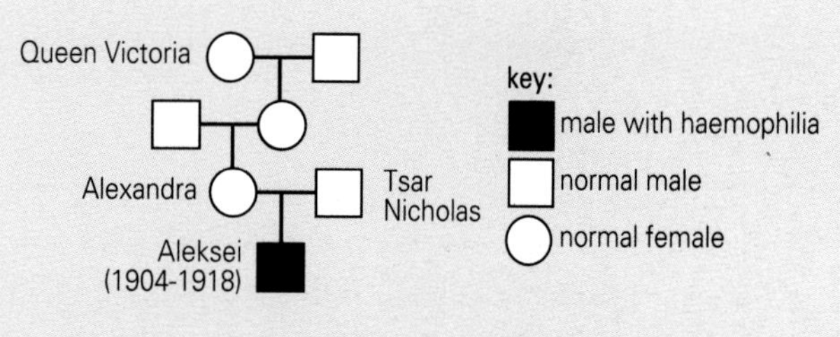

Use genetic diagrams to explain the following:

a Aleksei inherited haemophilia even though his father and grandfather did not have the disease.

b Haemophilia cannot pass from a man to his sons unless their mother is a carrier of the disease.

c There are very few women with haemophilia.

10 Some rocks such as the Burgess Shale in Canada are extremely rich in fossils of many different species, which have been extinct for many millions of years. A rich deposit, like the Burgess Shale, tells us about the organisms that lived when the rock was formed and what the environment was like. Many of the organisms in the Burgess Shale are arthropods although they do not resemble any that exist today.

a What feature of arthropods explains why they are likely to be preserved as fossils?

b Explain why some rocks, like the Burgess Shale, contain many fossils.

c Explain how studying fossils can help us find out how species have evolved.

SECTION D: QUESTIONS

11 When bacteria are spread on agar in a Petri dish they grow into colonies. Each colony arises from one bacterial cell. The bacterium *Salmonella typhi* causes food poisoning. An outbreak of food poisoning was traced to some meat. A sample of bacteria from the meat was grown and then treated in the following way:

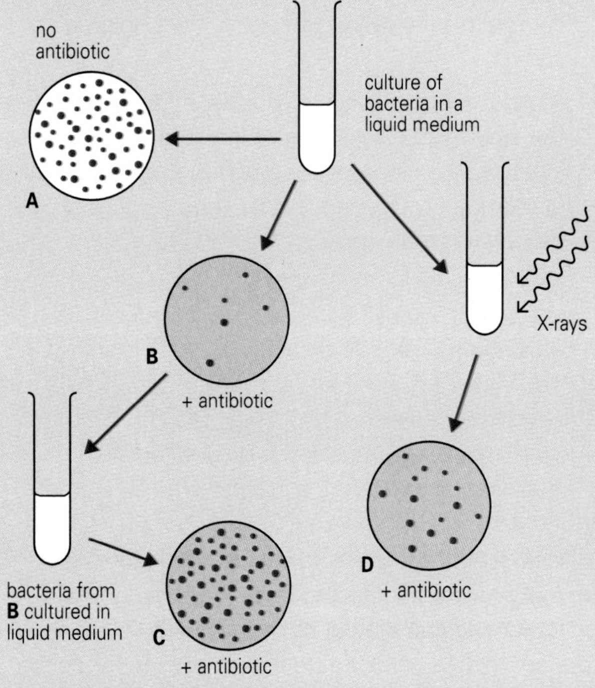

a What is an antibiotic?

b Explain the following:

i the purpose of dish **A**

ii the reason for the presence of a few colonies in dish **B**, but more in dish **C**.

c Explain why more bacteria grew in **D** than in **B**.

d Suggest why it is important to test food poisoning bacteria (as in dish **B**) before choosing a type of antibiotic to treat people.

12 A snail known as *Partula* lived only on the Pacific island of Moorea. Then humans introduced the Giant African Snail to Moorea because it was good to eat, but it soon became a pest. A carnivorous snail, *Euglandina*, was introduced to control the numbers of the Giant African Snail. However, *Euglandina* preferred to eat *Partula*, and *Partula* soon became extinct in the wild.

a Explain why some species are only found on islands.

b Discuss why the introduction of animals and plants to new habitats should be carefully controlled.

c Make a list of other species which have become extinct over the last 200 years and try to find out the reasons in each case.

Seven different species of *Partula* were rescued from Moorea just before they became extinct on the island. Five of the species have now bred successfully in captivity and it is hoped that they can be reintroduced to Moorea. Other species, such as the Hawaiian goose and the Arabian oryx (a type of antelope), have been saved from extinction and released into the wild after several years of captive breeding in zoos. In this way zoos can help to maintain biodiversity. Many plant species are also in danger of becoming extinct and these too can be rescued and grown in botanic gardens.

d Explain:

i why we should try to maintain biodiversity

ii what we can do to reduce the numbers of species that become extinct.

13 Darwin's finches live on the Galapagos Islands and they are thought to have evolved from a species with a large beak that lives on the mainland of South America. Suggest how the four species shown in 7.3 may have evolved from the mainland species. Use the following terms in your answer: variation in beak size, competition, adaptation, natural selection.

14 Zimbabwe suffers from severe drought. One farmer has used selective breeding to help his farm survive. He has selected strains of grasses that his cattle like to eat and that grow well in dry conditions. He has bred miniature cattle (the smallest being 0.6 m) which are small enough to graze on the grass that grows beneath his Pecan nut trees. These miniature cattle grow well during the dry season and they do not produce any calves until the rains start. They eat little but produce more milk for their size than bigger cattle. The farmer used the three breeds of cattle shown in the table to develop his miniature breed.

Breed	Height (metres)	Features
Tuli (African)	2.0–2.5	drought and disease resistant produces milk for 6–7 months every year
Redpoll (European)	1.5–1.8	tolerant of hot and cold dual purpose – milk and beef produces high yields of milk produces milk for 10 months every year
Jersey (European)	1.3–1.5	tolerant of hot and cold produces lower yields of milk milk has high fat content produces milk for 10 months every year

a State the features that you think the farmer selected from each breed of cattle.

b Suggest the steps he might have taken to breed his miniature cattle.

c Explain why this is an example of artificial selection.

d Explain how selective breeding of cattle and grass helps his farm survive during a drought.

The Munchken breed of cat has front legs that are only 80 mm long and are shorter than its hind legs.

e Discuss whether there should be any restrictions on the selective breeding of animals.

15 The table shows features of four varieties of wheat.

Variety	Yield	Resistance to disease	Resistance to water shortage	Height (m)
A	very high	low	low	1.0
B	high	high	low	0.3
C	medium	high	high	0.3
D	low	low	low	0.5

a Explain what is meant by the term selective breeding.

b Why might a farmer choose to grow varieties **B** and **C** at the same time?

c Explain how a plant breeder might use selective breeding to produce a very high yielding dwarf variety (0.3 m high).

d Variety **D** has good bread-making qualities. How might a plant breeder use the other varieties to improve **D**'s yield and resistance to disease.

16 Human growth hormone promotes growth. It is a protein made of 188 amino acids.

a How many bases in DNA code for this protein? Explain your answer.

The gene for human growth hormone has been isolated and cloned in bacteria.

Genetic engineering involves removing a gene from one species and placing it into the DNA of another species. The gene for human growth hormone has been removed from human DNA and inserted into bacteria. When these genetically engineered bacteria divide they produce more copies of the gene. This is called gene cloning.

b Outline the method used to clone human genes in bacteria.

Genetically engineered bacteria make human growth hormone and a similar hormone found in cattle. Human growth hormone made by bacteria is used to treat children who do not grow normally. There may be a genetic reason for abnormal growth in children or they may have received radiation treatment for leukaemia or have had a brain tumour. Growth hormone from cattle (also known as bovine growth hormone) is injected into cows to increase their milk yield.

c State the advantages and disadvantages of using genetic engineering to produce:

i human growth hormone

ii bovine growth hormone.

d Discuss the arguments for and against putting genes into human embryos.

17 Most humans are genetically different. An exception is identical twins.

a Explain why identical twins have the same DNA.

b Describe how animals are cloned so that they have identical DNA.

c Discuss the advantages and the disadvantages of cloning farm animals.

8.1 *Habitats and communities*

Estuaries

An estuary is a widening of a river as it flows into the sea. Here, fresh water mixes with salt water. Most plants cannot survive in estuaries because it is too salty and the shifting sands and mud make it difficult to put down roots. Rivers carry dissolved minerals, which are absorbed by tiny algae growing on the surface of the mud, and small pieces of food suspended in the water, brought by rivers and by the tide. Many bacteria and small invertebrates such as ragworms, lugworms, mud snails, cockles, tellins and small shrimps feed on these suspended food particles.

The conditions in estuaries change with the tides. At high tide the water is very salty; at low tide it is less salty. The temperature increases at low tide and mud dries out and contains little oxygen.

Few animals are adapted to these conditions, but those that can cope are found in huge numbers because of the rich supply of food. At low tide shore birds such as shelducks, curlews, plovers and oystercatchers feed on these invertebrates. At high tide when the water is too deep for birds, fish feed on invertebrates instead. Other birds like cormorants dive for the fish.

Mudflats look very lifeless. There are no large plants and no large animals, but many shore birds feed there.

This oystercatcher finds its food by probing in the estuary mud with its beak.

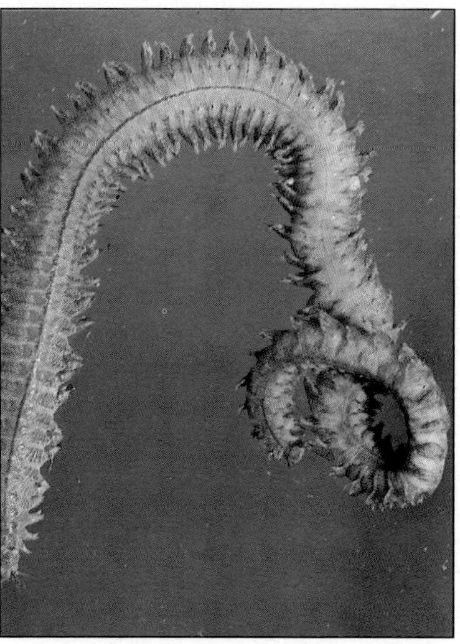

This ragworm is one of the invertebrates which provide food for birds and fish.

What happens in the spring?

Many birds that feed on estuaries migrate north to the Arctic to breed, where the days are long and the food supply even richer. Fish, e.g. bass, migrate into estuaries to breed and eat large numbers of invertebrates.

Habitat

An estuary is a **habitat**. A habitat is where organisms live. You can think of a habitat as an organism's 'address'. Habitats provide the requirements or **resources** for plants, animals and microbes. Migrant birds use the resources of two or more habitats.

All the organisms in a habitat form a **community**. Not many species live in estuaries because the conditions are so extreme. Other communities, like those in woodlands and coral reefs, have many different species.

Animals like cockles and ragworms belong to the communities living in estuaries. They feed on the food brought in by the river and the sea, they burrow into mud, they breed here and they are eaten by larger animals such as birds and fish. Their **niche** is their 'way of life' or 'profession' in this community. It describes the way they interact with other species and with their physical environment. Ragworms are scavengers - that is their niche.

Feeding preferences

Even though there is a large food supply on mudflats and estuaries, different birds do not feed in the same way. Some, like terns, dive for fish; plovers, oystercatchers, curlews and knots probe the mud with their beaks. Shelducks sieve small worms and mud snails from the surface of the mud. These birds are specialised feeders only taking a few food species. They have different niches which means that food resources are shared between them.

RESOURCES

	Animals	Plants
water	✓	✓
light	✗	✓ } for: photosynthesis
CO_2	✗	✓ } for: photosynthesis
O_2 for respiration	✓	✓
living space	for: territories, nesting sites, shelter from weather and predators	for: root growth in soil, spreading leaves to absorb light
minerals	calcium, phosphate, iron and others	nitrate, phosphate, potassium and others

These are the resources that habitats provide.

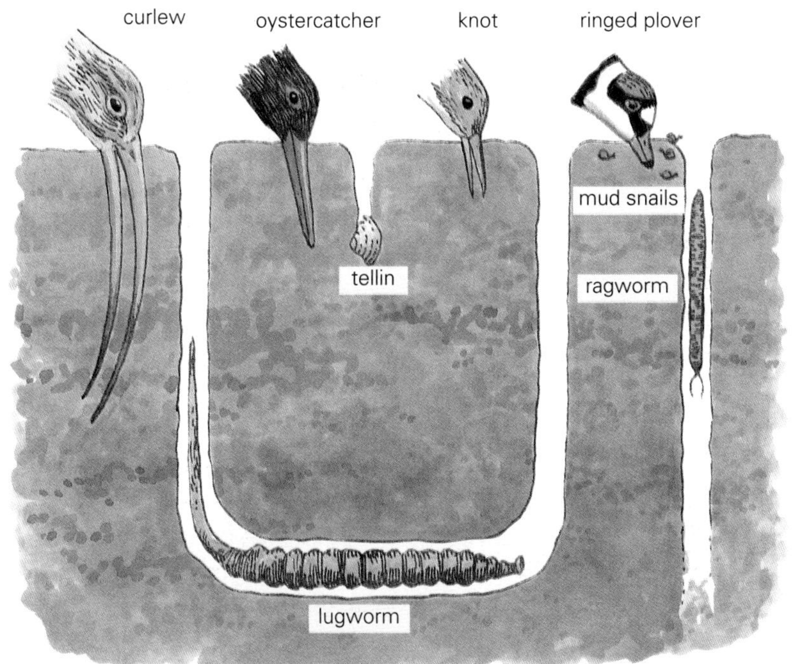

This shows how four birds search for food at different depths in the mud so they do not compete for the same food.

QUESTIONS

1. Explain the terms habitat, community and niche.
2. Describe the changes that occur in an estuary every twelve hours.
3. Explain why only a few different species live in estuaries.
4. Why do estuaries attract so many birds?
5. Explain how the food resources in an estuary are shared between the different bird species.

8.2 *The physical environment*

Ecology

Living things are very complex. They do not live in isolation. Animals, plants and microbes live in communities where they are influenced by many factors. Organisms are affected by their physical surroundings and other organisms in the same habitat. The study of how organisms interact with their environment is called **ecology**.

The animals and plants in this dry forest in the tropics have to cope with high temperatures and little water.

Physical factors

The physical (or non-living) conditions influencing organisms determine the characteristics of each habitat. Some of these are:

- temperature
- rainfall
- light
- soil type
- shelter
- concentrations of oxygen and carbon dioxide.

To survive in any habitat an organism must be adapted to cope with the physical conditions. These are different in each habitat. For example, tropical frogs cannot survive in very cold places like the Arctic. Few fish can survive outside water for very long. No plant can grow at the bottom of the ocean because there is no light for photosynthesis. In an estuary most sea and river life cannot cope with the changing salt concentrations: those that are adapted to cope with these changes thrive in large numbers.

Four main habitats

There are four main groups of habitats:

- land habitats, such as deserts, forests, grassland
- freshwater habitats, such as puddles, ponds, streams, lakes, rivers
- marine habitats, such as open ocean, seashore, ocean floor, coral reef
- estuaries that have water which changes between salty and fresh.

Each of these habitats has different physical factors. Some habitats, such as estuaries and deserts (see 8.9), have very extreme conditions and the communities have few species. Others, such as oak woodland, are very species rich: they have great biodiversity.

Plants

Light is necessary for plants to photosynthesise. Soil factors, such as depth, soil type, soil pH and mineral content, control where plants can grow. Some plants only grow during one season of the year when conditions are favourable. For the rest of the year they are dormant as seeds or bulbs.

Wood anemones grow in woodlands; they photosynthesise and flower in the spring before the trees are in leaf.

Stonefly nymphs live in clean, unpolluted rivers and streams where there is plenty of oxygen dissolved in the water.

Animals

Physical factors influence animal distribution. Unlike plants, animals can move from place to place, but when an animal reaches a new habitat it may not be able to survive there. It may not fit into the community already established there.

Tench can live in water with little dissolved oxygen.

Measuring physical factors

Factors such as temperature, humidity, pH and wind speed are fairly easy to measure. However, all these change during the day and throughout the year, so it is better to take continuous readings rather than occasional ones. Often it is the highest, or lowest temperature that determines where an organism can live. It is quite a task to think of all the physical factors that *might* influence a species and then organise ways of measuring them over a long period of time.

Here three physical factors are being measured and recorded with a data logger.

QUESTIONS

1 Make a table to show the main physical factors that influence the following habitats: pond, rocky seashore, woodland, desert.

2 List the physical factors that determine where plants can grow.

3 Plan an investigation to find out what physical factors control the distribution of wood anemones.

8.3 Ecosystems

Taking everything together

The communities in different habitats are not the same because the physical factors influencing the habitats are different. The term **ecosystem** is used to describe a habitat, the community that lives there and the physical factors that influence it. All the individuals of one species living in an ecosystem make a **population**.

Biotic factors

The different species making up a community interact with each other. For example, plants may be pollinated by insects and eaten by grazers such as rabbits. The interactions between living organisms in an ecosystem are called **biotic factors**. Other biotic factors include competition, parasites and disease.

Think of an ecosystem as a jigsaw consisting of all the living organisms and their physical surroundings.

Closed and open

Some ecosystems are 'closed' because few animals migrate in or out and all food resources are produced within the ecosystem. Most ponds and forests are 'closed' ecosystems. Others, like estuaries, are 'open' because food enters the ecosystem from elsewhere and some of the animals in the community may be visitors not permanent residents.

A woodland ecosystem

Oak is a producer making food by photosynthesis.

This fungus is a decomposer – it feeds on dead and decaying matter in the soil.

These looper caterpillars are primary consumers feeding on oak leaves.

Moles are carnivores, they feed on earthworms.

This great tit is a secondary consumer. It eats caterpillars and other insects.

Earthworms are decomposers, they feed on dead oak leaves.

Owls are carnivores, and tertiary consumer They feed on mice an small birds.

Feeding levels

The organisms in an ecosystem are divided into five groups according to the way in which they feed.

Producers These are green plants and algae. They convert light energy from the Sun into chemical energy as food. Plants use light energy, to convert carbon dioxide into sugars and other carbohydrates. Producers provide food directly or indirectly for all the organisms in a community.

Primary consumers These are herbivores – animals that feed on plants.

Secondary consumers These are carnivores – animals which eat other animals. They are predators.

Tertiary consumers These are 'top' carnivores that eat other carnivores.

Decomposers These organisms obtain their energy by feeding on the remains of dead plants and animals.

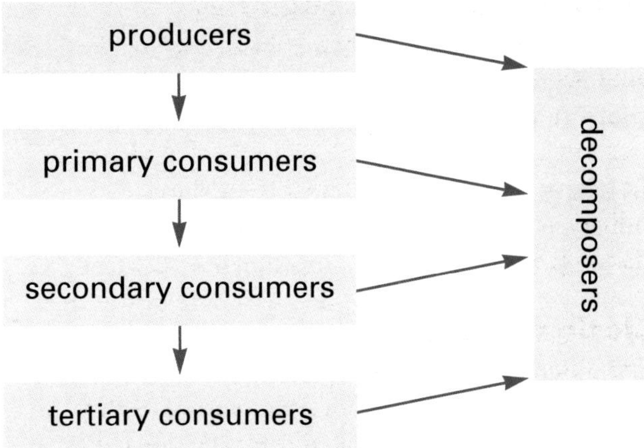

*A food chain shows that energy passes through **feeding (trophic) levels** from plants to consumers and decomposers.*

Food chains and webs

Food chains are usually short with no more than four or five links. In an ecosystem like an oak woodland it is possible to draw many different food chains. Here are three examples that you can follow in the food web shown. Note that the producer in all three is the oak.

oak leaves ➤ caterpillar ➤ great tit ➤ tawny owl

dead oak leaves ➤ earthworm ➤ mole ➤ weasel

acorns ➤ mice ➤ tawny owl

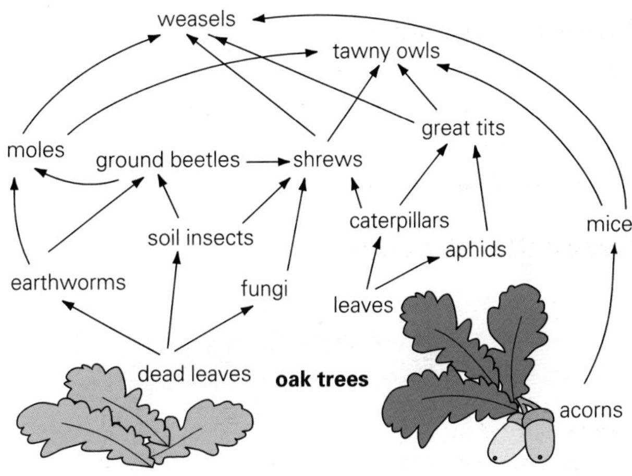

*Food chains can be combined to give a **food web**.*

You can see that many primary consumers and decomposers feed directly on oak leaves or acorns. Animals like caterpillars and earthworms provide food for the small birds that are in turn eaten by 'top' carnivores such as owls and weasels. In Britain, oaks support over 200 different species. Some of these, like caterpillars, feed on oaks; others, such as tawny owls, use old trees for nesting.

QUESTIONS

1 Draw up a table to explain the following terms: producer, primary consumer, secondary consumer, tertiary consumer, decomposer. Include in your table the names of species found in an oak woodland at each feeding level.

2 Explain the importance of oak trees in a woodland ecosystem.

3 In oak woodland name the animal(s) that feeds

a both as a primary and a secondary consumer

b both as a secondary and a tertiary consumer

c on earthworms.

4 Make a table to show the biotic and physical factors that you think may influence an oak woodland.

5 Explain the difference between *open* and *closed* ecosystems.

8.4 *Sampling ecosystems*

Making lists

When studying an ecosystem it is usual to make a list of all the species that live there and use identification keys to help you name them. An ecosystem may contain many different species of insects, fungi and bacteria so it can take a long time to identify them all.

Taking samples

You can count all the trees in a wood. It takes time, but it can be done. Large animals such as roe deer and tawny owls can be counted but with difficulty as they are not always easy to see. However, you cannot count *all* the caterpillars in the wood. To find the numbers of small animals, you have to take a **sample** and then make an estimate of the numbers in the population.

A sample is a small area of the ecosystem that can be studied carefully. This small area could be one square metre. As it is unlikely that any one square metre will be representative of the whole wood, several samples are taken at random. The results are averaged to give an estimate for the woodland.

These students are using a computer program to identify woodland plants.

Using a quadrat to measure the number of plants growing in a wood.

Sampling plants

A **quadrat** is a frame made of wood, metal or plastic. It covers a known area such as $1\,m^2$ or $0.25\,m^2$. The number of plants growing within the area of the quadrat are counted. If the total area of a wood is known then the total number of plants can be estimated.

Quadrats can be used to find out if plants are distributed randomly or in clusters. For instance, you might notice that there are more species growing at the edge of the wood than beneath the trees. You could make the prediction that the number of species is associated with the light intensity. The canopy of the trees may absorb so much light that only a few species can grow beneath them.

Placing quadrats along a line (known as a **transect**) into the wood allows you to take samples at regular intervals to test your prediction. You can also use a light meter to measure the light intensity at each sampling point on the transect.

Percentage cover

Some small plants, e.g. grass, grow in dense clumps so it is not easy to count them. Measuring **percentage cover** is easier. A quadrat divided into 100 smaller squares with string or wire is placed on the ground. Squares completely filled by one species are counted. Squares that are only partly filled are estimated in terms of full squares and added to make a total. One square is equal to 1% cover.

How to use a quadrat to estimate percentage cover.

Percentage cover is a more useful measurement than counting individual plants because it shows how efficient different species are at capturing light energy. A quadrat may include a large number of grasses, with small percentage cover, and one bramble with many large leaves. Counting numbers will underestimate the importance of the bramble in the ecosystem.

Sampling animals

Animals present many problems because they move, burrow into trees or into the soil. Many are active only at night or are present in ecosystems for short periods during the year. Ecologists use a variety of techniques for collecting small animals. Some of them are shown here.

Counting larger animals can be difficult. Birds may be caught and rings placed on their legs. Counting large flocks of birds or herds of deer is done by counting a small group and estimating how many groups of that size there are altogether. Wardens in African game reserves often use aerial photographs to count the numbers of animals like zebras and wildebeest.

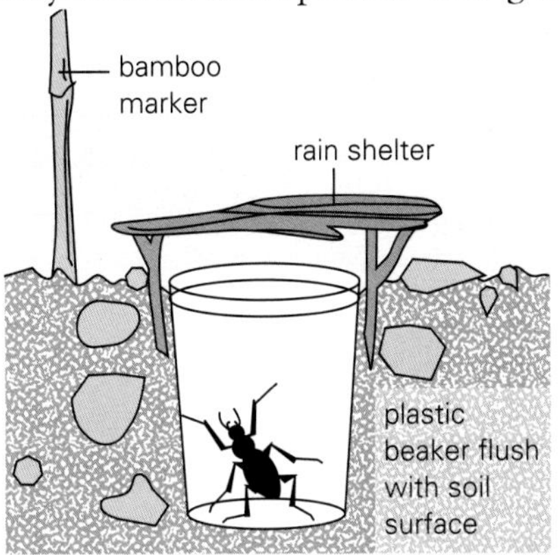

Pitfall traps are useful for collecting nocturnal ground-dwelling animals like this carabid beetle.

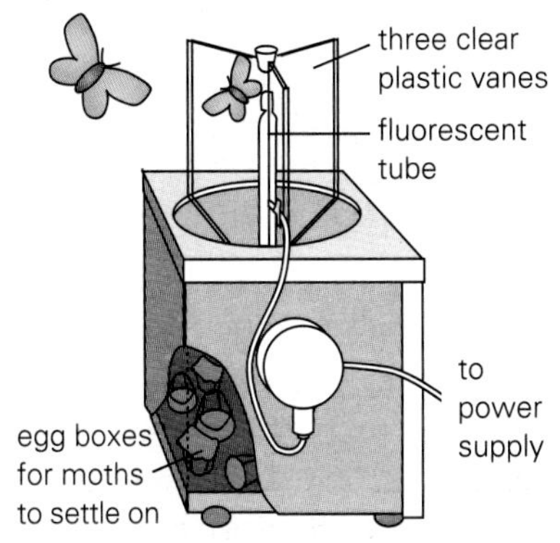

Moth traps use light to attract these night-flying animals.

Insects and spiders can be collected using a sweep net.

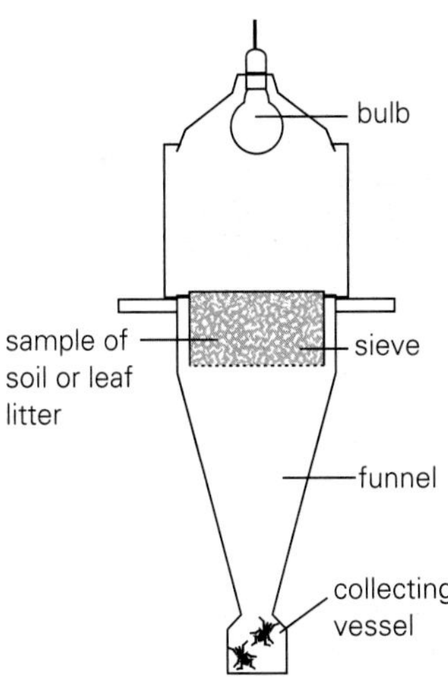

This Tullgren funnel is used to collect small soil animals. They move down the funnel away from the light and are collected in the liquid at the bottom.

QUESTIONS

1 Describe how you would use a quadrat to find the numbers of buttercups growing in a field.

2 Describe how you would use a quadrat to find the percentage cover of grass in a wood.

3 Describe three ways to collect small woodland animals such as beetles, spiders and aphids.

4 Plan an investigation to find out if light intensity, temperature or soil moisture influences the distribution of plants in a wood.

8.5 *Pyramids*

Building pyramids

Counting numbers of plants and animals in a field shows that there are huge numbers of plants. These are the producers which provide food for primary consumers. The number of herbivorous animals like aphids, beetles and caterpillars is smaller. There are fewer secondary consumers such as ladybirds, and even fewer birds feeding as 'top' carnivores (or tertiary consumers) on herbivores and carnivores.

You can plot the number in each feeding level as a **pyramid of numbers** (see pyramid 1). Notice as you move up the pyramid the numbers get smaller.

This old meadow is a very rich habitat full of many different species.

Not so simple

In the summer a beechwood has few plants growing under the shade of the trees, so almost the only producers are the trees. A pyramid of numbers for a beechwood in summer would look like the one shown in pyramid 2.

The pyramid is this shape because of the relatively small number of beech trees. Pyramids of numbers usually show that there are always more primary consumers than secondary consumers in most ecosystems. There are always few tertiary consumers.

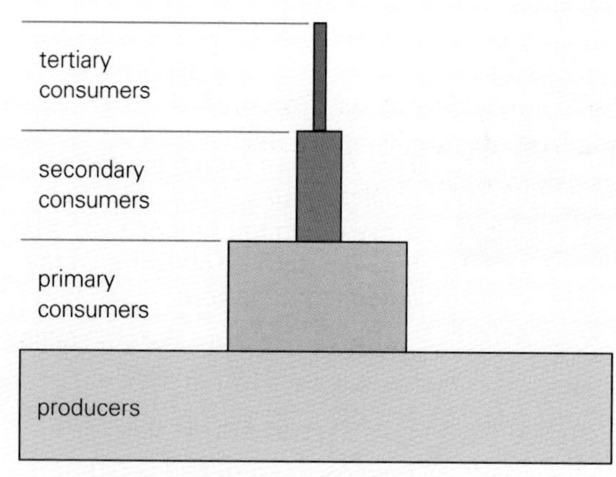

Pyramid 1: the blocks are used to represent the feeding levels and are centred to give a pyramid.

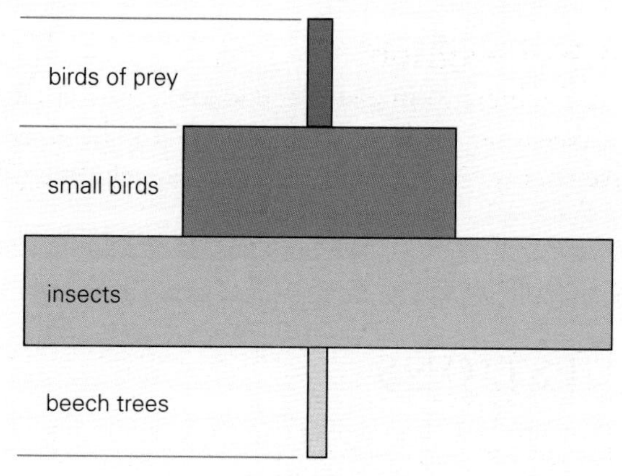

Pyramid 2: an inverted pyramid of numbers.

What about decomposers and parasites?

Decomposers are also a part of ecosystems. As they mostly decompose dead plants they are often put on the same level as the primary consumers but as a separate bar (see pyramid 3). While it is possible to count numbers of decomposers such as earthworms and springtails, it is impossible to count numbers of fungi or bacteria. In practice, when drawing pyramids, the animals are usually included with the primary consumers and the fungi and bacteria are quietly forgotten!

Most animals like badgers, foxes, squirrels and birds have **parasites**. In fact almost all animals have them (including humans). Plants also have parasites, e.g. fungi. Parasites are often small animals like ticks, lice or fleas.

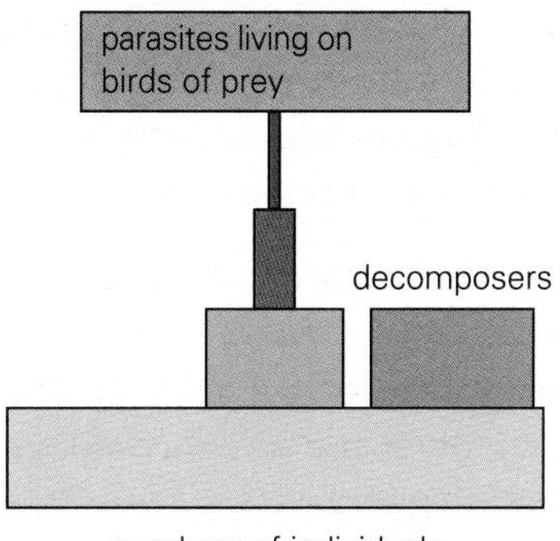

Pyramid 3: if you drew in the large number of parasites that live on carnivores the pyramid becomes top heavy and no longer looks like a pyramid at all.

Biomass

Large trees and tiny insects are counted as being equal, regardless of their sizes, when you draw a pyramid of numbers. This is obviously nonsense - you need to find another way to measure the animals, plants and microbes so that you can consider them in terms of food, not numbers.

To find how much food is available for consumers and decomposers you can weigh organisms at each feeding level in an ecosystem. The mass of living matter is called **biomass**, which is short for biological mass. It is calculated as mass per unit area, e.g. kilograms per square metre. A pyramid of biomass is shown in pyramid 4.

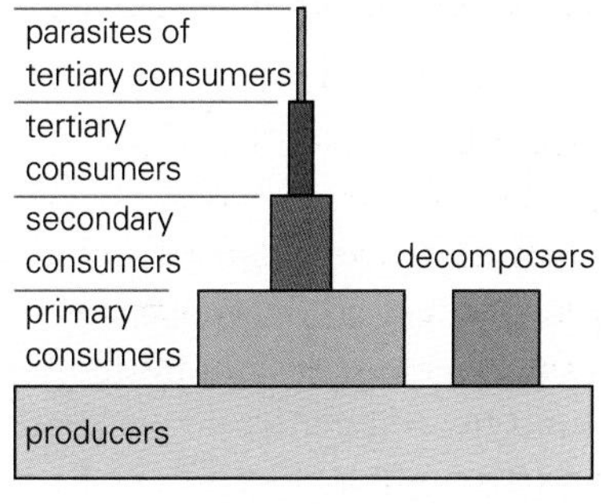

Pyramid 4: this pyramid of biomass shows how much food is available at each feeding level.

Weighing up the difficulties

The **fresh mass** of organisms includes a great deal of water. Almost 90% of the fresh mass of leaves may be water. This has no energy value to the consumers as energy is in the fats, proteins and carbohydrates of the leaves. The quantity of food in samples of leaves is found by drying them. This gives you their **dry mass**.

Samples of animals are weighed to find their biomass. About 30% of their fresh mass consists of organic compounds and skeleton so it is easy just to multiply fresh mass results by 0.3 to estimate the dry mass of animals.

Another problem

Not all the biomass in plants and animals provides energy for the animals at the next feeding level. Skeletons, shells, feathers and fur may be eaten but they are not digested and respired to give energy. For example, humans eat cellulose (fibre) but we cannot digest it.

QUESTIONS

1 Explain how a pyramid of numbers is drawn for a named ecosystem.

2 Explain the disadvantages of using a pyramid of numbers to show the feeding relationships in an ecosystem.

3 Explain the term biomass.

4 Explain why it is better to measure the dry mass of animals and plants rather than fresh mass when working out a pyramid of biomass for an ecosystem.

5 Plan an investigation to find out if treating a lawn with fertiliser increases the growth of grass.

8.6 *Energy flow*

Sunlight provides energy

Living things need energy. Without it they cannot stay alive, they do not grow or reproduce. Plants gain their energy by absorbing sunlight and converting it into chemical energy in sugars. The sugars produced can be turned into fats. By combining sugars with minerals from the soil, plants make molecules such as proteins, chlorophyll and DNA. Animals gain energy by eating plants or other animals.

A very small part of the solar energy which reaches plants is captured for photosynthesis. This is transferred to chemical energy which is mostly used to drive the chemical processes that occur in their cells. The rest of the energy goes into new growth and stored compounds like starch. This provides food for primary consumers. But before they are eaten, plants have already used much of the energy they converted in photosynthesis, so only a proportion is left for the primary consumers.

Energy for animals

Herbivores consume plants. Some of what they eat passes straight through their guts undigested. The rest is absorbed into their bodies and the energy used in respiration. The rest is used for growth. Only energy in herbivore flesh is available to carnivores. So only part of the energy that herbivores consume is available to carnivores.

Some animals need less energy than others. Fish, reptiles and amphibians do not eat as much as mammals and birds of similar size. This is because birds and mammals maintain constant body temperatures which are usually higher than their surroundings. They continually lose heat to the atmosphere or water in which they live and this energy loss has to be replaced by eating large quantities of food.

Pyramids explained

The diagram shows that energy is lost from each feeding level. When animals, plants and decomposers respire part of the energy is transferred to the atmosphere as heat. Some energy is also lost from each feeding level to decomposers. Leaves that are not eaten fall off and decay; trees die, fall over and decay. Decomposers also feed on animal urine and faeces.

All this means that compared with the energy that enters a feeding level little is available to be eaten by the next level because most has been transferred as heat or in waste materials. This explains why ecosystems do not support large numbers of carnivores. Birds of prey, lions, and killer whales are rare because they are at the top of food chains.

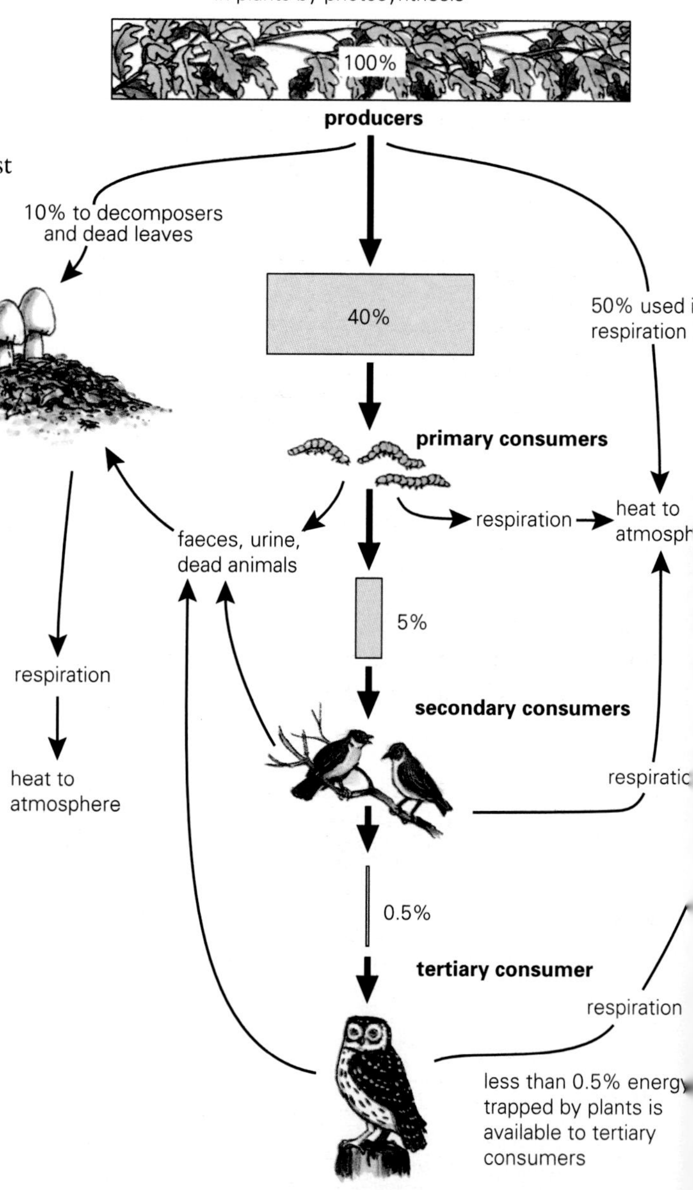

This diagram shows energy transfer along a food chain. The blocks represent energy transferred from one feeding level to the next.

Energy flow on the farm

Arable farmers have a free source of energy - the Sun. To make the best use of this energy farmers

- plant crops to absorb sunlight efficiently by sowing them so plants do not shade each other
- remove weeds which compete with crop plants
- apply fertilisers
- irrigate during dry spells.

In spite of all this effort crop plants only convert about 2–5% of the light energy they receive into food, not all of which is available to humans. When crop plants are used as human food (e.g. wheat flour for bread) we gain much of this energy. However, if plants are used to feed cattle and pigs (e.g. wheat or barley in animal feed) about 5–20% of the energy that the animals consume is available to us as meat. This means that only 0.1–0.5% of the energy available to plants reaches us. Energy available as food can be increased by reducing the number of stages in the food chain.

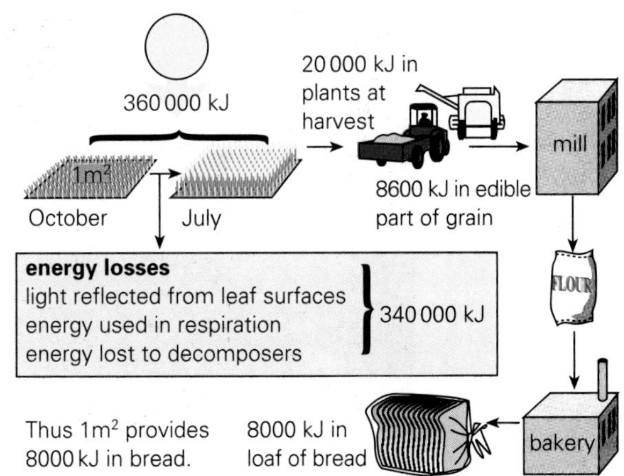

In arable farming the energy in wheat is passed directly to humans.

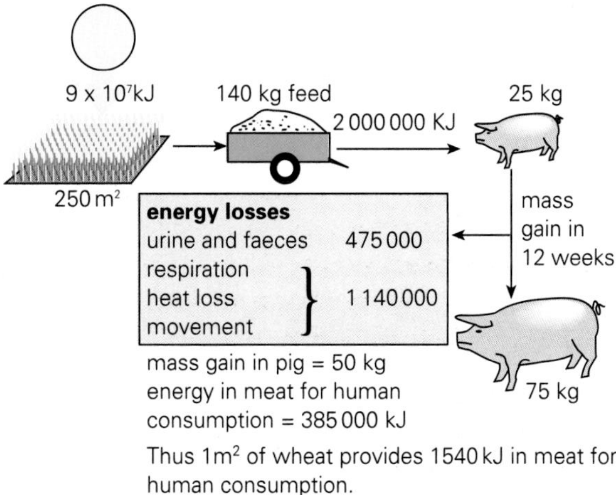

In livestock farming less energy is passed to humans. Most is used by the animals or is lost in their waste.

Another way in which farmers increase the energy flow to humans is by reducing the energy losses from cattle and pigs by keeping them indoors.

These piglets are kept under heat lamps so that they use less energy to keep warm and put on weight quickly.

QUESTIONS

1 Explain what happens to the energy absorbed by plants in photosynthesis as it flows through an ecosystem.

2 Why do mammals and birds eat more food compared with reptiles of similar size?

3 Explain, in terms of energy flow through ecosystems, why there are very few big carnivores such as lions and killer whales.

4 Explain why livestock farming is less efficient in providing food for humans than arable farming.

8.7 *Population growth and decline*

Reproductive potential

An oak tree may live for many hundreds of years and produce many thousands of acorns, but very few of them will ever become mature oak trees. The chances of any one acorn growing to maturity are very small because

- they are eaten by animals
- they may not gain enough resources (light, carbon dioxide, mineral ions) to grow successfully
- they may die of disease.

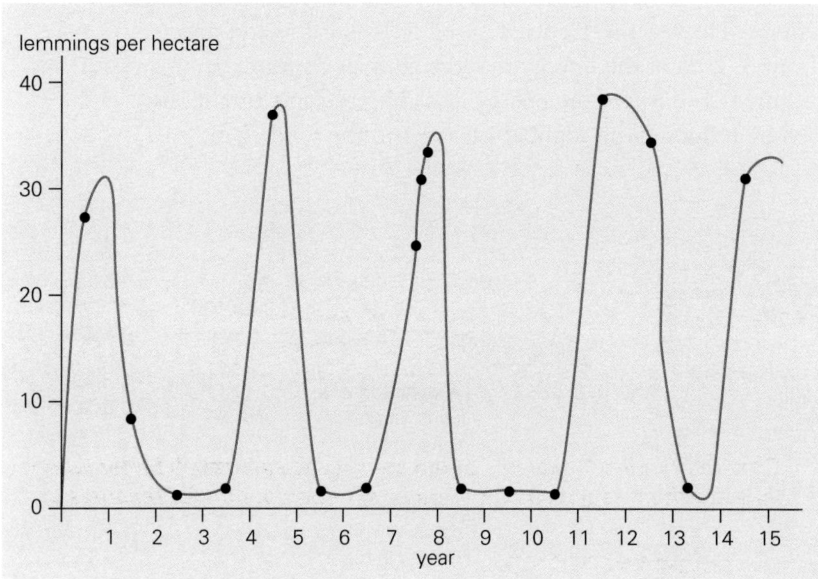

Every four years the number of lemmings increases. For reasons not fully understood these population explosions are followed by population crashes.

A Norwegian lemming

Too many lemmings

Every four years the number of lemmings in Norway increases suddenly. When this happens many migrate from the mountains down into the valleys. Many die of starvation, are eaten by predators or drown when swimming across rivers or fjords. After a short while the population falls, mainly because the survivors fail to reproduce.

The populations of animals that feed on lemmings, such as Arctic foxes and snowy owls, show a similar cycle. When there are many lemmings, these predators have plenty of food for their young and many survive. When there are few lemmings many young foxes and owls die of starvation.

Limiting factors

Algae in lakes reproduce rapidly when the water is warm and there is plenty of light. Their numbers decrease if they are grazed heavily by waterfleas. In Alderfen Broad in Norfolk, fish feed on waterfleas at certain times of the year. With fewer waterfleas, the algae increase in numbers. This shows how **grazers** control populations of producers and **predators** control populations of consumers and producers.

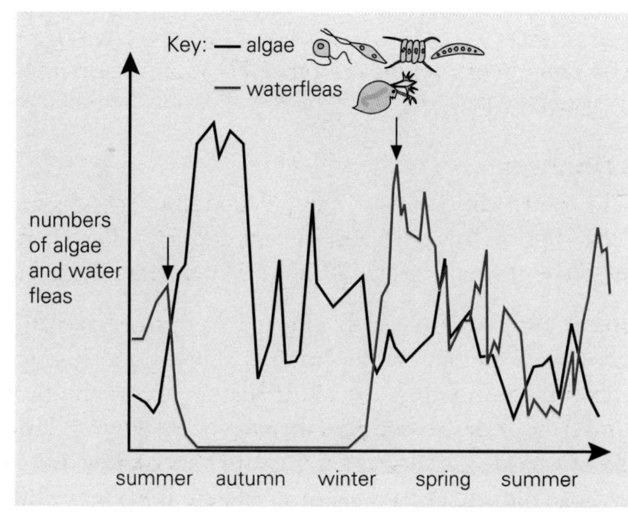

The arrows show when fish start to feed on water fleas.

Populations increase when there is nothing to limit their reproduction. In a complex ecosystem, e.g. an oak woodland, a population does not usually increase rapidly in numbers as there are numerous checks on population growth such as:

- physical factors such as climate (e.g. cold winters kill many organisms)
- lack of space
- predators
- competition for food between members of the same species
- disease.

Space as a limiting factor

Plants compete for growing space. They need space above ground to spread leaves to absorb light. They need space in the soil for roots to absorb water and minerals ions.

Animals compete for space. Some birds guard territories during the breeding season. All the food they collect to feed their young comes from within the territory. Any bird that does not have a territory does not breed. This keeps bird populations constant from year to year.

Growth of individual plants of the same species is much better when they are thinned out so that there is less competition for resources.

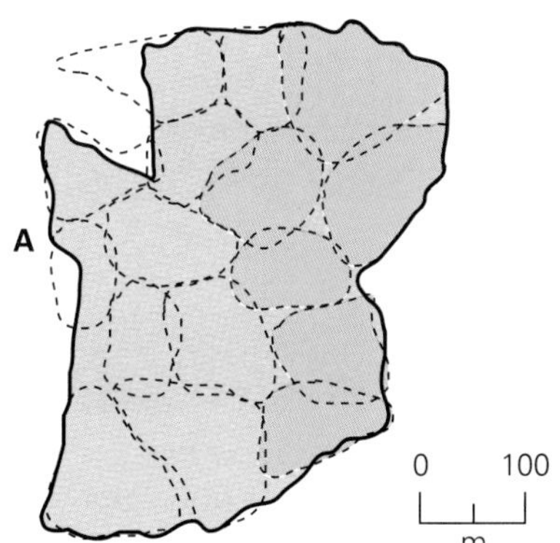

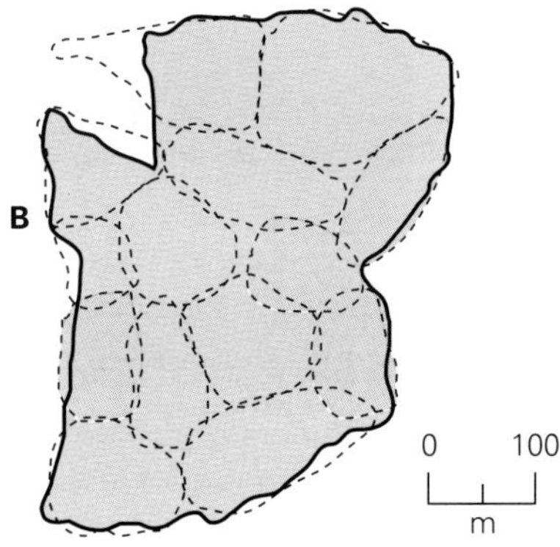

Competition for space among the great tit in a wood. When six male great tits were removed from their territories (shaded brown in A), four new males moved in (shaded purple in B) and others expanded their territories.

Disease

The greater the density of a population, the faster disease can spread through it. This happens to both plants and animals. Elms were common trees in Britain until about twenty years ago when Dutch elm disease killed many of them.

Biotic and physical factors interact to control populations. In most ecosystems physical factors such as climate and shortage of space and food serve to control most species. Predators become important when populations of prey animals increase quite quickly. However, most predators do not have much effect on the numbers of prey. Instead they usually just remove old and diseased animals. There is evidence that predators have quite a different effect. They maintain the biodiversity in ecosystems.

QUESTIONS

1 Describe the population cycle of lemmings and suggest some reasons for it.

2 Explain why Arctic foxes and snowy owls have a similar cycle to lemmings.

3 Explain the effect on the numbers of algae in Alderfen Broad when fish start feeding on waterfleas.

4 Make a list of the physical and biotic factors that limit population growth.

5 Plan an investigation to find out how different biotic and physical factors influence the growth of a population of waterfleas.

8.8 *Survival in the cold*

Life is just about everywhere

About four-fifths of the living space on Earth is very cold. This is the deep sea and the polar regions - the Arctic and the Antarctic. Very few species live in the deep sea because, as it is dark, there are no producers.

Everywhere else - even the Arctic - it is different. In the short Arctic summer there is daylight for nearly 24 hours a day. Nutrients are plentiful so there are large numbers of algae. The sea teems with fish. Seals feed on fish and polar bears feed on seals. Polar bears are often followed by a pair of Arctic foxes waiting to scavenge a meal. If none is forthcoming foxes will catch ptarmigan, one of the few birds to live in the Arctic all the year round.

Why waste your energy when you can get someone else to catch your food?

Survival in the cold

Most animals that live in Arctic habitats avoid the worst of the weather.

- Rodents like lemmings make burrows under the snow where they feed, breed and raise several litters and are safe from predators like snowy owls.
- Most birds fly south for the winter.
- Large carnivores like bears sleep for long periods, but do not hibernate. They use their large stores of body fat as insulation and as a food store to keep a warm body temperature.
- Some small animals hibernate by allowing their body temperature to drop to that of their surroundings. The Barrow ground squirrel that lives in Alaska hibernates for nine months of the year. In May it wakes from hibernation and is active for up to 17 hours a day collecting food to store in its body as fat.

Caribou migrate south across the open wastes of the Canadian tundra in search of food and to avoid the worst of the northern winter.

Keeping warm

Conditions in the Arctic are very severe, but animals survive there. The Arctic fox is probably the best survivor. One was once kept at a temperature of –73°C. The Arctic fox has a number of adaptations for survival in the cold as shown in the diagram at the top of the next page.

The Arctic fox – superbly adapted to life in the cold.

The Arctic fox is so well insulated that it does not start to increase its body heat production until the air temperature is as low as –50°C. We start to increase our heat production when the air temperature drops to 28°C.

The thick coat of large mammals like polar bears and Arctic foxes provides a good insulation. Cold air cannot reach the skin surface. Air is trapped in the underfur and this reduces heat loss to the atmosphere. Polar bears have black skins which absorb heat. Any that is reflected from the skin's surface is retained by the white fur. Small mammals cannot carry long coats, this explains why most of them hibernate or live beneath the snow where they can build nests.

Arctic foxes, and many other Arctic mammals such as caribou and polar bears, have small ears. In most mammals ears are thin, have a large surface and have blood vessels very close to the surface. They can therefore lose a lot of heat. By having small ears covered in fur these animals do not lose too much heat.

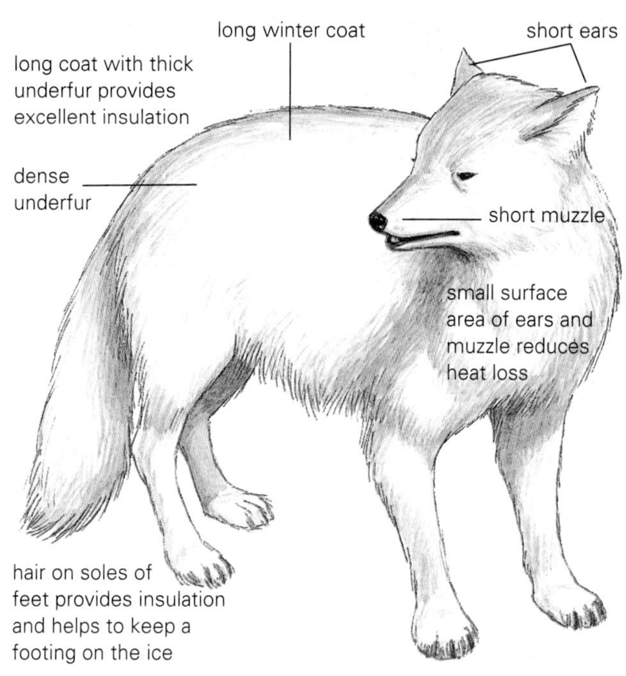

The Arctic fox has various ways of retaining its body heat.

Many animals lay down stores of fat under their skin in summer when food is plentiful. This insulates their bodies in the winter cold and provides a store of energy for respiration. Fat is one of the keys to survival in the Arctic.

Avoiding predators

Ptarmigan change their plumage three times every year. In spring and summer they are brownish, in autumn they are greyer in colour, but in winter they are white. Each plumage provides camouflage as they blend in with their surroundings. Brown birds show up very clearly against snow and soon fall prey to foxes.

Ptarmigan are well camouflaged in the winter and summer.

QUESTIONS

1 Describe different ways in which three named animals respond to the changing seasons in the Arctic.

2 Explain how the Arctic fox is adapted to survive the severe cold of an Arctic winter.

3 There are penguins in Antarctica and as far north as the Galapagos Islands in the Pacific. Suggest why penguins are not found in the Arctic.

4 Describe an investigation you could carry out to find the best type of clothing to take on an Arctic expedition.

8.9 Life in the desert

This saguaro cactus is well adapted to cope with the extreme conditions in the Arizona desert. They can grow up to 20 metres in height and store several tonnes of water.

Lands without water

Deserts cover much of the Earth's land mass. There are several different types of desert, but the one thing they all have in common is shortage of water. Either water is frozen (as in Antarctica) or there is very little rainfall. The Gobi Desert in Asia is very hot in summer and freezing cold in winter. Deserts that are hot during the day are often very cold at night. Deserts have less than 50 mm of rainfall every year. Rainfall is erratic: sometimes a year's rain can fall on one day.

Deserts are not lifeless. Death Valley in California has 600 plant species and 30 different types of mammal.

An extreme habitat

Plants and animals that live in deserts have a range of adaptations that equip them to survive wide fluctuations in temperature and the shortage of water. In similar very dry habitats in Africa, Asia and the Americas different species of animals and plants have much the same adaptations. Cacti in America and the totally unrelated euphorbias (spurges) in Africa are adapted to survive hot, dry conditions by having:

- a small surface area to reduce water loss by transpiration
- a vertical shape to reduce absorption of heat around midday when the Sun is directly overhead
- long roots to absorb water from deep in the ground
- leaves reduced to spines which give protection against herbivores
- photosynthesis taking place in the stem
- fleshy stems to store water.

Desert shrubs have roots which are widespread and shallow. They make best use of the rainfall before it drains away or evaporates. To avoid competition they secrete toxic compounds into the soil to prevent other plants growing nearby. This means that they are not crowded together but are widely spaced across the desert. Many small plants survive the driest times as seeds. They germinate when it rains, grow very quickly, produce flowers, shed seeds and then die.

This creosote bush has thick leaves to reduce water loss and to prevent damage by frost. It can provide useful shade for animals. When it is very dry the plant sheds its leaves.

Small mammals in deserts

Many rodents, like rats and mice avoid the fierce heat and extreme cold by burrowing into the ground, where the temperature does not change as much as it does on the surface. Here they can shelter, store food, build nests and avoid being caught by predators. As there is so little shelter above ground they often have very large hind legs to make a rapid escape from predators. Many only come out at night so avoiding the daytime heat.

Desert mammals survive with little or no water. Some, like the fennec fox can survive without drinking. It gets all its water from eating small rodents. Like them it conserves water by living in burrows which are moist. This reduces the amount of water lost in sweat or by panting. Rodents eat seeds and dry vegetation that contain very little water. They can survive on this dry diet by conserving the water they produce during respiration. All organisms produce water in this way, but few can conserve it so well as desert animals.

These small mammals are adapted to a desert habitat. They have strong front legs for burrowing, long hind legs for jumping and large ears.

The fennec fox lives in the Sahara and Arabian deserts. It digs extensive burrows one metre deep and up to eleven metres long. It emerges at night to prey on rodents and lizards.

The fennec fox is superbly adapted to life in the desert because it has:

- strong forepaws for digging
- dry faeces, concentrated urine to reduce water loss
- little sweating
- yellow/white fur for camouflage
- large ears (15 cm long) for heat loss, excellent hearing to detect prey
- thick fur to insulate against cold night air
- nocturnal so avoids overheating.

QUESTIONS

1 Describe the physical factors that affect the animals and plants in desert habitats.

2 Describe the adaptations shown by desert plants to **a** reduce water loss, **b** make use of water when it falls as rain.

3 Explain how the fennec fox survives the severe conditions in the Sahara desert.

8.10 *Recycling carbon*

Carbon – the element of life

All life on Earth is based on the element carbon. Plants absorb it as carbon dioxide and convert it to sugars in photosynthesis. This is called **carbon fixation**. Plants use sugars to make starch and cellulose. They also make fats and oils such as those we extract from sunflowers and olives to use for cooking. Plants absorb mineral ions from the soil and use them to make amino acids, proteins, nucleic acids, e.g. DNA, chlorophyll and many more compounds (see 5.6). All these carbon compounds are called **organic compounds**.

Recycling keeps life going

There is a limited supply of carbon on Earth. Only carbon dioxide gas in the atmosphere and the dissolved carbon dioxide in water can be used for photosynthesis. Plants continually remove carbon dioxide from the air, but it does not run out because it is constantly being replaced.

All organisms respire. They use organic compounds as sources of energy and release carbon dioxide back into the atmosphere.

This fungus is a decomposer. It is releasing the carbon in the tree stump as carbon dioxide.

Decomposers

Most dead plant matter is made of cellulose, which most animals cannot digest. Bacteria and fungi have the enzymes to digest cellulose. They digest cellulose into sugars which they use for their respiration and so release carbon dioxide into the air. Without the decomposers much of the carbon in the atmosphere would be locked up in cellulose, would not be recycled as carbon dioxide and life would end.

Decomposition is fast when it is warm, moist and there is plenty of air. Enzymes in the bacteria and fungi work faster when it is warm. Decomposers grow quickly when water is available and it also helps with the digestion of their food. Most respire aerobically so they need a good supply of oxygen. Decomposers inside a compacted mass of vegetation have little oxygen and respire slowly. In cold, dry conditions with little oxygen, decomposition is very slow. Peat forms where the soil is cold, wet and very acid. Few decomposers can live in these conditions.

Termites feed on wood. Bacteria in their guts digest cellulose in the wood releasing sugars which the termites absorb.

Earthworms feed on dead leaves. Much of what they eat passes straight through their guts to provide food for soil bacteria.

This dung beetle is doing its bit for carbon recycling.

Recycling carbon

Carbon is also recycled in the atmosphere by burning fossil fuels. Coal was formed from huge forests which grew in swamps about 350 million years ago. When trees and other plants died and fell into the swamps, they did not decay because there was not enough oxygen present for decomposers. This plant life became fossilised as coal. Burning coal and other fossil fuels such as oil adds carbon dioxide to the atmosphere (see 9.5).

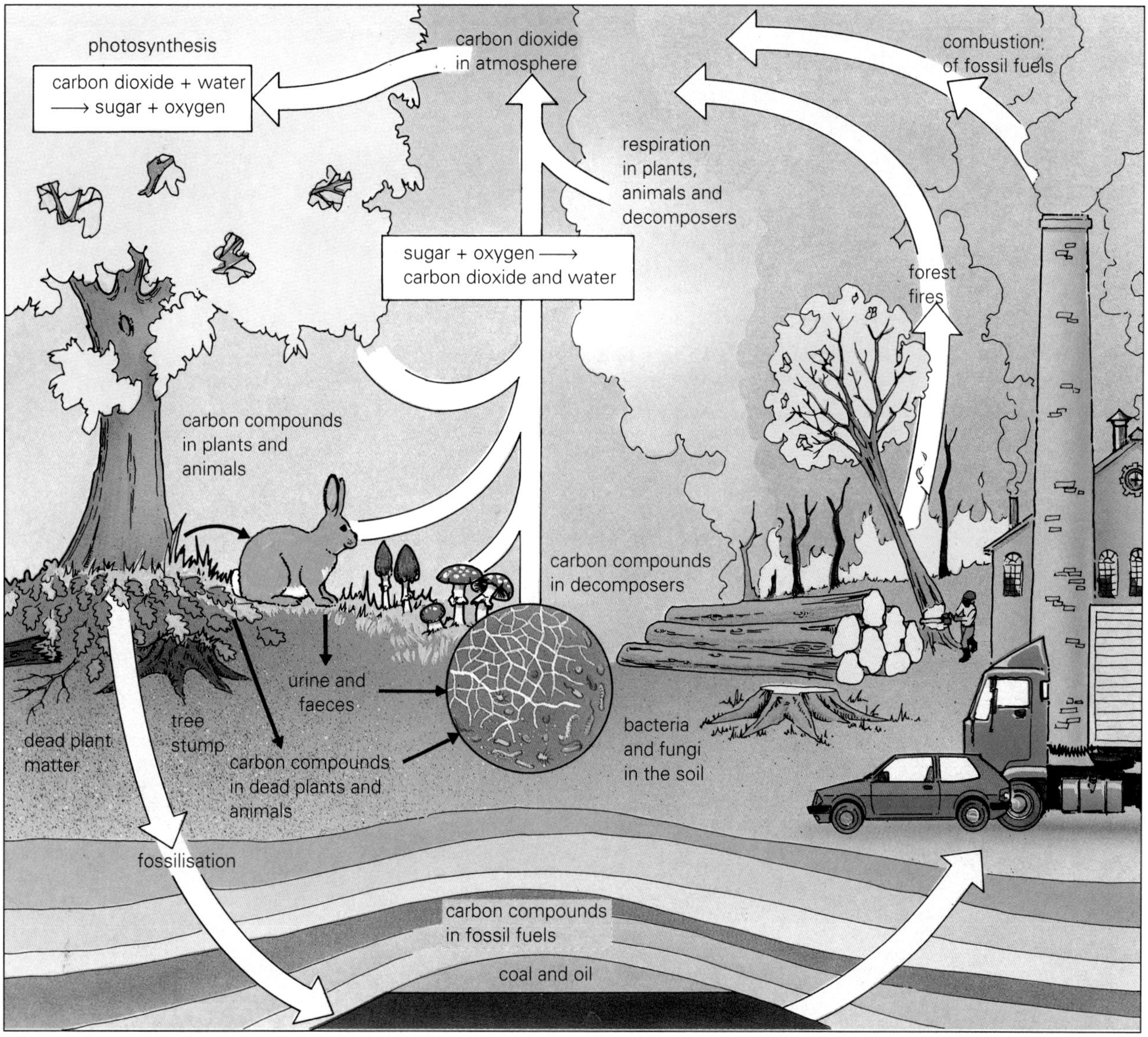

photosynthesis
carbon dioxide + water ⟶ sugar + oxygen
carbon dioxide in atmosphere
combustion of fossil fuels
respiration in plants, animals and decomposers
sugar + oxygen ⟶ carbon dioxide and water
forest fires
carbon compounds in plants and animals
carbon compounds in decomposers
urine and faeces
tree stump
dead plant matter
carbon compounds in dead plants and animals
bacteria and fungi in the soil
fossilisation
carbon compounds in fossil fuels
coal and oil

The carbon cycle

QUESTIONS

1 Describe two processes that release carbon dioxide into the atmosphere.

2 Name one process that takes carbon dioxide from the atmosphere.

3 Describe how decomposers help the recycling of carbon.

4 Explain why it is important that carbon is recycled.

5 Plan an investigation to find out how oxygen, temperature and moisture influence how quickly foods like peas or bread decay.

8.11 *Recycling nitrogen*

Nitrogen

Nitrogen gas (N_2) forms nearly 80% of the atmosphere. Unlike carbon dioxide very few organisms use nitrogen because this gas is very unreactive. But nitrogen is an important element for life: all organisms need it for amino acids, proteins and nucleic acids. Plants need it for chlorophyll. As most plants cannot obtain nitrogen from the air they absorb it from the soil or from water as nitrate ions (NO_3^-). Plants then use energy to combine nitrate with compounds derived from sugars to form amino acids. This occurs in chloroplasts where light energy is trapped.

Along the food chain

Animals need to absorb amino acids to make their own proteins. Herbivores use plant protein as their source of amino acids to make their own protein. Carnivores digest meat protein to amino acids and use them to build their protein. Animals turn excess amino acids that they cannot store into urea and excrete urea in their urine (see 2.10).

Putrefaction

Decomposers break down the proteins in dead plants and animals to amino acids. Some bacteria use amino acids as a source of energy and in the process produce ammonium ions (see 2.10). Bacteria also use urea as a source of energy turning it into ammonium ions. This process of producing ammonium ions from organic compounds such as proteins is called **putrefaction**. The bacteria that do this are **putrefying bacteria**.

Nitrification

Ammonium ions released by decomposers are changed into nitrate by **nitrifying bacteria**. This process releases energy for the bacteria. This occurs in two stages. Some nitrifying bacteria oxidise ammonium ions to nitrite ions:

$$\text{ammonium ions } (NH_4^+) \longrightarrow \text{nitrite ions } (NO_2^-) + \text{energy.}$$

Others oxidise nitrite ions to nitrate ions:

$$\text{nitrite ions } (NO_2^-) \longrightarrow \text{nitrate ions } (NO_3^-) + \text{energy.}$$

Plants absorb nitrate ions and use them to make amino acids and so the cycle is complete. This cycling of nitrogen is important in all ecosystems. Without it life would stop because there are few other supplies of nitrates for plants.

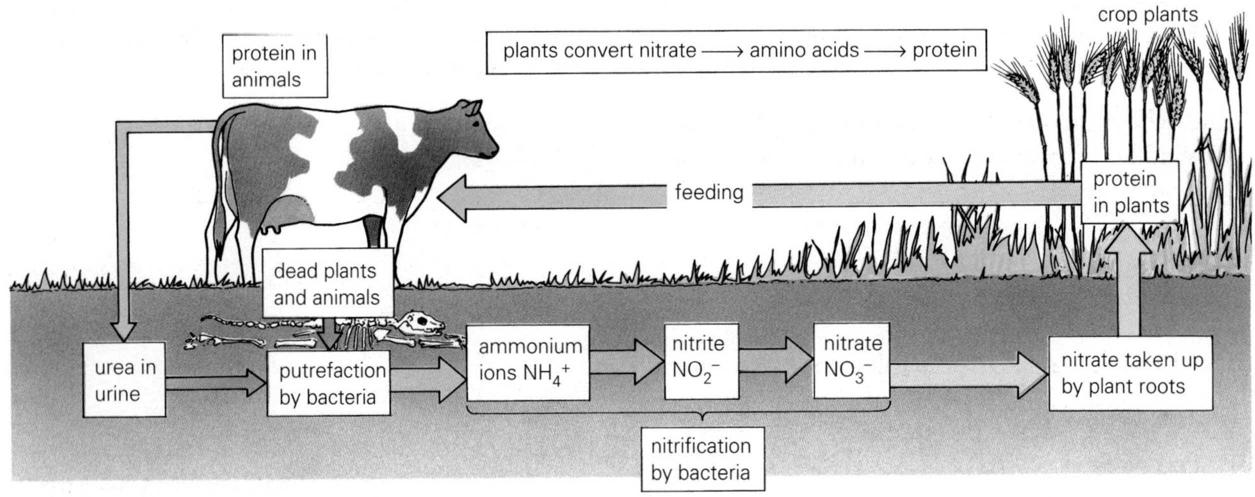

Nitrogen is recycled by bacteria into nitrates which are absorbed by plants and used to make proteins.

Nitrogen in the atmosphere

As in the carbon cycle (see 8.10), nitrogen is exchanged between living organisms and the atmosphere. Some bacteria absorb nitrogen from the air and convert it into ammonium ions and then into amino acids and proteins. As nitrogen is so unreactive, it requires a lot of energy from respiration to do this. The process is **nitrogen fixation**.

Nitrogen fixation in plants

Many of the bacteria that fix nitrogen live in the soil, compost heaps or in water. Some live inside the roots of plants. Swellings on the roots of legumes, e.g. peas, beans and clover, are full of nitrogen-fixing bacteria that absorb nitrogen from the air in the soil and convert it into ammonium ions and then into amino acids. The host plants supply the bacteria with the large amounts of food they need for fixing nitrogen and keep the oxygen concentration very low as oxygen interferes with the enzymes that fix nitrogen. In return, the plants receive a supply of amino acids.

Some nitrogen in the air is converted into nitrogen oxide during electrical storms. This dissolves in rainwater to form nitric acid which is a source of nitrate in the soil.

In this oasis legumes are grown with other crops because they replace the nitrate taken up by other crops.

These root nodules contain nitrogen-fixing bacteria. The plant supplies them with food.

Plants whose roots contain nitrogen-fixing bacteria are used in crop rotations because their roots contain high concentrations of nitrogen compounds which are converted into nitrate by soil bacteria. This is a natural alternative to using fertilisers.

Denitrification

Some bacteria that live in anaerobic conditions such as waterlogged soils use nitrate to help them respire. They convert nitrate to nitrogen gas. This replaces the nitrogen taken out of the air by nitrogen fixation, helping to keep the atmospheric concentration at about 80%.

QUESTIONS

1 Explain why nitrogen is an important element in organisms.

2 Describe the roles of the following bacteria in recycling nitrogen
a putrefying bacteria
b nitrifying bacteria
c nitrogen-fixing bacteria.

3 Draw out a complete nitrogen cycle using all the information given here.

9.1 Human populations

Human population growth

In about 1830 the human population reached 1000 million. There are now somewhere between 5000 and 6000 million of us and the number is growing at a phenomenal rate.

In the past, human populations were kept in check by famine, war and disease. But humans have invented technologies to control their environment and so support an ever-increasing population. These technologies also provide higher standards of living for many people, but have had enormous consequences for natural ecosystems.

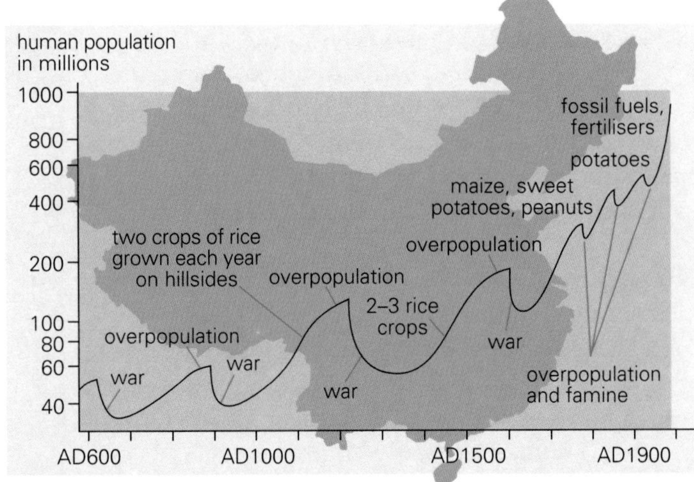

Some of the reasons for periods of increase and decrease in the Chinese population.

Humans need space

Our growing population takes space from other species. People cleared the lowland forest covering Britain to make space for farms, towns and roads. Many habitats were destroyed and many species driven to extinction. Through ignorance people have polluted the environment. This puts our survival and the survival of other species at risk.

This quarry in Britain is in an area of outstanding natural beauty. The stone is used for building houses and roads.

Using too much fertiliser will pollute water supplies.

As farming has become more industrialised, fewer people are required to work on the land to produce the food we need. Instead to help produce their crops farmers use agrochemicals – fertilisers, insecticides and herbicides – which can pollute the soil and waterways if misused.

Industry needs raw materials and energy

Quarrying, mining and drilling for oil extract raw materials we need from the Earth. These activities can destroy ecosystems and produce poisonous wastes. The waste from mining contains toxic substances which few plants can tolerate. By using fossil fuels we are using up non-renewable resources.

Pollution

Industrial and domestic waste has to be disposed of and this causes **pollution**. This is the harm done to the environment by the release of substances produced by human activities. The table shows some pollutants of air, water and land.

	Pollutant	**Effects on humans and the environment**
Air	smoke	makes breathing difficult
	sulphur dioxide	causes acid rain
	ozone	damages leaves
	CFCs	damage ozone layer
	carbon dioxide	increases the greenhouse effect
Water	sewage	eutrophication (see 9.3)
	fertilisers	eutrophication (see 9.3)
	acid rain	makes soils, lakes and rivers acidic
	oils spills	kill fish
	toxic chemicals, e.g. mercury	kill fish and other aquatic life
Land	solid waste disposal in landfill sites	methane causes explosions and increases the greenhouse effect
	mining waste, e.g. lead	water run-off poisons plants and animals
		heavy metals kill most plants and animals

How many humans?

How many people can the Earth support? In natural ecosystems limiting factors such as space, food and water determine how large populations will grow. Most species never reach their maximum numbers because of disease and physical factors such as climate and predation. In any large population there is intense competition between individuals and many die. Our population is not limited by the same factors. If our species behaves like others it will increase its numbers until resources run out. So far our technology has allowed us to maximise our resources and find new ones. Maybe this will continue.

QUESTIONS

1 Explain why the human population has increased so much over the past 250 years.

2 Explain why the Chinese population did not increase evenly over the last 1500 years.

3 Describe ways in which human activities have polluted land, water and air.

9.2 *Managing artificial ecosystems*

Harvesting from the wild

People harvest materials from natural ecosystems for food, fuel and building materials. Forests or individual trees are cut down and fish are taken from the sea. Apart from these activities most of our needs come from **artificial ecosystems** such as farms.

As the human population grows the pressure on natural ecosystems increases. If too many trees or fish are harvested and not replaced, populations will be severely depleted and ecosystems will be damaged.

This has happened in many places with modern fishing methods. Boats equipped with large nets and sophisticated sonar equipment often take so many fish that there are not enough left to reproduce and maintain the stock at the same level.

Indians in Amazonia harvest Brazil nuts. The people do not harm their natural habitat.

Modern food production

Farms and market gardens supply large quantities of food. In the past most farms in Britain had a mixture of livestock and crops. Now most farmers concentrate on just a few crops such as wheat, barley, oilseed rape or potatoes or on livestock. Crops are grown in large fields to make it easy to use machinery for ploughing, sowing, applying fertilisers, spraying pesticides and harvesting. Animals are reared intensively (see 8.6).

In the past land used to be left fallow or crops were rotated so that the natural fertility of the land could be restored. Legumes (e.g. peas, beans and clover) which contain nitrogen-fixing bacteria were used to return the nitrogen absorbed by cereal crops to the soil (see 8.11). In the 1940s British farmers were encouraged to grow as much as possible so that the country could become self-sufficient in food. Trad*i*titional farming practices were neglected. Farmers ploughed up land previously only used for livestock production. New crop varieties were developed by selective breeding (see 7.5). However, increasing crop yields were mainly the result of the increased use of artificial fertilisers.

Mechanised food production is efficient, but requires large areas of land for just one crop. An artificial ecosystem is created.

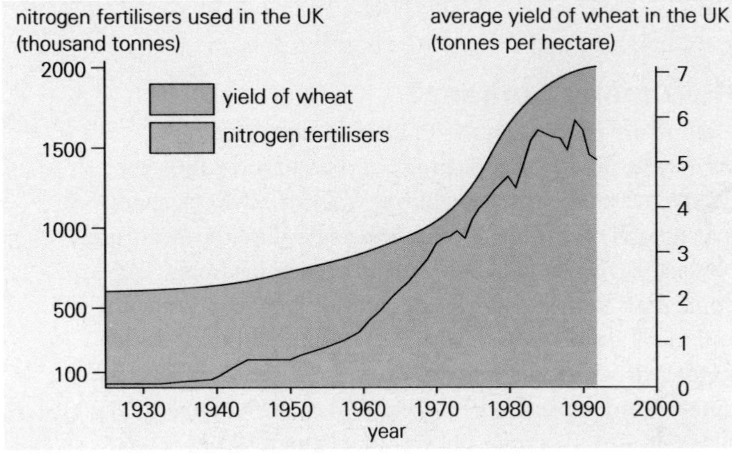

As farmers used more and more fertiliser, yields increased.

Energy for fertilisers

The production of nitrogen fertiliser requires great amounts of energy from fossil fuels. Once the fertiliser is produced it has to be transported, stored and applied to crops. All this uses more fossil fuel.

Modern farming is very successful but if you consider the total quantity of energy used to grow crops compared with the quantity of food energy produced, it is not very efficient. Compare this with the energy needed to grow food in New Guinea, as illustrated in the diagram (left, below).

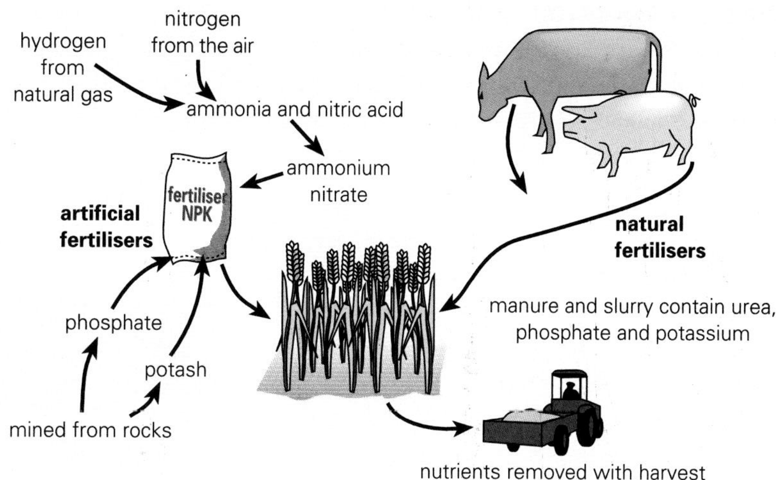

Fertilisers replace the nutrients taken from the soil.

Fish farming

Fish are also farmed. Many peasant farmers in Asia keep fish in irrigation channels. In the Philippines milkfish are captured in the wild and reared in ponds. These are simple methods of **fish farming**.

In Britain, both freshwater and marine fish are farmed. Salmon are reared in large cages in Scottish lochs. They are kept at high density and fed a high protein diet. They grow quickly and have the advantage over cattle or pigs in that they do not use energy to maintain a constant body temperature.

Farmed salmon and trout are prone to catch parasites such as fish lice and diseases caused by bacteria and fungi. Parasites are likely to spread quickly as the animals are kept close together. Pesticides are used to treat them, but the environmental effects are unknown. Predators like sea otters, seals and fish-eating birds, like herons, can take many fish from farms.

Mechanised farming requires large energy inputs from fossil fuels but it requires fewer workers and produces more food per hectare than subsistence (non-mechanised) farming.

Salmon are farmed in Scottish lochs.

QUESTIONS

1 Give three examples of artificial ecosystems and describe the main features of each one.

2 Explain the ways that mechanised farming is
a more efficient and
b less efficient than subsistence farming.

3 Explain why mechanised farming uses large inputs of energy.

4 What are the advantages of fish farming over keeping pigs and cattle for meat production?

9.3 *Water pollution*

Waste disposal

In Britain most domestic sewage and industrial waste is treated in sewage plants to remove dissolved and suspended organic matter. Intensive animal production produces slurry – a mixture of urine and faeces. Some of this waste is applied to farmland and may be washed off into waterways.

The careless disposal of waste material has destroyed many freshwater ecosystems, such as the Great Lakes of North America and parts of the Norfolk Broads.

Organic pollution

When domestic sewage flows directly into a river its organic content provides food for decomposers like bacteria and fungi. Their numbers increase and they use up much of the dissolved oxygen. Many invertebrates and fish cannot survive in low oxygen conditions. Other species, like midge larvae, can and their numbers increase because they now have few competitors or predators.

Unless there is another source of pollution, the river improves downstream as bacteria decompose the sewage or it settles out on the river bed. However, putrefying bacteria release ammonium ions which are converted into nitrate by nitrifying bacteria (see 8.11). This makes nutrients available for plants in the water.

Measuring the oxygen content of a river can show if it is polluted.

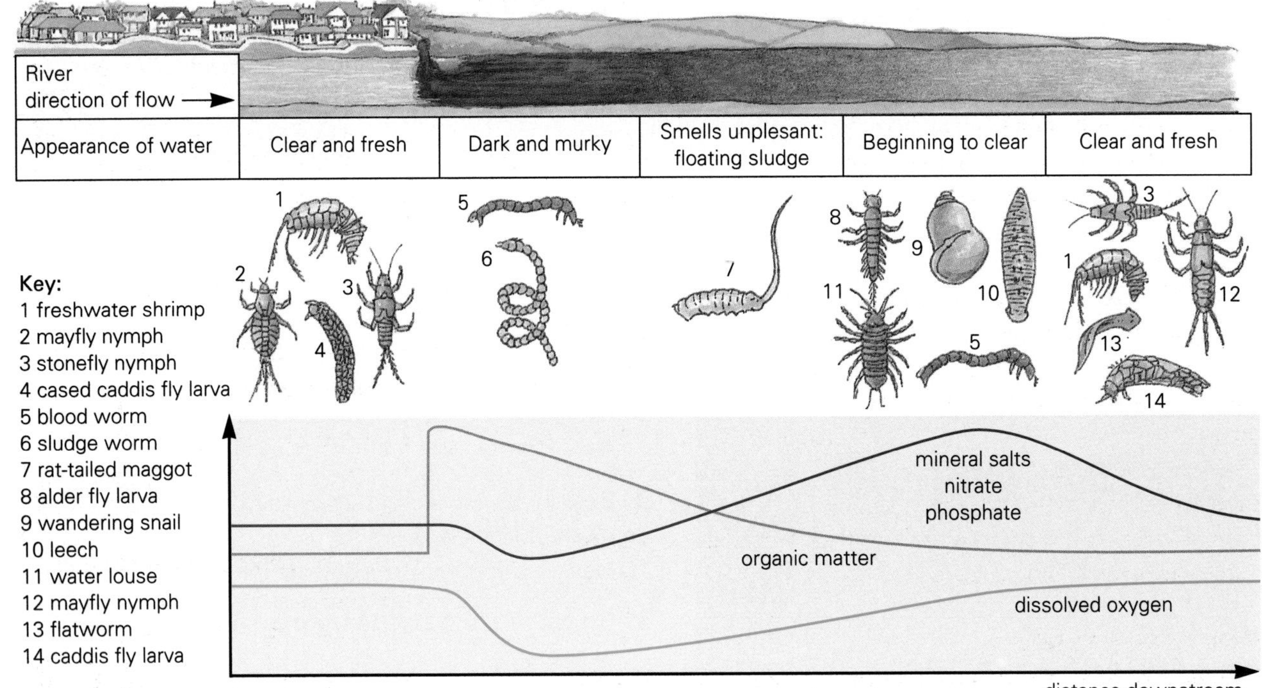

When raw sewage enters a river the community changes considerably. Stoneflies and freshwater shrimps indicate that the river is unpolluted. Blood worms and sludge worms indicate that there is little oxygen and the river is heavily polluted with organic matter.

Eutrophication

Both nitrates and phosphates encourage the growth of algae. When they enter waterways they alter the balance of organisms.

- Algae grow rapidly to give an algal bloom over the surface of the water.
- Many blue-green algae produce toxins which kill plants and some animals such as fish.
- Small animals that feed on algae do not multiply fast enough to check the increase in the algae.
- Algae block out the light for the rooted plants growing on beds of lakes and they die. This reduces the amount of oxygen.
- The algal population crashes due to competition for resources. The algae are then decomposed by bacteria which use the oxygen in the water.
- The lack of oxygen kills many invertebrates and fish.

This process is called **eutrophication**.

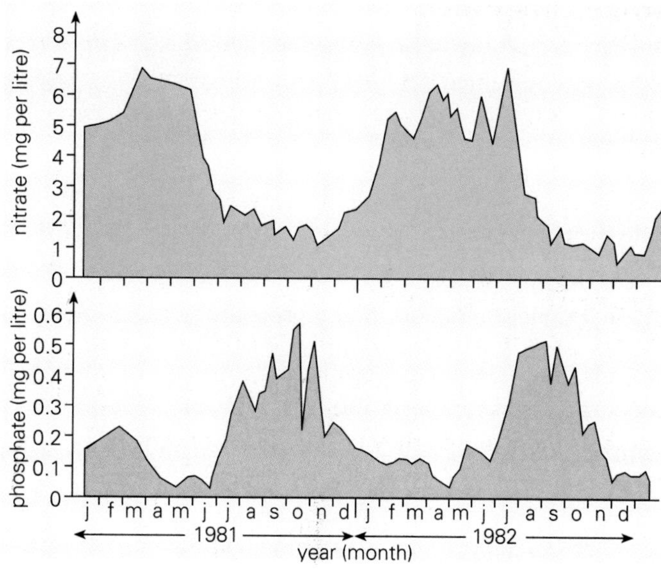

This graph shows the concentration of nitrate and phosphate in a reservoir in eastern England over two years. Algal blooms occurred in the summer months when the concentration of phosphate was high.

Nitrates and phosphates

Nitrate from organic and artificial fertilisers is very soluble and if it is not absorbed by plants, it is easily washed away through the soil. However, nitrate is not the main limiting factor for the growth of freshwater plants. It is rarely in short supply. The main limiting factor is phosphate. Phosphate in fertilisers is not as soluble as nitrate and it tends to remain in the soil. The main sources of phosphate are domestic washing powders and detergents and the waste from farm animals.

Algal bloom on the water's surface.

Solutions

Eutrophication can be reduced by limiting the levels of nitrate and phosphate entering waterways. Sewage works can reduce levels of phosphate. However, the problem of nitrate is more difficult. Farmers try to apply the minimum amount of fertilisers necessary at the times of year when crops absorb them. This does not solve the problem as most nitrate comes from the natural decay by soil bacteria of organic matter when the crops have been harvested. Nitrate levels in Britain's rivers have increased mainly because so much farmland has been ploughed up over the past 50 years.

Another problem

Nitrate is responsible for algal blooms in the sea. These have occurred in the North Sea where rivers drain from intensively farmed areas of Holland, Germany, Denmark and Belgium. These blooms produce toxins that kill fish and contaminate shellfish.

QUESTIONS

1. Make a list of the substances that pollute water and their sources.
2. Describe the changes that occur in a river after it receives raw sewage.
3. Name the sources of nitrate and phosphate which cause eutrophication in freshwater.
4. Describe what can be done to reduce the problem of eutrophication in lakes and rivers.

9.4 *Controlling pests*

Crop protection

Farmers spend millions of pounds every year on crop protection chemicals:

- **herbicides** to control weeds, e.g. black grass, bind and wild oats
- **insecticides** to control insect pests, e.g. aphids
- **fungicides** to control fungal diseases, e.g. blight, mildew.

Before the development of crop protection chemicals farmers often lost great quantities of food to pests and disease either before harvest or during storage.

Insecticides

DDT and **dieldrin** are chlorine-containing compounds. DDT is an insecticide that controls many pest species including mosquitoes that carry malaria. Its use freed some countries of malaria, making previously inhospitable areas habitable and increasing crop yields. Like DDT, dieldrin was used to kill many pest species, but it also killed many useful insects as well.

Crop plants are sources of food for many organisms and are under constant attack from many pests and diseases.

Moving up the food chain

One of the earliest warnings that something was wrong with these insecticides was the decrease in the number of birds of prey which occupy the role of top carnivore in many ecosystems. In Britain peregrine falcon numbers decreased as they did not reproduce very well because their eggshells became thinner. Concentrations of DDT and dieldrin were found to increase up the food chain.

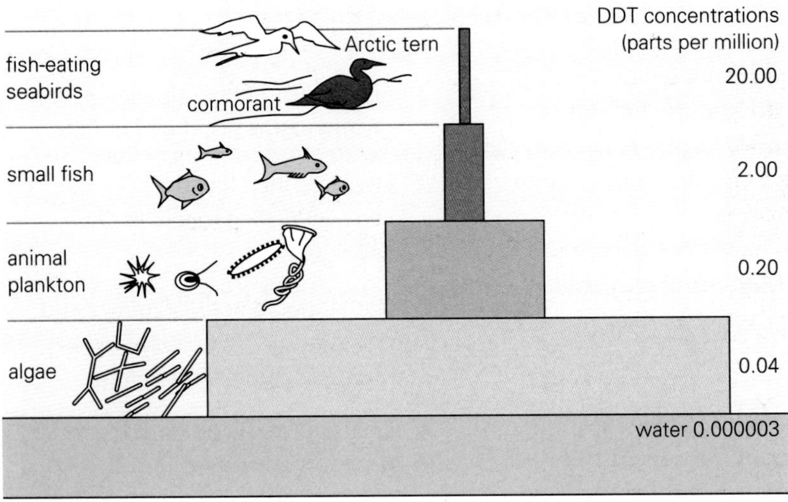

This shows how concentrations of DDT increase along food chains.

DDT is not broken down by animals and plants. It is a **persistent** chemical. When animals eat plants containing DDT it accumulates in their fat stores. Animals toward the top of the food chain live a long time and take in a large amount of DDT over their lifetime which they are unable to excrete. The use of DDT and dieldrin in Britain was reduced in the 1960s; both were finally banned in 1986. However, they are still used in other parts of the world. DDT is cheap and it seems not to do any serious damage to people. This means that these insecticides will be having their effects on wildlife for many years to come.

The problem: whitefly feed on sap. Much of this passes through their guts as honeydew which sticks to the leaves. Fungi grow on the honeydew and prevent light reaching the leaves.

Biological control

For some crops farmers are now using **biological control** methods, using natural predators to control pests. For example, whiteflies are a problem on many glasshouse crops. Whitefly are now resistant to many pesticides. A tiny wasp is used to control them. Female wasps lay their eggs in the young whitefly. When the young wasp hatches it eats the whitefly from the inside. This control is very effective as female wasps search out the whitefly when they lay their eggs. If the control is to continue throughout the growing season, there must always be some whitefly for the wasps to lay their eggs inside.

The solution: packets of wasp pupae are hung on tomato plants in the greenhouse when the whitefly start to increase in number.

These whitefly pupae (black) contain parasitic wasps.

The tiny wasp crawls out from the body of the whitefly ready to mate and find more whitefly to lay its eggs inside.

QUESTIONS

1 Explain why farmers use crop protection chemicals.

2 What were the first signs that insecticides like DDT and dieldrin were harming wildlife?

3 Explain how DDT accumulates in food chains.

4 Explain why growers of glasshouse crops use predators of whitefly rather than spraying insecticides.

5 Describe how parasitic wasps control whitefly in greenhouses.

9.5 *Fossil fuels*

Energy

Fossil fuels such as oil and coal are made of complex mixtures of chemicals. The compounds in them are mainly composed of the elements carbon, hydrogen and small quantities of sulphur and nitrogen. When they are burnt they release carbon dioxide, water, sulphur dioxide(SO_2) and oxides of nitrogen (known as NO_x) into the air. Smoke is also released – this is made of particles of soot.

Acid rain

When sulphur dioxide and nitrogen oxides are deposited on the surfaces of plants or on buildings they do considerable damage. This is called **dry deposition**. They also dissolve in water in the atmosphere to form sulphuric acid and nitric acid. These lower the pH of rain and snow. In some parts of Europe the pH can be as low as 3.0. When they fall to the ground it is called **wet deposition**. The term **acid rain** refers to both types of deposition.

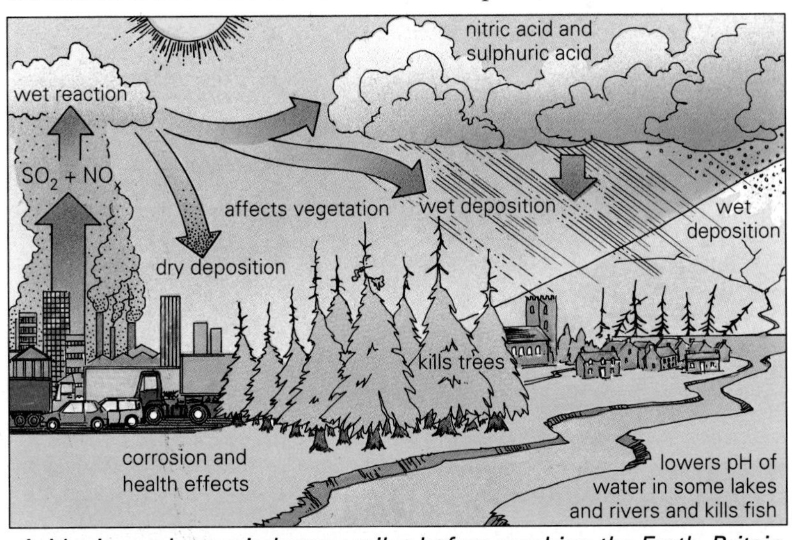

Acid rain can be carried many miles before reaching the Earth. Britain is responsible for some of the acid rain that falls in Scandinavia.

Sources of acid rain

The problem of acid rain began at the time of the Industrial Revolution with industries burning coal. Thanks to the development of smokeless fuels, and the use of electricity and gas in homes, there has been a reduction in the pollution from homes. However, factories that make smokeless fuel and power stations that burn coal still produce sulphur dioxide. Sulphur dioxide is carried through the air to southern Scotland and Scandinavia.

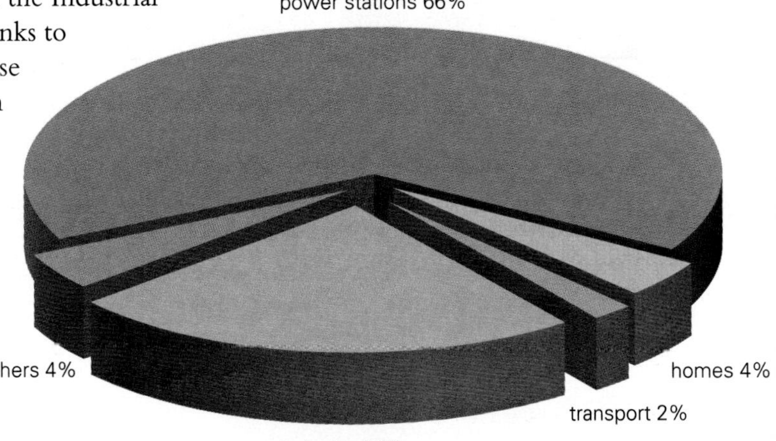

Sources of emissions of sulphur dioxide in the UK.

Acid rain and ecosystems

When acid rain falls on deep soils on limestone or chalk, there is little effect. The natural alkalinity of the soil neutralises the acid.

When it falls on trees it causes the leaves to die and it may also reduce their ability to resist attack from disease. In areas with hard rock and acid soil or peat the deposited rain is not neutralised. Water runs into streams and lakes causing communities there to change. As the pH decreases many species disappear and their places are taken by species able to survive in acid conditions.

One effect of acid water is that aluminium compounds become soluble. There are large quantities of aluminium compounds in soils which only become soluble below pH 5.5. When there is a large amount of rainfall the aluminium levels in streams can increase tenfold in a few hours. Compounds of aluminium are highly toxic to fish and they are now extinct in some lakes in southern Norway which receive very high quantities of acid rain. Lakes are treated with alkali and plant nutrients to reverse these effects.

Lichens as pollution monitors

Lichens grow on rocks and on trees. They are formed by algae and fungi growing together. They do not have roots and obtain all their water and minerals from the air and rainwater. Lichens have proved useful in detecting the levels of sulphur dioxide pollution in the air. Where the concentration in the air is very high, no lichens will grow at all. However, as the concentration decreases more and more lichens can grow. Only a few can tolerate quite high concentrations.

The areas around heavily industrialised areas have no lichens at all. This is another example of human activity reducing the diversity of ecosystems.

Lichens are very slow growing. These lichens are growing in an unpolluted atmosphere in Wales.

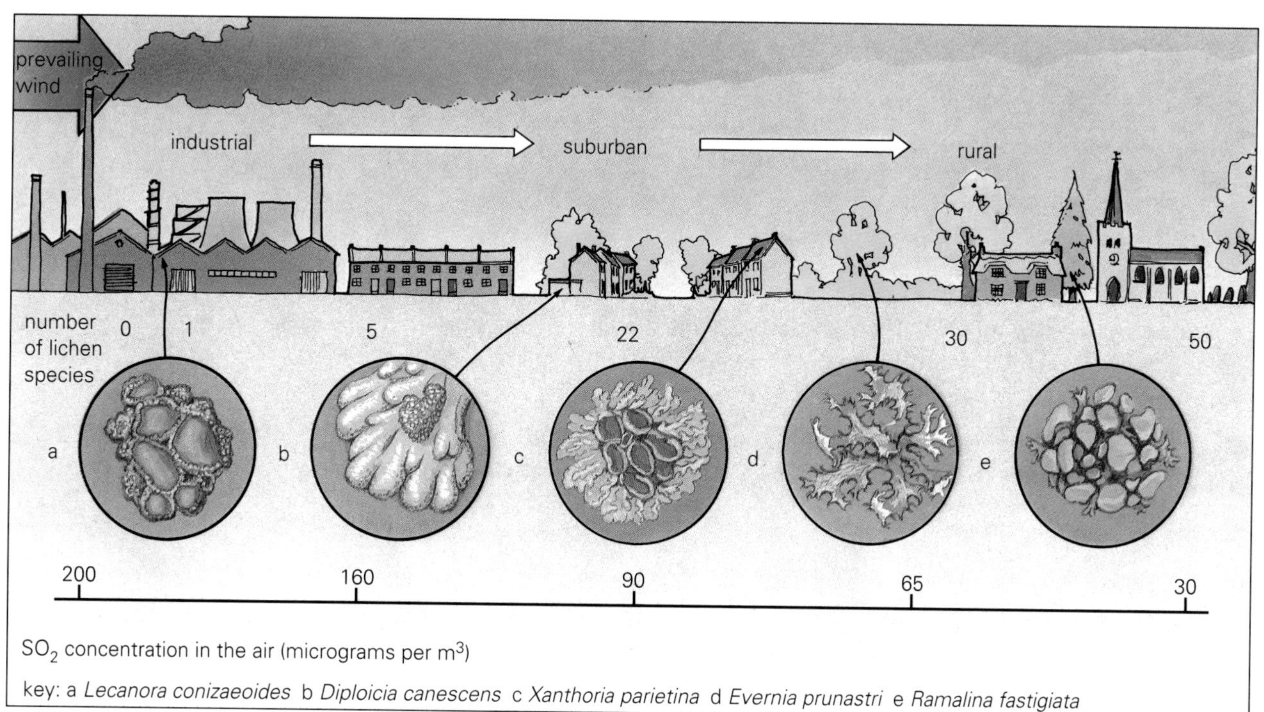

The presence or absence of lichen species indicates the degree of sulphur dioxide pollution in the air.

Cleaning up

Over the last few decades the levels of sulphur dioxide emitted in Britain have decreased. To reduce the problem of acid rain still further, power stations can be fitted with gas flue desulphurisers and cars fitted with catalytic converters. This helps to remove the sulphur dioxide and NO_x from emissions.

QUESTIONS

1 What is acid rain?

2 Explain why acid rain has its worst effects on ecosystems in places such as Scotland and Scandinavia.

3 Explain how lichens are used as monitors of pollution.

4 How can the problem of acid rain be solved?

9.6 Life in the 'greenhouse'

The Earth should be very cold

The average global temperature on Earth is 15°C. The average temperature for a planet of this size situated 150 million kilometres from the Sun should be -17°C, as it is on the Moon. The reason the Earth is 32°C warmer is our atmosphere. It acts like a blanket around the Earth keeping in much of the heat that would otherwise be radiated into space.

The 'greenhouse effect'

The effect of trapping some of the Sun's radiation is called the **'greenhouse effect'**. The Sun radiates energy in many wavelengths. Some of this radiation is reflected by the atmosphere. Some is absorbed by the atmosphere. The rest passes through and is absorbed by the Earth. Some energy passes through food chains (see 8.6). Eventually most of this energy is emitted from the Earth's surface at a longer wavelength than it entered. The Earth emits radiation in the infrared (IR) region of the spectrum.

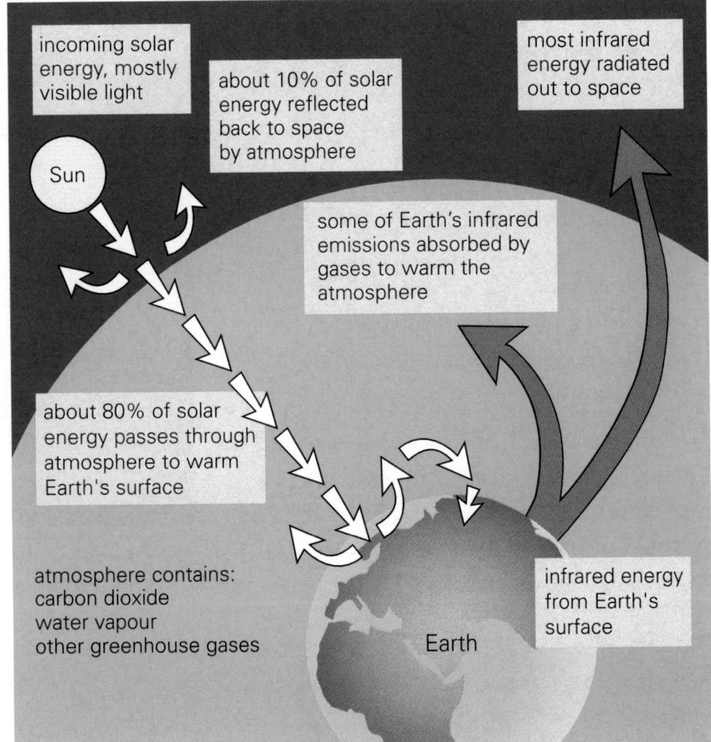

The greenhouse effect provides the Earth with an environment that supports life.

If all the IR left the atmosphere the Earth would be very cold, as cold as the Moon. But because the atmosphere contains gases such as water vapour, carbon dioxide and methane, which absorb in this region of the spectrum, the energy is not lost but warms the atmosphere. If *all* the IR emitted by the Earth was trapped in this way global temperatures would increase steeply.

Gas	Concentration in the atmosphere in certain years (parts per million)			Approximate length of time a molecule will remain in the atmosphere (years)	Relative effect as greenhouse gas compared to CO_2	Main sources
	1890	1990	2030			
Carbon dioxide (CO_2)	290	354	400–550	100	1	burning fossil fuels, deforestation, burning wood
Methane (CH_4)	0.9	1.7	2.2–2.5	10	30	bacterial activity in rice fields, cattle guts, waste dumps
Nitrous oxide (N_2O)	0.28	0.3	0.33–0.35	150	160	fertilisers, vehicle emissions
CFCs (e.g. $CFCl_3$)	0.0	0.003	0.002–0.006	60–130	17 000	aerosols, coolants in fridges, freezers and air conditioners, production of foams, solvents

The table shows how the concentrations of four greenhouse gases have increased over the last 100 years and how far they are expected to increase by 2030. It also shows how long the molecules remain in the atmosphere and how effective they are as greenhouse gases compared with carbon dioxide.

The main gas which contributes to the reflection of IR is water vapour, present in the atmosphere at a concentration of 10 000 parts per million. It is not much affected by human activities. Oxygen and nitrogen although making up a large proportion of the atmosphere, have little effect.

The composition of the atmosphere is such that it makes Earth suitable for life. But to a large extent the atmosphere has been formed by the activities of living organisms that maintain it in a constant state. One species appears to be doing its best to upset this balance – humans.

Life regulates the atmosphere

In the past the Earth's tilt has changed and there have been marked changes to the climate. There have been periods when the Earth has become very cold ('global cooling') and others when it has been very warm and moist. The quantity of water vapour in the atmosphere depends on the temperature. As temperature rises more water evaporates and the Earth heats up (water vapour is a greenhouse gas). In these warmer conditions, rates of photosynthesis increase so that carbon dioxide is taken out of the atmosphere. This decreases the greenhouse effect so more heat is radiated from the Earth's surface into space and so temperature decreases. This is like a global homeostasis preventing the Earth from becoming too hot or too cold to sustain life. There is evidence for this: carbon dioxide concentrations have fluctuated in the past along with global temperatures.

The enhanced greenhouse effect

Since the start of the Industrial Revolution the concentration of carbon dioxide in the atmosphere has increased due, in part, to an increase in the use of fossil fuels. Other greenhouse gases such as nitrous oxide and methane have increased rapidly.

It is thought that more carbon dioxide makes the atmosphere better at trapping the radiation emitted by the Earth, so raising the global temperature. However, carbon dioxide is not as effective as a greenhouse gas as others like methane, nitrous oxide and CFCs. In addition, these are increasing at a much faster rate than carbon dioxide.

Human activities are increasing the concentration of greenhouse gases in the atmosphere. It is likely that they are increasing faster than any natural process can remove them. In some cases they remain in the atmosphere for a long time – it is estimated up to 100 years.

Global average temperatures have increased. The southern hemisphere has warmed by 0.1–0.5°C every decade since 1950. The enhanced greenhouse effect may well be increasing the temperature of the Earth, although the evidence for this is not conclusive. Climates have changed in the past and human activities may just be accelerating a change that would happen anyway. We are living in a relatively warm period, but 400 years ago in the 'mini-ice age' winters were very severe – even the river Thames froze over. Curiously, acid rain and ozone destruction may be reducing the warming effect – we still do not fully understand what is happening to the atmosphere.

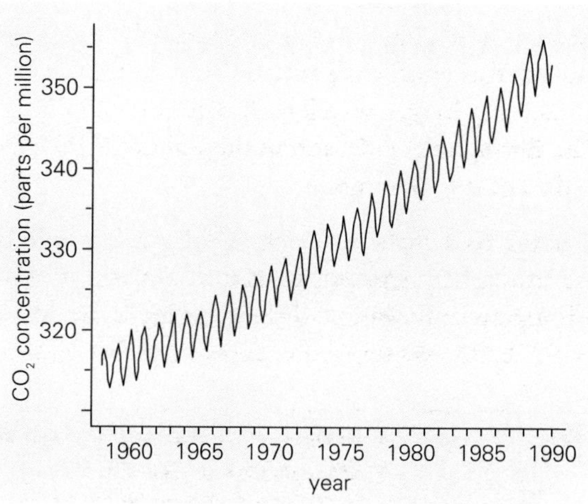

Readings of carbon dioxide concentrations taken in Hawaii show that they have been increasing this century. (350ppm = 0.035%)

QUESTIONS

1 Explain why the Earth is much warmer than the Moon.

2 Name the greenhouse gases.

3 Explain what is meant by the 'enhanced' greenhouse effect.

4 Explain why the concentrations of greenhouse gases in the atmosphere have increased.

5 Suggest why the concentrations of carbon dioxide measured in Hawaii fluctuate each year.

9.7 Ozone protection

Ozone – poisonous and protective

Ozone (O_3) is a blue, pungent smelling gas. At ground level it causes damage to trees and other plants and it irritates the human lungs and windpipe causing respiratory illness. However, at 19–48 kilometres above the Earth's surface in the stratosphere there is a layer of ozone. There is not much: if it was all brought down to ground level it would give a layer 3 mm thick.

Ozone absorbs most of the short wavelength radiation from the Sun. It absorbs ultraviolet (UV) and other high-energy radiation, preventing much of it reaching the Earth. If UV was not absorbed it would damage plant and animal tissues. Just enough UV light reaches the Earth's surface to cause some mutations in DNA (see 6.12) and produce vitamin D in our skin (see 2.2).

Thinning of the ozone layer

When oxygen in the atmosphere absorbs ultraviolet radiation it splits into two parts: each part combines with another oxygen molecule forming ozone. In 1984 a 'hole' was detected in the ozone layer above Antarctica. This was not a complete gap in the ozone layer but a thinning of the layer. The graph shows the thinning of ozone over Halley Bay Station in Antarctica between August and October in 1987.

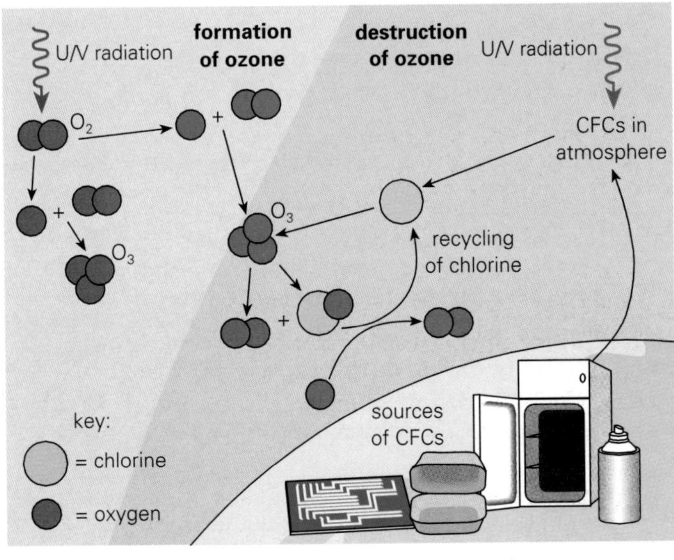

Chlorine from CFCs destroys ozone.

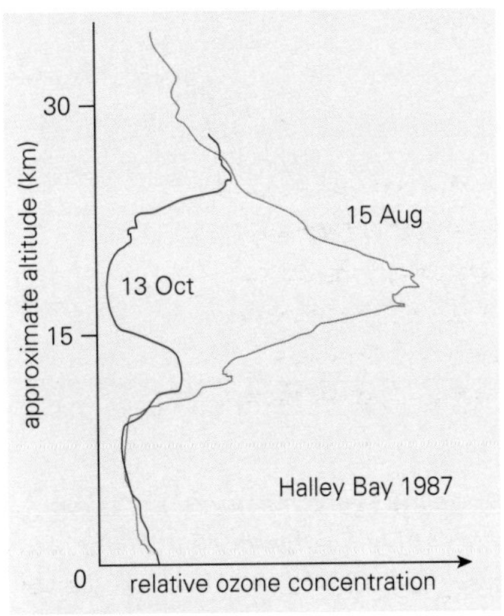

In the period shown, some 95% of the ozone between 14 and 23km altitude was destoyed over Halley Bay.

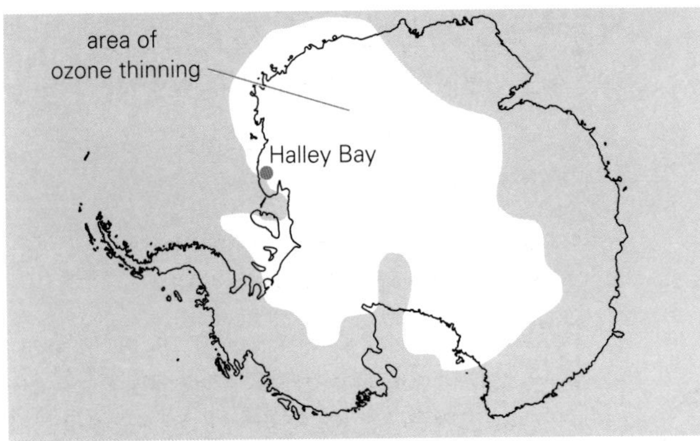

Antarctica: ozone layer thinned over an area as large as the United States.

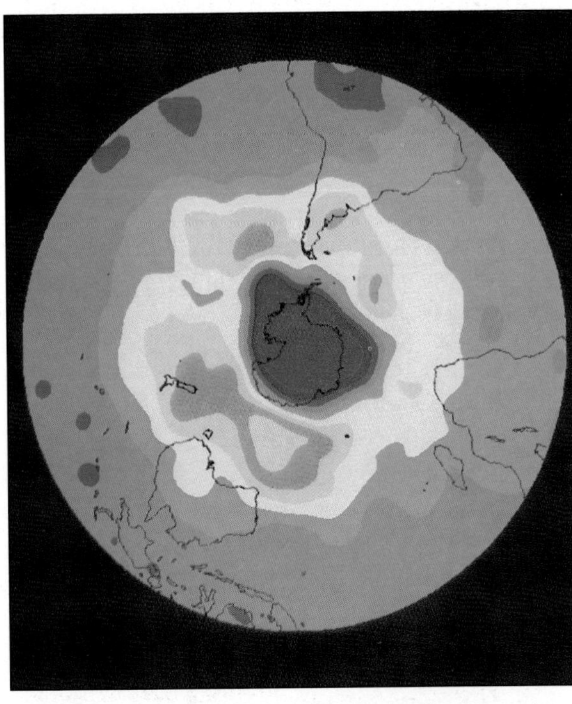

Satellite image taken in 1995 shows the ozone has thinned. Blue, purple and pink = ozone 'hole'.

CFCs are the culprits

It was thought that synthetic chlorofluorocarbons were responsible for the thinning of the ozone layer. Conclusive proof was not found for this theory until 1987 when an aeroplane flew through the ozone 'hole' over Antarctica to sample the atmosphere at 18 km. Thinning of ozone was found and a high concentration of chlorine. The source of the chlorine is the CFCs. Ultraviolet radiation causes CFCs to break down releasing chlorine. This acts as a catalyst turning ozone into oxygen. Each chlorine molecule destroys 100 000 molecules of ozone before it is removed from the atmosphere.

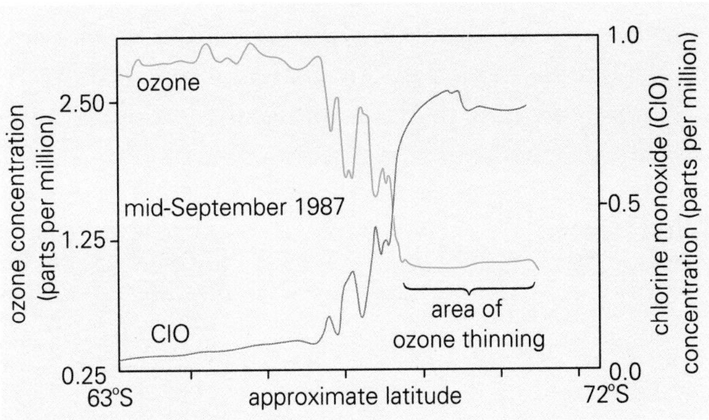

This graph shows that ozone decreases at just the same place where chlorine monoxide, ClO, accumulates in the atmosphere.

CFCs are harmless!

CFCs were developed in the 1930s as a safe substance to use in refrigerators as a coolant. They also have a variety of other uses:

- coolant in air conditioners
- propellant in aerosols
- 'blowing' agent in foamed plastics
- solvent in the electronics industry.

The great advantages of CFCs are that they are not toxic, they are stable and do not decay at ground level, and they are not flammable.

Why Antarctica?

The extreme cold of the Antarctic winter isolates the polar atmosphere from the rest and creates a large swirl of air over the continent. When this is warmed by the spring Sun (in September) the ice particles have many molecules of ozone destroying chemicals on their surface. In other parts of the world nitrogen oxides interfere with this destruction and protect ozone, but not in the air above Antarctica where the cold temperature reduces the concentrations of these gases. Thinning of the ozone layer has been observed in both the southern and northern hemispheres.

Ban them

As the seriousness of ozone thinning was realised, developed countries decided to stop production in January 1996. Several firms are producing alternatives that do not have as much effect as CFCs in destroying ozone. But developing countries still have ten years to phase out CFCs.

Skin cancer

Thinning of the ozone layer means that there will be more UV radiation reaching the Earth's surface. It is thought that this will result in

- an increase in skin disorders including one form of cancer
- many plants which are sensitive to UV radiation growing less well
- a slowing of the growth of marine organisms that play an important part in removing carbon dioxide from the atmosphere.

QUESTIONS

1. Explain why ozone is harmful at ground level but useful in the atmosphere.
2. Explain how the thinning of ozone over Antarctica has happened.
3. Summarise the environmental effects of ozone thinning.
4. Suggest what could be done to reduce the effects of CFCs already in refrigerators and aerosols.
5. Explain why, even if the production of CFCs was stopped immediately, the ozone layer would still keep thinning for years to come.

9.8 *Global climate change*

In the history of the Earth great changes in climate have occurred. But we think these have usually happened quite slowly. In the 1980s we became aware for the first time of changes in greenhouse gases (see 9.6), acid rain (9.5) and ozone depletion (9.7). While there is no doubt about ozone destruction, no one knows definitely whether the Earth is warming up and if it is, whether humans are causing it.

Methane

Methane is a greenhouse gas, and its concentration in the atmosphere has risen steeply over the last 100 years (in line with the increase in the human population) because it:

- is emitted by the digestive processes, e.g. cows
- is produced by anaerobic bacteria living in marshes and paddy fields
- is released from coal and oil extraction
- is formed in the incomplete burning of fossil fuels
- leaks from landfill sites.

The areas of land used to grow rice have increased over the past twenty years. Paddy fields release large quantities of methane.

Deforestation

Demand for land and timber leads to large tracts of forest being cleared. Large areas of rainforest in Amazonia and South East Asia have already been cleared for subsistence farming, plantations and for cattle ranches.

Many of these forests are on thin soils which soon wash away. When bare land is exposed to the Sun it absorbs more heat than if it was covered in vegetation. This increases the temperature of the lower atmosphere and creates more frequent and intense storms.

When vegetation is removed heavy rains wash away soil and cause gully erosion.

Carbon sinks

Tropical forests are often claimed to be important in regulating the level of carbon dioxide in the atmosphere. However, as the carbon compounds are recycled so quickly in such forests, tropical forests are in fact **carbon neutral**. When they are burnt they do release large quantities of carbon dioxide, but otherwise they do not reduce the carbon dioxide concentration of the atmosphere.

The major sites of carbon removal from the atmosphere – which can offset our increasing production of carbon dioxide – are places like the Flow country in northern Scotland. Carbon is fixed by mosses and other plants, but the soil is acid so few decomposers live in it. Carbon compounds remain in the soil to form peat. This helps to remove carbon from the atmosphere. Places like this are known as **carbon sinks**.

We should be as concerned about the conservation of areas like the Flow country as we are about tropical rainforests.

The effects of global warming

It is predicted that the world's average temperature will be 1°C higher in 2025 than it is now. By 2050 it is also predicted that it will be higher than it has ever been over the last 150 000 years. These predictions are based on current trends in temperature rise and the continued increase in emissions of greenhouse gases. If this happens there will be thermal expansion of water and the ice caps will melt raising sea levels by a predicted 20 cm by 2030.

Most of the world's population lives on low-lying land. In fact 3000 million people live within a few centimetres of sea level. Many large cities and much rich farmland is situated in low lying areas.

Global warming could also cause changes in climate in the centre of continents. The severe droughts and flooding that have occurred in the United States over the last decade are thought to be a forerunner of future changes to the weather pattern.

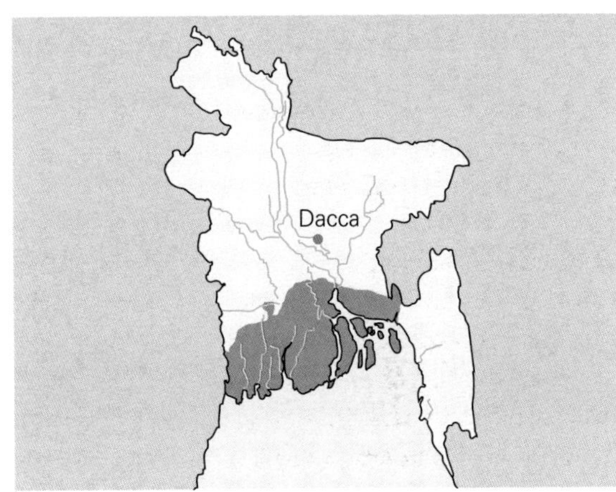

This map of Bangladesh shows the area likely to be flooded by a sea level rise of one metre.

Farms in the United States have suffered several droughts over the last decade.

QUESTIONS

1. Explain how our knowledge of the Earth's atmosphere has changed over the last ten years.
2. Describe the sources of methane and explain why it is an important pollutant.
3. Describe the environmental effects of deforestation.
4. Explain why the Flow country in Scotland is a carbon sink, but tropical rainforests are not.
5. Describe the likely effects on the Earth of global warming.

SECTION E: QUESTIONS

1 The table shows some of the organisms that live in a pond and their food. Detritus is dead plant material some of which falls into the pond from the surrounding trees.

Organism	Food
trout	water boatman, hoglouse, minnow, shrimp
minnow	water boatman, hoglouse, shrimp, water beetle
water boatman	phantom midge larva
water beetle	hoglouse, shrimp
phantom midge larva	waterflea
hoglouse	detritus
shrimp	detritus, pond weed
waterflea	planktonic algae

a State the source of energy for all the organisms in the pond.

b Use the information in the table to draw:

i four food chains that begin with producers. Identify the different feeding (trophic) levels in each food chain

ii a food web showing all the feeding relationships given in the table.

c Is this a 'closed' ecosystem? Explain your answer.

2 Explain how a pond ecosystem differs from a river ecosystem. Refer to physical and biotic factors in your answer.

The diagram shows part of a food web in a river.

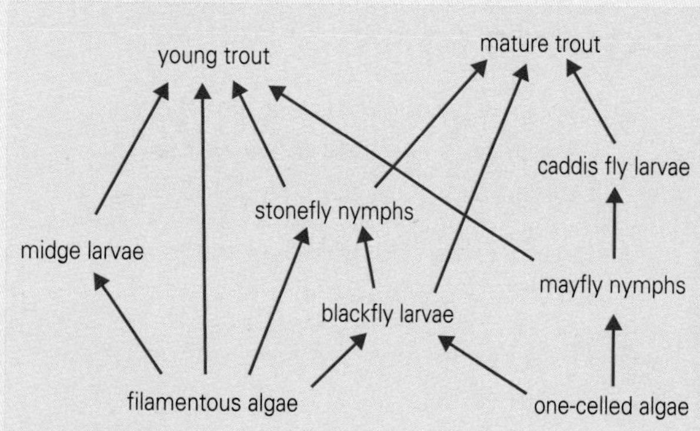

Predict the effects of the following changes on the species in the food web. Give explanations for your answers in each case.

a The oxygen concentration falls so that there are no stonefly nymphs.

b Extra nutrients in the water leads to an increase in filamentous and one-celled algae.

c Blackfly larvae change into flies and leave the river.

d The river is stocked with more young trout from a fish farm.

3 A large species of starfish is the top carnivore in a rocky shore ecosystem. It feeds on eight other species – mainly shrimps and snails. Its prey are either herbivores or predators. In an experiment all the starfish were removed from an area of rock. A nearby area was left as a control. The experiment ran for six years. After the starfish were first removed the community began to change. The number of barnacles increased, but they were soon replaced by mussels; fewer seaweeds grew. The herbivores migrated away. The number of species decreased from 15 to 8. There was no change in the other area where starfish were left to feed.

a Explain why a control was used in this experiment.

b Describe what the experimenters found out about top carnivores from this study.

4 Some students conducted a study of energy flow in a mixed oak and birch woodland during one week in August. The diagram below shows their results.

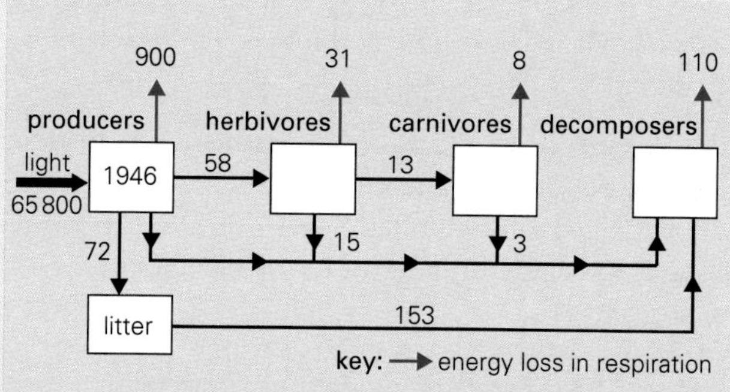

All figures are kJ per m^2 per week. The total amount of energy captured by the plants in photosynthesis is 1946 kJ/m^2 per week.

a Calculate:

i the energy captured by the plants as a percentage of the energy that reached them;

ii the total energy used in respiration by the community.

b Calculate the amount of energy retained by **i** herbivores, and **ii** carnivores.

c Use the data in the diagram and your answers to **a** and **b** to explain why the students found more herbivores than carnivores in the wood.

d Name three decomposers that are likely to be in this ecosystem.

The students measured the total energy in the leaf litter as 15 899 kJ per m^2. They noticed that the waste materials from the animals decomposed more quickly than dead leaves.

e Explain the importance of leaf litter to the community.

f Why does animal waste decompose faster than dead leaves?

g Suggest what you might expect to find if you investigated the flow of energy in this wood in January.

h What happens eventually to the energy in the ecosystem?

5 The food conversion ratio (FCR) for livestock is:

$$\frac{\text{mass of food eaten}}{\text{gain in mass}}$$

a Use the data in the table to calculate the FCR for each animal.

Animal	Food per animal (kg)	Gain in mass (kg)
beef cattle	1785	340
pig	140	51
trout	0.35	0.25
turkey	13.4	4.7

b Explain the differences in FCRs between the animals.

c Explain why farmers want to raise animals with a low FCR.

A Friesian cow produces 6000 litres of milk per year. The energy content of milk is 3000 kJ per litre. Each year she also produces a calf with an energy value of 300 000 kJ. She eats grass, hay and cattle cake (made from cereals and beans) consuming 6000 kg (DM) each year. She is fed 1400 kg (DM) of cattle cake. The energy content of grass is 17.5 kJ per gram (DM) and for cake it is 21 kJ per gram (DM).

DM = dry mass.

d Calculate:

i the dry mass of grass and hay she consumes each year

ii her total energy intake

iii the energy value of her milk and calf as a percentage of her total energy intake.

6 The table shows the increase in crop yields from 1885 to 1984 in the UK.

Crop	Yield (tonnes per hectare)		
	1885–89	**1950–54**	**1984**
wheat	2.06	2.81	7.71
barley	1.96	2.62	5.59
potatoes	14.70	19.90	37.00

a Calculate the percentage increase in yields for each crop between 1950–54 and 1984.

b Suggest reasons for the low yields in the 1880s.

c List the factors that were responsible for the steeper increase in yields between the1950s and 1984.

7 The graph shows data about the population of peregrine falcons in north-west England.

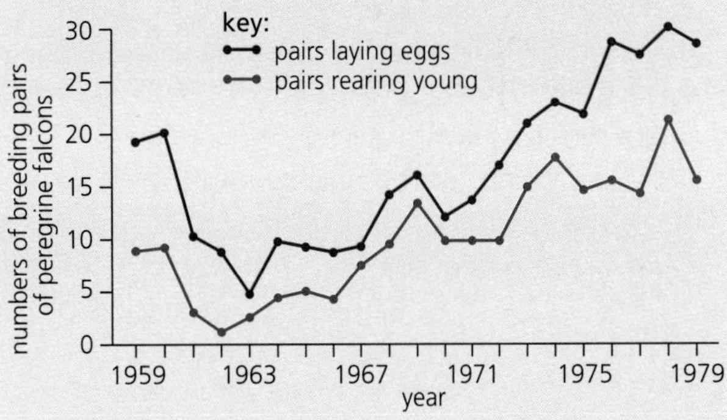

a Suggest reasons for the differences between the number of pairs laying eggs and the number of pairs rearing young in all years.

b Use the graph to describe the changes in the peregrine falcon population between 1959 and 1979.

c Explain the decrease in the number of breeding pairs in the early 1960s.

d Explain why the number has increased since then.

8 The graph shows the annual catches of herring in the North Sea.

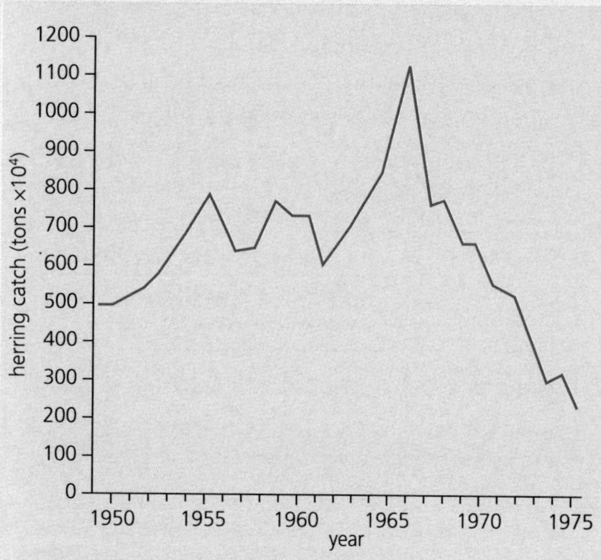

a Use the graph to describe the changes in herring catches between 1950 and 1975.

b Suggest reasons for the changes.
After the collapse of herring stocks in the North Sea, a ban was declared. Many fishermen caught haddock and cod instead. Cod catches in Britain dropped from 366 674 tonnes in 1970 to 74 000 tonnes in 1990. Catches for haddock showed the same trend.

c Suggest ways in which the catches of fish like herring, cod and haddock can be maintained.

9 The graph shows the production of salmon in Scottish fish farms.

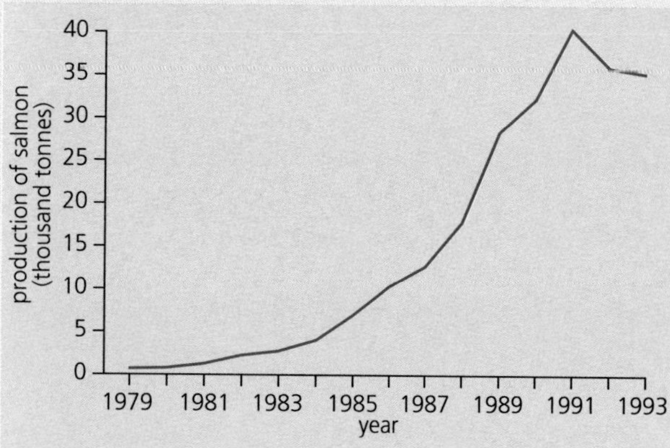

a Describe the trend shown in the graph.

b Explain the reasons for the trend you describe.

c Discuss the environmental problems posed by intensive rearing of salmon in Scottish lochs.

10 Some lakes and ponds often look green, especially when they receive water draining from farmland. The green colour is caused by algae growing in the water. Some students predicted that algae in ponds grow much better in water that is given extra fertiliser.
They planned the following experiment to test their prediction.

1 Six beakers were each filled with 100 cm^3 of pond water. The water level was marked on the side of each beaker.
2 Garden fertiliser (containing a mixture of phosphate, nitrate and potassium) was put into five of the beakers in the following quantities: **A** 0.5 g; **B** 1.0 g; **C** 1.5 g; **D** 2.0 g; **E** 2.5 g.
3 No fertiliser was added to beaker **F**.
4 The beakers were placed in a room with a constant temperature of 25°C. They were put under some lamps so that they received the same illumination.
5 The water levels in the beakers were checked every day. If any water had evaporated from one of the beakers then distilled water was added to keep the level of water in each beaker constant.
6 Every day for three weeks the growth of the algae was measured by two methods:
   - putting a white plastic disc under each beaker and noting whether the disc was visible through the water
   - shining a lamp at the side of each beaker and using a light sensor to record how much light passed through.

a Name the factor that was being investigated.

b List the factors that were kept constant.

c Explain why beaker **F** was included in the plan.

d Predict the results that might be obtained with the light sensor over the three weeks of the experiment if the students' prediction is correct.

e Describe ways in which the reliability of the experiment could be improved.

f Suggest how results from this type of experiment could be used to investigate eutrophication in ponds and lakes.

g Explain how you could extend this experiment to investigate the effect of individual plant nutrients (e.g. phosphate, nitrate and potassium) on eutrophication.

11a What is acid rain and how is it formed?

400 cress seeds were divided into four groups. Three groups were soaked in different concentrations of dilute sulphuric acid solution and one was soaked in water. The seeds were then placed on to pieces of moist filter paper and left to germinate. The lengths of roots and shoots were measured at three time intervals and the results averaged.

Concentration of sulphuric acid solution	Mean length (mm)					
	roots			shoots		
	21 h	41 h	65 h	21 h	41 h	65 h
low	3.8	20.9	63.4	0.9	11.3	18.4
medium	1.7	3.1	6.5	0.8	6.3	9.5
high	0.4	0.7	0.7	0.0	0.0	0.0
water	4.7	20.8	55.5	0.4	12.3	25.2

b Explain why a large number of seeds was used for this investigation.

c Why was one group of seeds soaked in water?

d Discuss the conclusions you can draw from this experiment.

e Discuss the relevance of experiments like this to our understanding of the environmental effects of acid rain.

12 Farmland is the habitat of many common British birds. The table shows the decline in four of these species between 1975 and 1995.

Bird species	Decline in numbers (%)	Decline in area inhabited (%)
tree sparrow	85	20
corn bunting	76	32
bullfinch	67	7
skylark	54	2

a What has happened to the population density of skylarks between 1975 and 1995?

b Describe what has happened to the population of corn buntings.

c Suggest reasons for the patterns shown in the table.

Many farmers are now encouraged to take land out of intensive production. This 'set aside' land can be used for a variety of purposes.

d Suggest ways in which farmers might manage 'set aside' land to encourage wildlife.

13a Explain why the Earth's surface is about 30°C warmer than it should be for a planet in its position in the Solar System.

The average surface temperature for different places on the Earth for the years 1951 to 1980 was 15°C. During the 1970s some years were hotter than this average and others were colder. The table below shows the average surface temperatures during the 1980s.

Year	Average surface temperature (°C)
1980	15.18
1981	15.20
1982	15.15
1983	15.30
1984	15.10
1985	15.09
1986	15.15
1987	15.32
1988	15.32
1989	15.21

b Plot the figures in the table as a graph.

c Use the graph to describe how temperatures in the 1980s differed from those in the 1970s.

d Explain why global temperatures have increased in the 1980s.

e Discuss the consequences of global warming for human activities.

Index

D

E

F

G

H

I

K

L

M